Merry Christmas, 1973
To Mom

Love,
Suzy + Rick

CHARLES LUTWIDGE DODGSON (LEWIS CARROLL).
(Photograph probably taken by Reginald Southey, May 10, 1856.)

Morris L. Parrish Collection, Princeton University Library

THE UNKNOWN
LEWIS CARROLL

EIGHT MAJOR WORKS AND
MANY MINOR

Former titles:
The Lewis Carroll Picture Book,
Diversions and Digressions of Lewis Carroll

EDITED BY

Stuart Dodgson
Collingwood

With a new selection
of Lewis Carroll's Photographs

DOVER PUBLICATIONS, INC.
NEW YORK

Published in Canada by General Publishing Com-
pany, Ltd., 30 Lesmill Road, Don Mills, Toronto,
Ontario.
Published in the United Kingdom by Constable
and Company, Ltd., 10 Orange Street, London
WC 2.

This Dover edition, first published in 1961, is an
unabridged republication of the work originally
published by T. Fisher Unwin in 1899 under the
title: *The Lewis Carroll Picture Book.*
The selection of illustrations which appeared in
the original edition has been slightly revised and
greatly augmented by the addition of forty-two
photographs from the Morris L. Parrish Collection
of the Princeton University Library, reproduced by
permission of the Princeton University Library and
through the cooperation of Mr. Alexander D.
Wainwright, Curator. Additional information concerning the Lewis Carroll photographs in the
Parrish Collection will be found preceding the
"Album of Photographic Portraits by Lewis Carroll"
which follows page 160. All illustrations from the
Parrish Collection are so credited on the List of
Illustrations, page xi. These illustrations may not
be reproduced without permission of the Princeton
University Library.

International Standard Book Number: 0-486-20732-3
Library of Congress Catalog Card Number: 61-2003

Manufactured in the United States of America
Dover Publications, Inc.
180 Varick Street
New York, N. Y. 10014

To

MY MOTHER.

PREFACE

THIS book is primarily, as its title denotes, a "picture book." The pictures have been taken from many sources; the magazines which Lewis Carroll edited for his brothers and sisters at Croft Rectory have furnished a considerable number; the innumerable photographs which he took in his studio at Christ Church have also been laid under contribution, and in addition to these two main sources to which I am principally indebted, I have collected from all quarters illustrations bearing upon the life and work of the author of "Alice."

Of the literary matter, much is here published for the first time; I would draw special attention to "Isa's Visit to Oxford" (Chapter VII.), which is to my thinking one of the most charming things that Lewis Carroll ever wrote. "Notes by an

Oxford Chiel," and several smaller efforts, are reprints, the old editions having long been unobtainable.

I have again to thank many kind friends for the help they have given me, and in particular I wish to acknowledge my gratitude to the following : Miss Dora Abdy, Mrs. Samuel Bickersteth, Mr. A. W. Dubourg, Mrs. Fuller, Mrs. Collier Foster, Mrs. Horniman, Miss Longley, Mrs. Paul Mason, Rev. Walter Scott, Mr. Lewis Sergeant, Miss Stevens, Miss Lucy Walters, Miss Menella Wilcox, and Mrs. Chivers-Wilson.

Two events which have occurred since the publication of " The Life " seem to call for some mention here ; I refer to the opening of the " Lewis Carroll " cot at the Great Ormonde Street Hospital for children, and to the recent successful performance of "Alice in Wonderland" at the Opera Comique Theatre. Both are pictorially commemorated in the present volume.

S. D. COLLINGWOOD.

The Chestnuts, Guildford.
  July, 1899.

CONTENTS

ix

LIST OF ILLUSTRATIONS

THE UNKNOWN
LEWIS CARROLL

CHAPTER I

" THE RECTORY UMBRELLA "

PEOPLE are accustomed to think of "Alice in Wonderland" as Lewis Carroll's earliest attempt at writing for children, but this is a great mistake. Indeed, the polished workmanship of that famous tale could hardly have come from a novice at story-telling, and one would have been forced to believe in earlier literary efforts in the same field even if there was no other evidence of their having existed. But the truth is that the author of "Alice" began to write for child-readers when he was himself a child, and continued to do so during the whole of his school and early college days.

His work took the form of periodicals edited for the amusement of his brothers and sisters at Croft ; the best account of them is that given in

the Preface to the last of the series, *Misch-Masch*.
Of the magazines whose rise and fall he there
describes, the only ones which still survive are

FRONTISPIECE TO " THE RECTORY UMBRELLA."

*Useful and Instructive Poetry, The Rectory
Magazine,* and *The Rectory Umbrella.*
    The first two contain nothing of any permanent

interest from his pen. When one remembers that only three or four years elapsed between the issuing of the *Magazine* and of the *Umbrella*, the contrast between them is most remarkable ; Lewis Carroll's contributions to the former might, except for their somewhat unusually pompous and affected style, have been written by any intelligent schoolboy ; in the latter we get the first real exhibition of his genius, undeveloped, of course, as yet, but none the less unmistakable and authentic.

Nothing in *The Rectory Umbrella* is more characteristic of Lewis Carroll's bent of mind than the two papers entitled " Difficulties," which I have thought worth reproducing in their entirety. No one who was not by nature a lover of logic, and an extreme precisian in the use of words and phrases, could have written the two " Alice " books ; their humour is not, as is, to take a well-known instance, the humour of Max Adeler, dependent upon a gush of unrestained animal spirits ; it is not the humour of the child, unconscious and funny just because it *is* unconscious ; it is the acute sense of paradox which revels in the most unlikely subjects, the habit of playing with words which is built upon an accurate conception of their proper use.   In a word, Lewis Carroll's humour is that of an educated man ; it is fun indeed, but of the most refined and exotic.   And that is why his books, popular as they are and as they deserve to be among children, can only be fully appreciated by grown-up readers.

DIFFICULTIES.

No. 1.

Half of the world, or nearly so, is always in the light of the sun : as the world turns round, this hemisphere of light shifts round too, and passes over each part of it in succession.

Supposing on Tuesday, it is morning at London ; in another hour it would be Tuesday morning at the west of England ; if the whole world were land we might go on tracing [1] Tuesday morning, Tuesday morning all the way round, till in 24 hours we get to London again.   But we *know* that at London 24 hours after Tuesday morning it is Wednesday morning.   Where then, in its passage round the earth, does the day change its name ? where does it lose its identity ?

Practically there is no difficulty in it, because a great part of its journey is over water, and what it does out at sea no one

---

[1] The best way is to imagine yourself walking round with the sun and asking the inhabitants as you go " What morning is this ? "   If you suppose them living all the way round, and all speaking one language, the difficulty is obvious.

can tell: and besides there are so many different languages that it would be hopeless to attempt to trace the name of any one day all round. But is the case inconceivable that the same land and the same language should continue all round the world? I cannot see that it is: in that case either [1] there would be no distinction at all between each successive day, and so week, month, &c., so that we should have to say, "The Battle of Waterloo happened to-day, about two million hours ago," or some line would have to be fixed, where the change should take place, so that the inhabitant of one house would wake and say "Heigh-ho, [2] Tuesday morning!" and the inhabitant of the next (over the line), a few miles to the west would wake a few minutes afterwards and say "Heigh-ho! Wednesday morning!" What hopeless confusion the people who happened to live *on* the line would always be in, it is not for me to say. There would be a quarrel every morning as to what the name of the day should be. I can imagine no third case, unless everybody was allowed to choose for themselves, which state of things would be rather worse than either of the other two.

I am aware that this idea has been started before, namely, by the unknown author of that beautiful poem beginning "If all the world were apple pie, &c." [3] The particular result here discussed, however, does not appear to have occurred to him, as he confines himself to the difficulties in obtaining drink which would certainly ensue.

Any good solution of the above difficulty will be thankfully received and inserted.

---

[1] This is clearly an impossible case, and is only put as an hypothesis.

[2] The usual exclamation at waking ; generally said with a yawn.

[3] " If all the world were apple pie,
And all the sea were ink,
And all the trees were bread and cheese,
What *should* we have to drink ? "

DIFFICULTIES,

No. 2.

Which is the best, a clock that is right only once a year, or a clock that is right twice every day?   "The latter," you reply, "unquestionably."   Very good, reader, now attend.

I have two clocks: one doesn't go *at all*, and the other loses a minute a day : which would you prefer?   "The losing one," you answer, "without a doubt."   Now observe : the one which loses a minute a day has to lose twelve hours, or seven hundred and twenty minutes before it is right again, consequently it is only right once in two years, whereas the other is evidently right as often as the time it points to comes round, which happens twice a day.   So you've contradicted yourself *once*. "Ah, but," you say, "what's the use of its being right twice a day, if I can't tell when the time comes?"   Why, suppose the clock points to eight o'clock, don't you see that the clock is right *at* eight o'clock?   Consequently when eight o'clock comes your clock is right.   "Yes, I see *that*," you reply.[1]   Very good, then you've contradicted yourself *twice* : now get out of the difficulty as you can, and don't contradict yourself again if you can help it.

To understand the very amusing article on "Fishs," which is one of a series of "Zoological Papers" in *The Rectory Umbrella*, it must be pre-

---

[1] You *might* go on to ask, "How am I to know when eight o'clock *does* come?   My clock will not tell me."   Be patient, reader : you know that when eight o'clock comes your clock is right ; very good ; then your rule is this : keep your eye fixed on your clock, and *the very moment it is right* it will be eight o'clock.   "But——" you say.   There, that'll do, reader ; the more you argue the farther you get from the point, so it will be as well to stop.

mised that the creatures intended are those metal
fish which children float in a basin of water, using
a magnet to make them swim about.

ZOOLOGICAL PAPERS.

No. 3.

Fishs.

The facts we have collected about this strange race of
creatures are drawn partly from observation, partly from the
works of a German author whose name has not been given
to the world. We believe that they [1] are only to be found
in Germany : our author tells us that they have "ordinarely [2]
angles [3] at them," by which they "can be fanged and heaved
out of the water." The specimens which fell under our
observation had *not* angles,
as will shortly be seen, and
therefore this sketch [4] is
founded on mere conjec-
ture.

What   the   "fanging"

consists of we cannot exactly say : if it is anything like a
dog "fanging" a bone, it is certainly a strange mode of

---

[1] *I.e.*, fishs.   [2] As he spells it.   [3] Or corners.
[4] The "angles," however, may be supposed to be correct.

capture, but perhaps the writer refers to otters. The
"heaving out of the water" we have likewise attempted to
pourtray, though here again fancy is our only guide. The
reader will probably ask, "Why put a *Crane* into the picture?"
Our answer is, "The only 'heaving' we ever saw done was
by a Crane."

This part of the subject, however, will be more fully treated
of in the next paper. Another fact our author gives us is
that "they will very readily swim [1] after the pleasing direction
of the staff": this is easier to understand, as the simplest
reader at once perceives that the only "staff" answering to
this description is a stick of barley sugar.[2]

---

[1] "Float" would be a better word, as their fins are immovable.

[2] There is an objection to this solution, as "fishs" have no mouths.

We will now attempt to describe the "fishs" which we examined. Skin hard and metallic; colour brilliant, and of many hues; body hollow (surprising as this fact may appear, it is *perfectly true*); eyes large and meaningless; fins fixed and perfectly useless. They are wonderfully light, and have a sort of beak or snout of a metallic substance : as this is solid, and they have no other mouth, their hollowness is thus easily accounted for. The colour is sticky, and comes off on the fingers, and they can swim back downwards  just as easily as in the usual way. All these facts prove that they must not on any account be confounded with the English "fishes," which the similarity of names might at first lead us to do. They are a peculiar race of animals,[1] and must be treated as such. Our next subject will be "The One-Winged Dove."

"Ye Fatalle Cheyse" and "Lays of Sorrow. No. I.," are good examples of Carroll's early fondness for versification; the latter refers, no doubt, to some incident at Croft Rectory. The lines—

> "And so it fell upon a day
> (That is, it never rose again,)"

are very characteristic of the misapplication of familiar phrases in which the author of "Alice" delighted.

---

[1] An incorrect expression : "creatures" would be better.

Yͤ "FATALLE CHEYSE"

1

Ytte wes a mirke ᴇn dreiry cave,
Weet scroggis[1] owr ytte creepe
Gurgles withyn yͤ flowan wave
Throw-channel braid an deip

2

Never withyn that dreir recesse
Wes sene yͤ lyghte of daye,
Quhat bode azont[2] yt's mirkinesse[3]
Nane kerid an nane mote saye

3

Yͤ monarche rade owr brake an brae
An drave yͤ yellynge packe
Hiz meany[4] au' richte cadgily[5]
Are wendynge[6] yn hiz tracke

4

Wi eager iye, wi yalpe an crye
Yͤ hondes yode[7] down yͤ rocks
Ahead of au' their companye
Renneth yͤ panky[9] foxe

5

Yͤ foxe hes soughte that cave of awe
Forewearied[9] wi' hiz rin,
Quha nou ys he sae bauld an braw[10]
To dare to enter yn?

6

Wi eager bounde hes ilka honde
Gane till that caverne dreir,
Foa[11] many a yowl ys[13] hearde arounde,
Fou[11] many a screech of feir

(1) bushes. (2) beyond (3) darkness (4) company (5) merrily (6) going journeying
(7) went (8) running (9) much wearied (10) brave (11) full (12) hour. (13) is

7

Like ane wi' thirstie appetite
  Quha swalloweth orange pulp,
Wes hearde a huggle an a bile,
  A swallow an a gulp

8

Yᵉ kynge hes lap frae aff hiz steid,
  Outbrayde[1] hiz trenchant brande;²
"Quha on my packe of hondes doth feed,
  "Maun deye benead thilke hande"

9

Sae sed, sae dune yᵉ stonderes[2] hearde
  Fou many a mickle[3] stroke,
Sowns[4] lyke yᵉ flappynge of a birde,
  A struggle an a choke

10

Owte of yᵉ cave scarce fette[5] they ytte,
  Wi pow[6] an push an hau[7]—
Whereof I've drawne a littel bytte,
  Bot durst nat draw ytte au[8]

[1] drawn [2] bystanders [3] heavy. [4] sounds [5] fetched [6] pull [7] haul. [8] all.

LAYS   OF   SORROW.

Nº 1.

The day was wet, the rain fell souse
  Like jars of strawberry jam,[1]
Sound was heard in the old hen house,
  A beating of a hammer.
Of stalwart form, and visage warm,
  Two youths were seen within it,
Splitting up an old tree into perches for their
                                          poultry
  At a hundred strokes[2] a minute.

The work is done, the hen has taken
Possession of her nest and eggs,
Without a thought of eggs and bacon,[3]
(Or I am very much mistaken;)
    She turns over each shell,
    To be sure that all's well,
    Looks into the straw
    To see there's no flaw,
    Goes once round the house,[4]
    Half afraid of a mouse,
    Then sinks calmly to rest
    On the top of her nest,
First doubling up each of her legs.

[1]. i.e. the jam without the jars observe the beauty of this rhyme.
[2] at the rate of a stroke and two thirds in a second.
[3] unless the hen was a poacher, which is unlikely. [4] 'the hen = house.

Time rolled away, and so did every shell,
"Small by degrees and beautifully less,"
As the sage mother with a powerful spell [1]
Forced each in turn it's contents to express, [2]
    But ah "imperfect is expression,"
Some poet said, I don't care who,
If you want to know you must go elsewhere,
One fact I can tell, if you're willing to hear,
He never attended a Parliament Session,
For I'm certain that if he had ever been there.
Full quickly would he have changed his ideas,
With the hissings, the hootings, the groans and
                                    the cheers,
And as to his name it is pretty clear
That it wasn't me and it wasn't you!

And so it fell upon a day,
    (That is, it never rose again,)
A chick was found upon the hay,
It's little life had ebbed away,
No longer frolicsome and gay,
No longer could it run or play,
"And must we, chicken, must we part?"
It's master [3] cried with bursting heart,
    And voice of agony and pain
So one, whose ticket's marked "Return," [4]

[1] beak and claw. [2] press out. [3] probably one of the two
stalwart youths. [4] the system of return tickets is an excellent one. People
are conveyed, on particular days, there and back again for one fare

When to the lonely road side station,
    He flies in fear and perturbation,
    Thinks of his home — the hissing urn —
    Then runs with flying hat and hair,
    And, entering, finds to his despair
        He's missed the very latest train[1]

Too long it were to tell of each conjecture
    Of chicken suicide, and poultry victim,
The deadly frown, the stern and dreary lecture,
    The timid guess, "perhaps some needle pricked him!"
The din of voice, the words both loud and many,
    The sob, the tear, the sigh that none could smother,
Till all agreed "a shilling to a penny
    It killed it self, and we acquit the mother!"
            Scarce was the verdict spoken,
            When that still calm was broken,
    A childish form hath burst into the throng,
            With tears and looks of sadness,
            That bring no news of gladness,
    But tell too surely something hath gone wrong!
    "The sight that I have come upon
        "The stoutest[2] heart would sicken,
    "That nasty hen has been and gone
        "And killed another chicken!"

(continued page 60.)

[1] an additional vexation would be that his "Return" ticket would
be no use the next day [2] perhaps even the "bursting" heart of its master

The whole of the *Umbrella* is written in manuscript, in that neat, exquisitely legible handwriting which Lewis Carroll always employed, but when we turn to *Misch-Masch* this is no longer the case. Many of the poems and articles in that miscellany had made an earlier appearance in various periodicals, such as *The Illustrated Times* and the *Whitby Gazette*. The extracts which follow are placed here in the order in which they occur in *Misch-Masch*, and cover a period of about seven years (1855–1862).

PREFACE.

" Yet once more " (to use the time-honoured words of our poet Milton) we present ourselves before an eager and expectant public, let us hope under even better auspices than hitherto.

In making our bow for the—may we venture to say so?—fourth time, it will be worth while to review the past, and to consider the probable future. We are encouraged to do so by Mrs. Malaprop's advice : " Let us not anticipate the past ; let all our retrospections be to the future," and by the fact that our family motto is " *Respiciendo prudens*."

We purpose then to give a brief history of our former domestic magazines in this family, their origin, aim, progress, and ultimate fate, and we shall notice, as we go on, the other magazines which have appeared, but not under our own editorship. We commence our history, then, with

USEFUL AND INSTRUCTIVE POETRY.

This we wrote ourselves about the year 1845, the idea of the first poem being suggested by a piece in the "Etonian:" it lasted about half a year, and was then very clumsily bound up in a sort of volume : the binding, however, was in every respect worthy of the contents : the volume still exists.

THE RECTORY MAGAZINE.

This was the first started for general contribution, and at first the contributions poured in in one continuous stream, while the issuing of each number was attended by the most violent excitement through the whole house : most of the family contributed one or more articles to it.   About the year 1848 the numbers were bound into a volume, which still exists.

THE COMET.

This was started by us about the year 1848.   It was the same shape as the former, but, for the sake of variety, opened at the end instead of the side.   Little interest attended this publication, and its contents were so poor, that, after 6 numbers were out, we destroyed all but the last, and published no more.   The last number, we believe, is still in existence.

THE ROSEBUD.

This was started in imitation of the Comet, but only reached a second number : the cover of each number was tastefully ornamented with a painted rosebud : the two numbers do not contain much worth notice, but are still preserved.

THE STAR.

Another imitator of the Comet, on a less ambitious scale even than the last : the manuscript and illustrations decidedly below par : some half-dozen numbers still survive.

THE WILL-O THE-WISP.

Even inferior to the last : the numbers were cut in a triangular shape : we believe some numbers are still to be found.

THE RECTORY UMBRELLA.

This we started, we believe, in 1849 or 1850, in a ready bound square volume. It was admired at the time, but wholly unsupported, and it took us a year or more to fill the volume by our own unaided efforts. The volume exists, and in good preservation, and therefore any further account of it is needless.

We will here notice one or two of our own writings, which have seen more extended publicity than the above mentioned. In the summer of 1854 we contributed two poems to the " Oxonian Advertiser," neither at all worth preservation ; and in the Long Vacation of the same year, when staying with a reading party at Whitby, we contributed " The Lady of the Ladle " and " Wilhelm von Schmitz," to the weekly Gazette of that place. Both will be found inserted in this volume. From this subject we hasten to the consideration of the present magazine.

MISCH-MASCH.

The name is German, and means in English " midge-madge,' which we need not inform the intelligent reader is equivalent to " hodge-podge " : our intention is to admit articles of every kind, prose, verse, and pictures, provided they reach a sufficiently high standard of merit.

The best of its contents will be offered at intervals to a contemporary magazine of a less exclusively domestic nature : we allude to the Comic Times ; thus affording to the contributors to this magazine an opportunity of presenting their productions to the admiring gaze of the English Nation.

CROFT, *Aug.* 13, 1855.

THE TWO BROTHERS.

There were two brothers at Twyford school,
    And when they had left the place,
It was, "Will ye learn Greek and Latin?
        Or will ye run me a race?
Or will ye go up to yonder bridge,
    And there we will angle for
        dace?"

"I'm too stupid for Greek and
        for Latin,
    I'm too lazy by half for a race,
So I'll even go up to yonder
        bridge,
    And there we will angle for dace."

He has fitted together two joints of his rod,
    And to them he has added another,
And then a great hook he took from his book,
    And ran it right into his brother.

Oh much is the noise that is made among boys
    When playfully pelting a pig,
But a far greater pother was made by his brother
    When flung from the top of the brigg.

The fish hurried up by the dozens,
   All ready and eager to bite,
For the lad that he flung was so tender and young,
   It quite gave them an appetite.

Said, "Thus shall he wallop
      about
   And the fish take him quite
         at their ease,
For me to annoy it was ever
      his joy,
   Now I'll teach him the
      meaning of 'Tees'!"

The wind to his ear brought
      a voice,
   "My brother you didn't
         had ought ter !
And what have I done that
      you think it such fun
   To indulge in the pleasure
      of slaughter ?

"A good nibble or bite is my
      chiefest delight,
   When I'm merely expected
         to *see*,
But a bite from a fish is not
      quite what I wish,
   When I get it performed upon *me* ;
      And just now here's a swarm of dace at my arm,
      And a perch has got hold of my knee.

" For water my thirst was not great at the first,
    And of fish I have quite sufficien——"
" Oh fear not ! " he cried, " for whatever betide,
    We are both in the selfsame condition !

" I am sure that our state's very nearly alike
    (Not considering the question of slaughter)
For I have my perch on the top of the bridge,
    And you have your perch in the water.

" I stick to my perch and your perch sticks to you,
    We are really extremely alike ;
I've a turn pike up here, and I very much fear
    You may soon have a turn with a pike."

" Oh grant but one wish !   If I'm took by a fish
    (For your bait is your brother, good man !),
Pull him up if you like, but I hope you will strike
    As gently as ever you can."

" If the fish be a trout, I'm afraid there's no doubt
    I must strike him like lightning that's greased ;
If the fish be a pike, I'll engage not to strike,
    Till I've waited ten minutes at least."

" But in those ten minutes to desolate Fate
    Your brother a victim may fall ! "
" I'll reduce it to five, so *perhaps* you'll survive,
    But the chance is exceedingly small."

"Oh hard is your heart for to act such
　　a part;
　　Is it iron, or granite, or steel?"
"Why, I really can't say—it is many
　　a day
　　Since my heart was accustomed to
　　feel.

"'Twas my heart-cherished wish for
　　to slay many fish,
Each day did my malice grow worse,
For my heart didn't soften with
　　doing it so often,
　　But rather, I should say, the
　　reverse."

"Oh would I were back at Twy-
　　ford school,
　　Learning lessons in fear of the
　　birch!"
"Nay, brother!" he cried, "for
　　whatever betide,
　　You are better off here with your
　　perch!

"I am sure you'll allow you are happier now,
　　With nothing to do but to play;
And this single line here, it is perfectly clear,
　　Is much better than thirty a day!

"And as to the rod hanging over your head,
　　And apparently ready to fall,
That, you know, was the case, when you lived in that place,
　　So it need not be reckoned at all.

" Do you see that old trout with a turn-up-nose snout ?
      (Just to speak on a pleasanter
        theme,)
      Observe, my dear brother, our
        love for each other—
He's the one I like best in the stream.

" To-morrow I mean to invite him to dine
   (We shall all of us think it a treat),
If the day should he fine, I'll just *drop him a line*,
   And we'll settle what time we're to meet.

" He hasn't been into society yet,
   And his manners are not of the best,
So I think it quite fair that it should be *my* care,
   To see that he's properly dressed."

Many words brought the wind of " cruel " and
   " kind,"
And that " man suffers more than the brute":
Each several word with patience he heard,
   And answered with wisdom to boot.

" What ? prettier swimming in the stream,
   Than lying all snugly and flat ?
Do but look at that dish filled with glittering fish,
   Has Nature a picture like that ?

" What ? a higher delight to be drawn from the sight
   Of fish full of life and of glee ?
What a noodle you are ! 'tis delightfuller far
   To kill them than let them go free !

" I know there are people who prate by the hour
    Of the beauty of earth, sky, and ocean ;
Of the birds as they fly, of the fish darting by,
    Rejoicing in Life and in Motion.

" As to any delight to be got from the sight,
    It is all very well for a flat,
But *I* think it all gammon, for hooking a salmon
    Is better than twenty of that !

" They say that a man of a right-thinking mind
    Will *love* the dumb creatures he sees—
What's the use of his mind, if he's never inclined
    To pull a fish out of the Tees ?

" Take my friends and my home—as an outcast I'll roam :
    Take the money I have in the Bank—
It is just what I wish, but deprive me of *fish*,
    And my life would indeed be a blank ! '

Forth from the house his sister came,
    Her brothers for to see,
But when she saw that sight of awe,
    The tear stood in her ee.

" Oh what bait's that upon your hook,
    My brother, tell to me ? "
" It is but the fantailed pigeon,
    He would not sing for me."

" Whoe'er would expect a pigeon to sing,
    A simpleton he must be !
But a pigeon-cote is a different thing
    To the coat that there I see ! '

" Oh what bait's that upon your hook,
  My brother, tell to me ? "
" It is but the black-capped bantam,
  He would not dance for me."

" And 'a pretty dance you are leading him
    now ! "
  In anger answered she,
" But a bantam's cap is a different thing
  To the cap that there I see ! "

" Oh what bait's that upon your hook,
  Dear brother, tell to me ? "
" It is my younger brother," he cried,
  " Oh woe and dole is me !

" I's mighty wicked, that I is !
  Or how could such things be ?
Farewell, farewell sweet sister,
  I'm going o'er the sea."

" And when will you come back again,
  My brother, tell to me ? "
" When chub is good for human food,
  And that will never be ! "

She turned herself right round about,
  And her heart brake into three,
Said, " One of the two will be wet through and through,
  And 'tother'll be late for his tea ! "

CROFT, 1853.

POETRY FOR THE MILLION.

The nineteenth century has produced a new school of music, bearing about the same relation to the genuine article, which the hash or stew of Monday does to the joint of Sunday.

We allude of course to the prevalent practice of diluting the works of earlier composers with washy modern variations, so as to suit the weakened and depraved taste of this generation : this invention is termed " setting " by some, who, scorning the handsome offer of Alexander Smith, to " set this age to music," have determined to set music to this age.

Sadly we admit the stern necessity that exists for such a change : with stern prophetic eye we see looming in the shadowy Future the downfall of the sister Fine Arts. The National Gallery have already subjected some of their finest pictures to this painful operation : Poetry must follow.

That we may not be behind others in forwarding the progress of Civilisation, we boldly discard all personal and private feelings, and with quivering pen and tear-dimmed eye, we dedicate the following composition to the Spirit of the Age, and to that noble band of gallant adventurers, who aspire to lead the Van in the great March of Reform.

THE DEAR GAZELLE.

arranged with variations

espressivo

"I never loved a dear gazelle,"
Nor aught beside that cost me much ;
High prices profit those who sell.
But why should I be fond of such ?

p.p   *cres:*

"To glad me with his soft black eyes,"
My infant son, from Tooting School,
Thrashed by his bigger playmate, flies,
And serve him right, the little fool !

con spirito

A Tempo

"But when he came to know me well,"
He kicked me out, her testy sire ;
And when I stained my hair, that Bell
Might note the change, and thus admire

dim.   *cadenza*   *D.C.*

"And love me, it was sure to die"
A muddy green, or staring blue,
While one might trace, with half an eye,
The still triumphant carrot through.

con dolore

SHE'S ALL MY FANCY PAINTED HIM

A POEM.

[This affecting fragment was found in MS. among the papers of the well-known author of " Was it You or I ? " a tragedy, and the two popular novels, " Sister and Son," and " The Niece's Legacy, or the Grateful Grandfather."]

She's all my fancy painted him
  (I make no idle boast);
If he or you had lost a limb,
  Which would have suffered most ?

He said that you had been to her,
  And seen me here before;
But, in another character,
  She was the same of yore.

There was not one that spoke to us,
  Of all that thronged the street;
So he sadly got into a 'bus,
  And pattered with his feet.

They sent him word I had not gone
  (We know it to be true);
If she should push the matter on,
  What would become of you ?

They gave her one, they gave me two,
  They gave us three or more;
They all returned from him to you,
  Though they were mine before.

> If I or she should chance to be
>   Involved in this affair,
> He trusts to you to set them free,
>   Exactly as we were.
>
> It seemed to me that you had been
>   (Before she had this fit)
> An obstacle, that came between
>   Him, and ourselves, and it.
>
> Don't let him know she liked them best,
>   For this must ever be
> A secret, kept from all the rest,
>   Between yourself and me.

The above poem is the germ of the well-known lines which were read by the White Rabbit at the trial of the Knave of Hearts, and which the King regarded as important evidence, and attempted to explain without any very conspicuous success. ("Alice in Wonderland," pp. 182–187.)

PHOTOGRAPHY EXTRAORDINARY.

The recent extraordinary discovery in Photography, as applied to the operations of the mind, has reduced the art of novel-writing to the merest mechanical labour. We have been kindly permitted by the artist to be present during one of his experiments ; but as the invention has not yet been given to the world, we are only at liberty to relate the results, suppressing all details of chemicals and manipulation.

The operator began by stating that the ideas of the feeblest intellect, when once received on properly prepared paper, could be "developed" up to any required degree of intensity. On hearing our wish that he would begin with an extreme case, he obligingly summoned a young man from an adjoining room, who appeared to be of the very weakest possible physical and mental powers. On being asked what we thought of him, we candidly confessed that he seemed incapable of anything but sleep ; our friend cordially assented to this opinion.

The machine being in position, and a mesmeric rapport established between the mind of the patient and the object glass, the young man was asked whether he wished to say anything ; he feebly replied "Nothing." He was then asked what he was thinking of, and the answer, as before, was "Nothing." The artist on this pronounced him to be in a most satisfactory state, and at once commenced the operation.

After the paper had been exposed for the requisite time, it was removed and submitted to our inspection ; we found it to be covered with faint and almost illegible characters. A closer scrutiny revealed the following :—

"The eve was soft and dewy mild ; a zephyr whispered in the lofty glade, and a few light drops of rain cooled the thirsty soil. At a slow amble, along the primrose-bordered path rode a gentle-looking and amiable youth, holding a light cane in his delicate hand ; the pony moved gracefully beneath him, inhaling as it went the fragrance of the roadside flowers : the calm smile, and languid eyes, so admirably harmonising with the fair features of the rider, showed the even tenor of his thoughts. With a sweet though feeble voice, he plaintively murmured out the gentle regrets that clouded his breast :—

'Alas ! she would not hear my prayer !
Yet it were rash to tear my hair ;
Disfigured, I should be less fair.

> ' She was unwise, I may say blind ;
> Once she was lovingly inclined ;
> Some circumstance has changed her mind. '

There was a moment's silence ; the pony stumbled over a stone in the path, and unseated his rider. A crash was heard among the dried leaves ; the youth arose ; a slight bruise on his left shoulder, and a disarrangement of his cravat, were the only traces that remained of this trifling accident."

" This," we remarked, as we returned the papers, " belongs apparently to the milk-and-water School of Novels."

" You are quite right," our friend replied, " and, in its present state, it is of course utterly unsaleable in the present day : we shall find, however, that the next stage of development will remove it into the strong-minded or Matter-of-Fact School." After dipping it into various acids, he again submitted it to us : it had now become the following :—

" The evening was of the ordinary character, barometer at ' change ': a wind was getting up in the wood, and some rain was beginning to fall ; a bad look-out for the farmers. A gentleman approached along the bridle-road, carrying a stout knobbed stick in his hand, and mounted on a serviceable nag, possibly worth some £40 or so ; there was a settled business-like expression on the rider's face, and he whistled as he rode ; he seemed to be hunting for rhymes in his head, and at length repeated, in a satisfied tone, the following composition :—

> ' Well ! so my offer was no go !
> She might do worse, I told her so ;
> She was a fool to answer ' No.'

> ' However, things are as they stood ;
> Nor would I have her if I could,
> For there are plenty more as good.'

At this moment the horse set his foot in a hole, and rolled over; his rider rose with difficulty; he had sustained several severe bruises and fractured two ribs; it was some time before he forgot that unlucky day."

We returned this with the strongest expression of admiration, and requested that it might now be developed to the highest possible degree. Our friend readily consented, and shortly presented us with the result, which he informed us belonged to the Spasmodic or German School. We perused it with indescribable sensations of surprise and delight :—

" The night was wildly tempestuous — a hurricane raved through the murky forest—furious torrents of rain lashed the groaning earth. With a headlong rush—down a precipitous mountain gorge—dashed a mounted horseman armed to the teeth—his horse bounded beneath him at a mad gallop, snorting fire from its distended nostrils as it flew. The rider's knotted brows—rolling eye-balls—and clenched teeth— expressed the intense agony of his mind—weird visions loomed upon his burning brain—while with a mad yell he poured forth the torrent of his boiling passion :—

> ' Firebrands and daggers ! hope hath fled !
> To atoms dash the doubly dead !
> My brain is fire—my heart is lead !

> ' Her soul is flint, and what am I ?
> Scorch'd by her fierce, relentless eye,
> Nothingness is my destiny ! '

There was a moment's pause. Horror ! his path ended in a fathomless abyss. . . . A rush—a flash—a crash—all was over. Three drops of blood, two teeth, and a stirrup were all that remained to tell where the wild horseman met his doom.

The young man was now recalled to consciousness, and shown the result of the workings of his mind; he instantly fainted away.

In the present infancy of the art we forbear from further comment on this wonderful discovery; but the mind reels as it contemplates the stupendous addition thus made to the powers of science.

Our friend concluded with various minor experiments, such as working up a passage of Wordsworth into strong, sterling poetry: the same experiment was tried on a passage of Byron, at our request, but the paper came out scorched and blistered all over by the fiery epithets thus produced.

As a concluding remark: *could* this art be applied (we put the question in the strictest confidence)—*could* it, we ask, be applied to the speeches in Parliament? It may be but a delusion of our heated imagination, but we will still cling fondly to the idea, and hope against hope.

" SHE DID SO ; BUT 'TIS DOUBTFUL HOW OR WHENCE."—*Keats.*
(*From an etching by Lewis Carroll in* "*Misch-Masch.*")

HINTS FOR ETIQUETTE: OR, DINING OUT MADE EASY.

As caterers for the public taste, we can conscientiously recommend this book to all diners-out who are perfectly unacquainted with the usages of society. However we may regret that our author has confined himself to warning rather than advice, we are bound in justice to say that nothing here stated will be found to contradict the habits of the best circles. The following examples exhibit a depth of penetration and a fulness of experience rarely met with.

V.

In proceeding to the dining-room, the gentleman gives one arm to the lady he escorts—it is unusual to offer both.

VIII.

The practice of taking soup with the next gentleman but one is now wisely discontinued; but the custom of asking your host his opinion of the weather immediately on the removal of the first course still prevails.

IX.

To use a fork with your soup, intimating at the same time to your hostess that you are reserving the spoon for the beefsteaks, is a practice wholly exploded.

XI.

On meat being placed before you, there is no possible objection to your eating it, if so disposed; still in all such delicate cases, be guided entirely by the conduct of those around you.

XII.

It is always allowable to ask for artichoke jelly with your boiled venison ; however there are houses where this is not supplied.

XIII.

The method of helping roast turkey with two carving-forks is practicable, but deficient in grace.

XVII.

We do not recommend the practice of eating cheese with a knife and fork in one hand, and a spoon and wine-glass in the other ; there is a kind of awkwardness in the action which no amount of practice can entirely dispel.

XXVI.

As a general rule, do not kick the shins of the opposite gentleman under the table, if personally unacquainted with him ; your pleasantry is liable to be misunderstood—a circumstance at all times unpleasant.

XXVII.

Proposing the health of the boy in buttons immediately on the removal of the cloth, is a custom springing from regard to his tender years, rather than from a strict adherence to the rules of etiquette.

LAYS OF MYSTERY, IMAGINATION, AND HUMOUR.

No. I.

The Palace of Humbug.   (For the end of 1855.)

I dreamt I dwelt in marble halls,
And each damp thing that creeps and crawls
Went wobble-wobble on the walls.

Faint odours of departed cheese,
Blown on the dank, unwholesome breeze,
Awoke the never-ending sneeze.

Strange pictures decked the arras drear,
Strange characters of woe and fear,
The humbugs of the social sphere.

One showed a vain and noisy prig,
That shouted empty words and big
At him that nodded in a wig.

And one, a dotard grim and grey,
Who wasteth childhood's happy day
In work more profitless than play.

Whose icy breast no pity warms,
Whose little victims sit in swarms,
And slowly sob on lower forms.

And one, a green thyme-honoured Bank,
Where flowers are growing wild and rank,
Like weeds that fringe a poisoned tank.

All birds of evil omen there
Flood with rich Notes the tainted air,
The witless wanderer to snare.

The fatal Notes neglected fall,
No creature heeds the treacherous call,
For all those goodly Strawn Baits Pall.

The wandering phantom broke and fled,
Straightway I saw within my head
A Vision of a ghostly bed,

Where lay two worn decrepit men,
The fictions of a lawyer's pen,
Who never more might breathe again.

The serving-man of Richard Roe
Wept, inarticulate with woe :
She wept, that waited on John Doe.

" Oh rouse," I urged, " the waning sense
" With tales of tangled evidence,
" Of suit, demurrer, and defence."

" Vain," she replied, " such mockeries :
" For morbid fancies, such as these,
" No suits can suit, no plea can please.'

And bending o'er that man of straw,
She cried in grief and sudden awe,
Not inappropriately, " Law ! "

The well-remembered voice he knew,
He smiled, he faintly muttered " Sue ! "
(Her very name was legal too.)

The night was fled, the dawn was nigh :
A hurricane went raving by,
And swept the Vision from mine eye.

Vanished that dim and ghostly bed,
(The hangings, tape ; the tape was red :)
'Tis o'er, and Doe and Roe are dead !

Oh yet my spirit inly crawls,
What time it shudderingly recalls
That horrid dream of marble halls !

OXFORD, 1855

Every reader of " Through the Looking-Glass " will recognise the following " Stanza of Anglo-Saxon Poetry," for it is the burden of the immortal " Jabberwocky." It is interesting to compare the commentary given here with the derivations suggested by Humpty Dumpty. (" Through the Looking-Glass," pp. 126–129.)

STANZA OF ANGLO - SAXON POETRY.

TWAS BRYLLYG, AND Yᵉ SLYTHY COVES
DID GYRE AND GYHBLE IN Yᵉ WABE :
ALL HIIHSY WERS Yᵉ BOROGOVES ;
AND Yᵉ IHOHE RATHS OUTGRABE.

This curious fragment reads thus in modern characters.

TWAS BRYLLYG, AND THE SLYTHY TOVES
DID GYRE AND GYMBLE IN THE WABE.
ALL MIMSY WERE THE BOROGOVES;
AND THE MOME RATHS OUTGRABE.

The meanings of the words are as follows:

BRYLLYG. (derived from the verb to BRYL or BROIL). "the time of broiling dinner, i.e the close of the afternoon "

SLYTHY (compounded of SLIMY and LITHE). " smooth and active.

TOVE a species of Badger. They had smooth white hair, long

hind legs, and short horns like a stag. lived chiefly on cheese

GYRE verb (derived from GYAOUR or GIAOUR, "a dog") "to scratch like a dog"

GYMBLE (whence GIMBLET) to screw out holes in anything

WABE (derived from the verb to SWAB or SOAK) "the side of hill. (from its being soaked by the rain)

MIMSY (whence MIMSERABLE and MISERABLE) "unhappy

BOROGOVE An extinct kind of Parrot The had no wings beaks turned up, and made their nests under sun-dials lived on veal

MOME (hence SOLEMOME SOLEMONE and SOLEMN) grave

RATH. A species of land turtle Head erect mouth like a shark the fore legs curved out so that the animal walked on it's knees. smooth green body lived on swallows and oysters

OUTGRABE. past tense of the verb to OUTGRIBE (it is connected with the old verb to GRIKE or SHRIKE, from which are derived "shriek" and "creak".) "squeaked"

Hence the literal English of the passage is:
"It was evening, and the smooth active badgers were scratching and boring holes in the hill side; all unhappy were the parrots; and the grave turtles squeaked out""

There were probably sun dials on the top of the hill, and the "borogoves" were afraid that their nests would be undermined The hill was probably full of the nests of "raths", which ran out squeaking with fear on hearing the "tones" scratching outside This is an obscure, but yet deeply affecting relic of ancient Poetry

Croft 1855   Ed

LEWIS CARROLL'S STUDY AT CHRIST CHURCH, OXFORD.

Morris L. Parrish Collection, Princeton University Library

PROFESSOR JOWETT.
(*From a photograph by Mr. Hay Cameron.*)

CHAPTER II

U NDER the above title Lewis Carroll issued in 1874 a collection of papers on Oxford matters which had appeared in separate form at various periods between 1865–1874. The volume has been long out of print, which is the more to be regretted as it contains some very brilliant writing, and the humour, which is apparent on almost every page, has lost but little of its force. However, as many of my readers will not, in all probability, be sufficiently conversant with Oxford affairs thirty years ago to fully appreciate these *jeux d'esprit* without some explanations, a short introduction, kindly supplied by my friend Mr. Lewis Sergeant, is prefixed to each of the papers.

It only remains to add that the present is a

reprint of the 1874 edition, which was originally published in one volume by Mr. James Parker of Oxford.

THE NEW METHOD OF EVALUATION
AS APPLIED TO π.

[The year 1865, when this playful reflex of academic affairs at Oxford was originally printed, found the University keenly interested in the case of Mr. Jowett, Regius Professor of Greek. The shabby treatment of the professor was matter of frequent comment in the public press. The details of this case are sufficiently familiar. It was early in the year 1865, ten years after the appointment of Jowett by Lord Palmerston, that the Dean and Chapter of Christ Church resolved to increase the salary of the professorship to £500. They had previously sought the opinion of counsel, according to which they were under no obligation to pay the Regius Professor more than £40 ; but their resolution to pay the larger sum was taken, as they declared, " on grounds of general expediency."

" The New Method " is to a large extent self-explanatory. The Π which it is required to evaluate stands for the proper payment to be assigned to Jowett. " Penrhyn's Method" refers, of course, to the action taken by Arthur Penrhyn Stanley : his "transformation into a new scale of notation," from the *senary* to the *denary*, signifies his appointment as Dean of Westminster in 1864. The " senary" may be an indirect allusion to Stanley's repeated travels, and the many " beautiful expressions " to the charming books in which he described them. His " exhaustive process for extracting the value of Π in a series of *terms*, by repeated *divisions* " signifies the persistence with which Stanley challenged the opinion of the University in the interests of Jowett.

The process of appealing to reason involved " the breaking up of U (the University) into its partial factions." Pusey and Liddon appear as E. B. P. and H. P. L. Pusey, though one of the keenest opponents of Jowett on the question of religious orthodoxy, accepted the decision of the Chancellor's court, that a professor's theological teaching could not be impugned unless it was given in his lectures as a professor ; he therefore voted in 1864 for the endowment of the chair by the University, and, this failing, he helped to promote the arrangement by which Christ Church found the necessary money. The "Patristic Catenary" was the edition of the Fathers on which Pusey had been engaged with others of the High Church school. The "Essays and Reviews," to which Jowett had contributed, were published in 1861 ; but they came into fresh prominence in 1864, after the reversal of the decree of the Court of Arches against Messrs. Williams and Wilson by the final Court of Appeal. The H. G. L. of the concluding chapter was the Dean of Christ Church ; and possibly ϕ (H. G. L.) may be taken as a gentle remonstrance with the Head of the House for yielding to pressure, and sacrificing "moral obligation" to "expediency."]

THE NEW METHOD

OF

EVALUATION

AS APPLIED TO π

―――

" Little Jack Horner
Sat in a corner,
Eating his Christmas Pie."

―――

FIRST PRINTED IN 1865

𝕺𝖗𝖋𝖔𝖗𝖉:

JAMES PARKER AND CO.

1874.

CONTENTS.

THE NEW METHOD OF EVALUATION
AS APPLIED TO π.

The problem of evaluating π, which has engaged the attention of mathematicians from the earliest ages, had, down to our own time, been considered as purely arithmetical. It was reserved for this generation to make the discovery that it is in reality a dynamical problem; and the true value of π, which appeared an *ignis fatuus* to our forefathers, has been at last obtained under pressure.

The following are the main data of the problem:

Let U = the University, G = Greek, and P = Professor. Then GP = Greek Professor; let this be reduced to its lowest terms, and call the result J.

Also let W = the work done, T = the Times, p = the given payment, π = the payment according to T, and S = the sum required; so that $\pi = S$.

The problem is, to obtain a value for π which shall be commensurable with W.

In the early treatises on this subject, the mean

value assigned to π will be found to be 40.000000. Later writers suspected that the decimal point had been accidentally shifted, and that the proper value was 400.00000 ; but, as the details of the process for obtaining it had been lost, no further progress was made in the subject till our own time, though several most ingenious methods were tried for solving the problem.

Of these methods we proceed to give some brief account. Those chiefly worthy of note appear to be Rationalisation, the Method of Indifferences, Penrhyn's Method, and the Method of Elimination.

We shall conclude with an account of the great discovery of our own day, the Method of Evaluation under Pressure.

I.—Rationalisation.

The peculiarity of this process consists in its affecting all quantities alike with a negative sign.

To apply it, let H = High Church, and L = Low Church then the geometric mean $= \sqrt{HL}$: call this " B " (Broad Church).

$$\therefore HL = B^2.$$

Also let x and y represent unknown quantities

The process now requires the breaking up of U into its partial factions, and the introduction of certain combinations. Of the two principal factions thus formed, that corresponding with P presented no further difficulty, but it appeared hopeless to rationalise the other.

A *reductio ad absurdum* was therefore attempted, and it was asked, " Why should π *not* be evaluated ? " The great difficulty now was, to discover y.

Several ingenious substitutions and transformations were then resorted to, with a view to simplifying the equation, and it was at one time asserted, though never actually proved, that the $y's$ were all on one side. However, as repeated trials produced the same irrational result, the process was finally abandoned.

II.--The Method of Indifferences.

This was a modification of "*the method of finite Differences*," and may be thus briefly described :—

Let E = Essays, and R = Reviews : then the locus of $(E + R)$, referred to multilinear co-ordinates, will be found to be a superficies (*i.e.*, a locus possessing length and breadth, but no depth). Let ν = novelty, and assume $(E + R)$ as a function of ν.

Taking this superficies as the plane of reference, we get—

$$E = R = B.$$
$$\therefore \ EB = B^2 = HL \text{ (by the last article).}$$

Multiplying by P, $EBP = HPL$.

It was now necessary to investigate the locus of EBP : this was found to be a species of Catenary, called the Patristic Catenary, which is usually defined as "passing through origen, and containing many multiple points." The locus of HPL will be found almost entirely to coincide with this.

Great results were expected from the assumption of $(E + R)$ as a function of ν : but the opponents of this theorem, having actually succeeded in demonstrating that the ν-element did not even enter into the function, it appeared hopeless to obtain any real value of π by this method.

III.—Penrhyn's Method.

This was an exhaustive process for extracting the value of π, in a series of terms, by repeated

DEAN STANLEY.

(From a photograph by Lewis Carroll.)

THE NEW BELFRY, CHRIST CHURCH, OXFORD.

Morris L. Parrish Collection, Princeton University Library

divisions. The series so obtained appeared to be convergent, but the residual quantity was always negative, which of course made the process of extraction impossible.

This theorem was originally derived from a radical series in Arithmetical Progression : let us denote the series itself by A.P., and its sum by (A.P.)S. It was found that the function (A.P.)S. entered into the above process, in various forms.

The experiment was therefore tried of transforming (A.P.)S. into a new scale of notation : it had hitherto been, through a long series of terms, entirely in the senary, in which scale it had furnished many beautiful expressions : it was now transformed into the denary.

Under this modification, the process of division was repeated, but with the old negative result ; the attempt was therefore abandoned, though not without a hope that future mathematicians, by introducing a number of hitherto undetermined constants, raised to the second degree, might succeed in obtaining a positive result.

IV.—Elimination of J.

It had long been perceived that the chief obstacle to the evaluation of π was the presence of J, and in an earlier age of mathematics J would probably have been referred to rectangular axes, and divided into two unequal parts—a process of arbitrary elimination which is now considered not strictly legitimate.

It was proposed, therefore, to eliminate J by an appeal to the principle known as "*the permanence of equivalent formularies:*" this, however, failed on application, as J became indeterminate. Some advocates of the process would have preferred that J should be eliminated "*in toto.*" The classical scholar need hardly be reminded that "*toto*" is the ablative of "*tumtum,*" and that this beautiful and expressive phrase embodied the wish that J should be eliminated by a compulsory religious examination.

It was next proposed to eliminate J by means of a "canonisant." The chief objection to this process was, that it would raise J to an inconveniently high power, and would after all only give an irrational value for π.

Other processes, which we need not here describe, have been suggested for the evaluation of π. One was that it should be treated as a *given* quantity: this theory was supported by many eminent men, at Cambridge and elsewhere ; but, on application, J was found to exhibit a negative sign, which of course made the evaluation impossible.

We now proceed to describe the modern method, which has been crowned with brilliant and unexpected success, and which may be defined as—

V.—Evaluation Under Pressure.

Mathematicians had already investigated the locus of HPL, and had introduced this function into the calculation, but without effecting the desired evaluation, even when HPL was transferred to the opposite side of the equation with a change of sign. The process we are about to describe consists chiefly in the substitution of G for P, and the application of pressure.

Let the function ϕ (HGL) be developed into a series, and let the sum of this be assumed as a perfectly rigid body, moving in a fixed line : let "μ" be the coefficient of moral obligation, and "e" the expediency. Also let "F" be a Force acting equally in all directions, and varying inversely as T : let A = Able, and E = Enlightened.

We have now to develope ϕ (HGL) by Maclaurin's Theorem.

The function itself vanishes when the variable vanishes :

$$
\begin{aligned}
\textit{I.e., } \phi(\circ) &= \text{O.} \\
\phi'(\circ) &= \text{C (a prime constant).} \\
\phi''(\circ) &= \text{2. J.} \\
\phi'''(\circ) &= \text{2.3.H.} \\
\phi''''(\circ) &= \text{2.3.4.S.} \\
\phi'''''(\circ) &= \text{2.3.4.5.P.} \\
\phi''''''(\circ) &= \text{2.3.4.5.6.J.}
\end{aligned}
$$

after which the quantities recur in the same order.

The above proof is taken from the learned treatise "*Augusti de fallibilitate historicorum*," and occupies an entire Chapter : the evaluation of π is given in the next Chapter. The author takes occasion to point out several remarkable properties possessed by the above series, the existence of which had hardly been suspected before.

This series is a function of μ and of e : but, when it is considered as a body it will be found that $\mu = \text{o}$, and that e only remains.

We now have the equation—

$$\phi\,(HGL) = O + C + J + H + S + P + J.$$

The summation of this gave a minimum value for π : this, however, was considered only as a first approximation, and the process was repeated under pressure EAF, which gave to π a partial maximum value ; by continually increasing EAF, the result was at last obtained, $\pi = S = 500.00000$.

This result differs considerably from the anticipated value, namely, 400.00000 : still there can be no doubt that the process has been correctly performed, and that the learned world may be congratulated on the final settlement of this most difficult problem.

THE END.

THE DYNAMICS OF A PARTI CLE.

[This is perhaps the best known, and in some respects the wittiest, of Mr. Dodgson's Oxford " Notes." The definitions, postulates, and axioms, as well as the " Dynamics of a Particle," will be familiar to many, and they arose out of circumstances which excited the University even more than the disputation over Jowett. In 1865 Mr. Gladstone was defeated at Oxford, after having represented his University in the House of Commons for eighteen years. The candidates, who appear in the following pages by their initials, were Sir W. Heathcote, Mr. Gathorne Hardy, and Mr. Gladstone. The polling extended over a week. On the third day Mr. Hardy led Mr. Gladstone by 230 ; but, after a strong appeal and rally on behalf of the Liberals, the final majority was no more than 180. The total number of voters was nearly twice as large as on any previous occasion—" whereby, the entry of the Convocation House being blocked up, men could pass neither in nor out."]

THE DYNAMICS

OF A

PARTI-CLE.

" 'Tis strange the mind, that very fiery particle,
Should let itself be snuff'd out by an article."

FIRST PRINTED IN 1865.

Oxford :

JAMES PARKER AND CO.

1874.

INTRODUCTION.

It was a lovely Autumn evening, and the glorious effects of chromatic aberration were beginning to show themselves in the atmosphere as the earth revolved away from the great western luminary, when two lines might have been observed wending their weary way across a plain superficies. The elder of the two had by long practice acquired the art, so painful to young and impulsive loci, of lying evenly between her extreme points ; but the younger, in her girlish impetuosity, was ever longing to diverge and become an hyperbola or some such romantic and boundless curve. They had lived and loved : fate and the intervening superficies had hitherto kept them asunder, but this was no longer to be : *a line had intersected them, making the two interior angles together less than two right angles.* It was a moment never to be forgotten, and, as they journeyed on, a whisper thrilled along the superficies in isochronous waves of sound, " Yes ! We shall at length meet if continually produced! " ' (Jacobi's Course of Mathematics, Chap. I.)

We have commenced with the above quotation

as a striking illustration of the advantage of introducing the human element into the hitherto barren
region of Mathematics. Who shall say what
germs of romance, hitherto unobserved, may not
underlie the subject? Who can tell whether the
parallelogram, which in our ignorance we have
defined and drawn, and the whole of whose
properties we profess to know, may not be all the
while panting for exterior angles, sympathetic
with the interior, or sullenly repining at the fact
that it cannot be inscribed in a circle? What
mathematician has ever pondered over an
hyperbola, mangling the unfortunate curve with
lines of intersection here and there, in his efforts
to prove some property that perhaps after all is a
mere calumny, who has not fancied at last that the
ill-used locus was spreading out its asymptotes as
a silent rebuke, or winking one focus at him in
contemptuous pity?

In some such spirit as this we have compiled
the following pages. Crude and hasty as they
are, they yet exhibit some of the phenomena of
light, or " enlightenment," considered as a force,
more fully than has hitherto been attempted by
other writers.

June, 1865.

CONTENTS.

CHAPTER I.

GENERAL CONSIDERATIONS.

Definitions.
Postulates.
Axioms.
Methods of Voting.
On Representation.

CHAPTER II.

DYNAMICS OF A PARTICLE.

Introductory.
Definitions.
On Differentiation.
Propositions.

CHAPTER I.

DEFINITIONS.

I.

PLAIN SUPERFICIALITY is the character of a speech, in which any two points being taken, the speaker is found to lie wholly with regard to those two points.

II.

PLAIN ANGER is the inclination of two voters to one another, who meet together, but whose views are not in the same direction.

III.

When a Proctor, meeting another Proctor, makes the votes on one side equal to those on the other, the feeling entertained by each side is called RIGHT ANGER.

IV.

When two parties, coming together, feel a Right Anger, each is *said* to be COMPLEMENTARY to the other, (though, strictly speaking, this is very seldom the case).

V.

OBTUSE ANGER is that which is greater than Right Anger.

POSTULATES.

I.

Let it be granted, that a speaker may digress from any one point to any other point.

II.

That a finite argument, (*i.e.*, one finished and disposed of,) may be produced to any extent in subsequent debates.

III.

That a controversy may be raised about any question, and at any distance from that question.

AXIOMS.

I.

Men who go halves in the same (quart) are (generally) equal to another.

II.

Men who take a double in the same (term) are equal to anything.

On Voting.

The different methods of voting are as follows :

I.

ALTERNANDO, as in the case of Mr. ——, who voted for and against Mr. Gladstone, alternate elections.

II.

INVERTENDO, as was done by Mr. ——, who came all the way from Edinburgh to vote, handed in a blank voting paper, and so went home rejoicing.

III.

COMPONENDO, as was done by Mr. ——, whose name appeared on both committees at once, whereby he got great praise from all men, by the space of one day.

IV.

DIVIDENDO, as in Mr. ——'s case, who, being sorely perplexed in his choice of candidates, voted for neither.

V.

CONVERTENDO, as was wonderfully exemplified by Messrs. —— and ——, who held a long and fierce argument on the election, in which, at the

end of two hours, each had vanquished and con
verted the other.

VI.

Ex Æquali in Proportione Perturbatâ seu
Inordinatâ, as in the election, when the result
was for a long time equalised, and as it were held
in the balance, by reason of those who had first
voted on the one side seeking to pair off with
those who had last arrived on the other side, and
those who were last to vote on the one side being
kept out by those who had first arrived on the
other side, whereby, the entry to the Convocation House being blocked up, men could pass
neither in nor out.

On Representation.

Magnitudes are algebraically represented by
letters, men by men of letters, and so on. The
following are the principal systems of representation :—

1. Cartesian : *i.e.*, by means of " cartes."
This system represents *lines* well, sometimes too
well ; but fails in representing *points*, particularly
good points.

2. Polar : *i.e.*, by means of the 2 poles,

" North and South." This is a very uncertain system of representation, and one that cannot safely be depended upon.

3. TRILINEAR : *i e.*, by means of a line which takes 3 different courses. Such a line is usually expressed by three letters, as W.E.G.

That the principle of Representation was known to the ancients is abundantly exemplified by Thucydides, who tells us that the favourite cry of encouragement during a trireme race was that touching allusion to Polar Co-ordinates which is still heard during the races of our own time, " $\rho 5$, $\rho 6$, cos ϕ, they're gaining !"

CHAPTER II.

DYNAMICS OF A PARTICLE.

Particles are logically divided according to GENIUS and SPEECHES.

GENIUS is the higher classification, and this, combined with DIFFERENTIA (*i.e.*, difference of opinion), produces SPEECHES. These again naturally divide themselves into three heads.

Particles belonging to the great order of GENIUS are called "able" or "enlightened."

DEFINITIONS.

I.

A SURD is a radical whose meaning cannot be exactly ascertained. This class comprises a very large number of particles.

II.

INDEX indicates the degree, or power, to which a particle is raised. It consists of two letters, placed to the right of the symbol representing the particle. Thus, " A.A." signifies the oth degree ; " B.A." the 1st degree ; and so on, till we reach " M.A." the 2nd degree (the intermediate letters indicating fractions of a degree); the last two usually employed being " R.A." (the reader need hardly be reminded of that beautiful line in *The Princess* " Go dress yourself, Dinah, like a gorgeous R.A.") and " S.A." This last indicates the 360th degree, and denotes that the particle in question (which is $\frac{1}{7}$th part of the function $\overline{E + R}$ " Essays and Reviews ") has effected a complete revolution, and that the result $= 0$.

III.

Moment is the product of the mass into the velocity. To discuss this subject fully, would lead us too far into the subject Vis Viva, and we must content ourselves with mentioning the fact that *no moment is ever really lost, by fully enlightened Particles.* It is scarcely necessary to quote the well-known passage : " Every moment, that can be snatched from academical duties, is devoted to furthering the cause of the popular Chancellor of the Exchequer." (Clarendon, " History of the Great Rebellion.")

IV.

A Couple consists of a moving particle, raised to the degree M.A., and combined with what is technically called a "better half." The following are the principal characteristics of a Couple : (1) It may be easily transferred from point to point. (2) Whatever *force of translation* was possessed by the uncombined particle (and this is often considerable), is wholly lost when the Couple is formed. (3) The two forces constituting the Couple habitually *act in opposite directions.*

On Differentiation.

The effect of Differentiation on a Particle is very remarkable, the first Differential being frequently of a greater value than the original Particle, and the second of less enlightenment.

For example, let L = " Leader," S = " Saturday," and then L.S. = " Leader in the Saturday " (a particle of no assignable value). Differentiating once, we get L.S.D., a function of great value. Similarly it will be found that, by taking the second Differential of an enlightened Particle (*i.e.*, raising it to the degree D.D.), the enlightenment becomes rapidly less. The effect is much increased by the addition of a C : in this case the enlightenment often vanishes altogether, and the Particle becomes conservative.

It should be observed that, whenever the symbol L is used to denote " Leader," it must be affected with the sign ± : this serves to indicate that its action is sometimes positive and sometimes negative—some particles of this class having the property of drawing others after them (as " a Leader of an army "), and others of repelling them (as " a Leader of the Times ").

PROPOSITIONS.

Prop. I. Pr.

To find the value of a given Examiner.

Example.—A takes in ten books in the Final Examination, and gets a 3rd Class : B takes in the Examiners, and gets a 2nd. Find the value of the Examiners in terms of books. Find also their value in terms in which no Examination is held.

Prop. II. Pr.

To estimate Profit and Loss.

Example.—Given a Derby Prophet, who has sent three different winners to three different betting men, and given that none of the three horses are placed. Find the total Loss incurred by the three men (a) in money, (β) in temper. Find also the Prophet. Is this latter generally possible?

Prop. III. Pr.

To estimate the direction of a line.

Example.—Prove that the definition of a line, according to Walton, coincides with that of Salmon, only that they begin at opposite ends.

If such a line be divided by Frost's method, find its value according to Price.

Prop. IV. Th.

The end (*i.e.*, " the product of the extremes,") justifies (*i.e.*, " is equal to "—see Latin " aequus,") the means.

No example is appended to this Proposition, for obvious reasons.

Prop. V. Pr.

To continue a given series.

Example.—A and B, who are respectively addicted to Fours and Fives, occupy the same set of rooms, which is always at Sixes and Sevens. Find the probable amount of reading done by A and B while the Eights are on.

We proceed to illustrate this hasty sketch of the Dynamics of a Parti-cle, by demonstrating the great Proposition on which the whole theory of Representation depends, namely, " To remove a given Tangent from a given Circle, and to bring another given Line into Contact with it."

To work the following problem algebraically,

it is best to let the circle be represented as referred to its two tangents, *i.e.*, first to WEG,
WH, and afterwards to WH, GH. When this
is effected, it will be found most convenient to
project WEG to infinity. The process is not
given here in full, since it requires the introduction of many complicated determinants.

Prop. VI. Pr.

To remove a given Tangent from a given
Circle, and to bring another given Line into
contact with it.

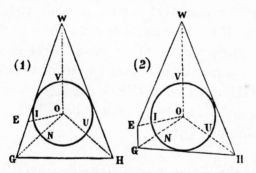

Let UNIV be a Large Circle, whose centre is
O (V being, of course, placed at the top), and let
WGH be a triangle, two of whose sides, WEG
and WH, are in contact with the circle, while
GH (called "the base" by liberal mathema-

ticians,) is not in contact with it. (See Fig. 1.) It is required to destroy the contact of WEG, and to bring GH into contact instead.

Let I be the point of maximum illumination of the circle, and therefore E the point of maximum enlightenment of the triangle. (E of course varying perversely as the square of the distance from O).

Let WH be fixed absolutely, and remain always in contact with the circle, and let the direction of OI be also fixed.

Now, so long as WEG preserves a perfectly straight course, GH cannot possibly come into contact with the circle ; but if the force of illumination, acting along OI, cause it to bend (as in Fig. 2), a partial revolution on the part of WEG and GH is effected, WEG ceases to touch the circle, and GH is immediately brought into contact with it. Q.E.F.

The theory involved in the foregoing Proposition is at present much controverted, and its supporters are called upon to show what is the fixed *point*, or " *locus standi*," on which they propose to effect the necessary revolution. To make this clear, we must go to the original Greek, and remind our readers that the true point or " locus standi " is in this case ἄρδις, (or ἄρδις according to modern usage), and therefore must not be assigned to WEG. In reply to this it is urged that, in a matter like the present, a single word cannot be considered a satisfactory explanation, such as ἀρδέως.

It should also be observed that the revolution here discussed is entirely the effect of enlightenment, since particles, when illuminated to such an extent as actually to become φῶς, are always found to diverge more or less widely from each other; though undoubtedly the *radical* force of the word is " union " or " friendly feeling." The reader will find in " Liddell and Scott " a remarkable illustration of this, from which it appears to be an essential condition that the feeling should be entertained φοράδην, and that the particle entertaining it should belong to the genus σκότος, and should therefore be, nominally at least, unenlightened.

THE END.

FACTS, FIGURES, AND FANCIES.

[The occasions of the three following papers are adequately explained by the Introductory matter prefixed to them by the Author. The notes to the first poetical epistle suffice to make its allusions clear. I will merely add that " C for Chairman" means the " see " of Chester for Dr. Jacobson, a distinguished Liberal who had been chairman of Mr. Gladstone's election committee.

" The Deserted Parks," in form a parody on " The Deserted Village," is a half serious protest against the over-encouragement of sports and ends with an appeal for the votes of independent electors against the proposed decree.]

FACTS, FIGURES, AND FANCIES,

RELATING TO

THE ELECTIONS TO THE HEBDOMADAL COUNCIL,

THE OFFER OF THE CLARENDON TRUSTEES,

AND

THE PROPOSAL TO CONVERT THE PARKS INTO CRICKET-GROUNDS.

" Thrice the brinded cat hath mewed."

FIRST PRINTED IN 1866–1868.

Oxford :

JAMES PARKER AND CO.

1874.

INTRODUCTORY.

§ I. The Elections to the Hebdomadal Council.

In the year 1866, a Letter with the above title was published in Oxford, addressed to the Senior Censor of Christ Church, with the twofold object of revealing to the University a vast political misfortune which it had unwittingly encountered, and of suggesting a remedy which should at once alleviate the bitterness of the calamity and secure the sufferers from its recurrence. The misfortune thus revealed was no less than the fact that, at a recent election of Members to the Hebdomadal Council, *two* Conservatives had been chosen, thus giving a Conservative majority in the Council; and the remedy suggested was a sufficiently sweeping one, embracing, as it did, the following details :—

1. "The exclusion" (from Congregation) "of the non-academical elements which form a main part of the strength of this party domination." These "elements" are afterwards enumerated as "the parish clergy and the professional men of the city, and chaplains who are without any academical occupation."

2. The abolition of the Hebdomadal Council.

3. The abolition of the legislative functions of Convocation.

These are all the main features of this remarkable scheme of Reform, unless it be necessary to add

4. "To preside over a Congregation with full legislative powers, the Vice-Chancellor ought no doubt to be a man of real capacity."

But it would be invidious to suppose that there was any intention of suggesting this as a novelty.

The following rhythmical version of the Letter developes

its principles to an extent which possibly the writer had never contemplated.

§ II. THE OFFER OF THE CLARENDON TRUSTEES.

Letter from Mr. Gladstone to the Vice-Chancellor.

DEAR MR. VICE-CHANCELLOR,—The Clarendon Trustees . . are ready, in concert with the University, to consider of the best mode of applying the funds belonging to them for "adding to the New Museum Physical Laboratories and other accommodation requisite for the department of Experimental Philosophy." . . .

I have the honour to remain,
Dear Mr. Vice-Chancellor,
Very faithfully yours,
May 3, 1867.   W. E. GLADSTONE.

The following passages are quoted from a paper which appeared on the subject.

"As Members of Convocation are called upon to consider the offer of the Clarendon Trustees, to employ the funds at their disposal in the erection of additional buildings to facilitate the study of Physics, they may perhaps find it useful to have a short statement of the circumstances which render additional buildings necessary, and of the nature of the accommodation required."

"Again, it is often impossible to carry on accurate Physical experiments in close contiguity to one another, owing to their mutual interference; and consequently different processes need different rooms, in which these delicate instruments, which are always required in a particular branch of science, have to be carefully and permanently fixed."

.　　　.　　　.　　　.　　　.

"It may be sufficient, in order to give an idea of the number of rooms required, to enumerate the chief branches of Physics which require special accommodation, owing to their mutual interference.

(1) Weighing and measuring.
(2) Heat.
(3) Radiant Heat.
(4) Dispersion of Light.　Spectrum Analysis, &c.
(5) General optics.
(6) Statical electricity.
(7) Dynamical electricity.
(8) Magnetism.
(9) Acoustics.

Of these, (5) requires one large room or three smaller rooms, and these, together with those devoted to (3) and (4), should have a south aspect. Besides the fixed instruments, there is a large quantity of movable apparatus, which is either used with them or employed in illustrating lectures; and this must be carefully preserved from causes of deterioration when not in use; for this purpose a large room fitted with glass cases is required. A store-room for chemicals and other materials used is also necessary."

.　　　.　　　.　　　.　　　.　　　.

"As Photography is now very much employed in multiplying results of observation, in constructing diagrams for lectures, &c., and as it is in fact a branch of Physics, a small Photographic room is necessary, both for general use and for studying the subject itself."

.　　　.　　　.　　　.　　　.

§ III. The Proposal to Convert the Parks into Cricket-Grounds.

Notice from the Vice-Chancellor.

" A form of Decree to the following effect will be proposed :—

" 1. That the Curators of the Parks be authorised to receive applications from Members of the University for Cricket-grounds in the Parks, and that public notice be issued to that effect, a time being fixed within which applications are to be sent in.

" 2. That at the expiration of such time the Curators be authorised to make Cricket-grounds, and allot them to Cricket-clubs or Colleges from which applications have been received, according to priority of application. . . .

" F. K. Leighton,

" *Vice-Chancellor.*

" *April* 29, 1867."

THE ELECTIONS TO THE HEBDOMADAL COUNCIL.

" Now is the winter of our discontent." [1]

" Heard ye the arrow hurtle in the sky ?
Heard ye the dragon-monster's deathful cry ? "—
Excuse this sudden burst of the Heroic ;
The present state of things would vex a Stoic !
And just as Sairey Gamp, for pains within,
Administered a modicum of gin,
So does my mind, when vexed and ill at ease,
Console itself with soothing similes.

---

[1] Dr. Wynter, President of St. John's, one of the recently elected Conservative members of Council.

The " dragon-monster " (pestilential schism !)
I need not tell you is Conservatism ;
The " hurtling arrow " (till we find a better)
Is represented by the present Letter.

'Twas, I remember, but the other day,
Dear Senior Censor, that you chanced to say
You thought these party-combinations would
Be found, " though needful, no unmingled good. '
Unmingled good?   They are unmingled ill ! [1]
I never took to them, and never will——— [2]
What am I saying?   Heed it not, my friend :
On the next page I mean to recommend
The very dodges that I now condemn   )
In the Conservatives !   Don't hint to them   }
A word of this !   (In confidence.   Ahem !))
    Need I rehearse the history of Jowett ?
I need not, Senior Censor, for you know it. [3]
That was the Board Hebdomadal, and oh !
Who would be free, themselves must strike the blow !
Let each that wears a beard, and each that shaves,
Join in the cry " We never will be slaves ! "
" But can the University afford
" To be a slave to any kind of board ?
" A *slave ?* " you shuddering ask.   " Think you it can,
    Sir ? "
" *Not at the present moment,*" is my answer. [4]

[1]   " In a letter on a point connected with the late elections to the
Hebdomadal Council you incidentally remarked to me that our combinations for these elections, ' though necessary were not an unmixed good.'
They are an unmixed evil."
[2]   " I never go to a *caucus* without reluctance : I never write a canvassing
letter without a feeling of repugnance to my task."
[3] " I need not rehearse the history of the Regius Professor of Greek."
[4]   " The University cannot afford at the present moment to be delivered
over as a slave to any non-academical interest whatever."

I've thought the matter o'er and o'er again
And given to it all my powers of brain ;
I've thought it out, and this is what I make it,
(And I don't care a Tory how you take it :)
It may be right to go ahead, I guess:
It may be right to stop, I do confess ;
Also, it may be right to retrogress.[1]
So says the oracle, and, for myself, I
Must say it beats to fits the one at Delphi !

   To save beloved Oxford from the yoke,
(For this majority's beyond a joke,)
We must combine,[2] aye ! hold a *caucus*-meeting,[3]
Unless we want to get another beating.
That they should " bottle " us is nothing new—
But shall they bottle us and *caucus* too ?
See the " fell unity of purpose " now
With which Obstructives plunge into the row ![4]
" Factious Minorities," we used to sigh—
" Factious Majorities ! " is now the cry.
" Votes—ninety-two "—no combination here :
" Votes—ninety-three "—conspiracy, 'tis clear ![5]
You urge " 'Tis but a unit." I reply
That in that unit lurks their " unity."

---

[1] " It may be right to go on, it may be right to stand still, or it may be right to go back."

[2] "To save the University from going completely under the yoke . . . we shall still be obliged to combine."

[3] " Caucus-holding and wire-pulling would still be almost inevitably carried on to some extent."

[4] "But what are we to do? Here is a great political and theological party . . . labouring under perfect discipline and with fell unity of purpose, to hold the University in subjection, and fill her government with its nominees."

[5] At a recent election to Council, the Liberals mustered ninety-two votes, and the Conservatives ninety-three ; whereupon the latter were charged with having obtained their victory by a conspiracy.

Our voters often bolt, and often baulk us,
But then, they never, never go to *caucus !*
Our voters can't forget the maxim famous
" *Semel electum semper eligamus* ";
They never can be worked into a ferment
By visionary promise of preferment,
Nor taught, by hints of " Paradise " [1] beguiled,
To whisper " C for Chairman " like a child ! [2]
And thus the friends that we have tempted down
Oft take the two-o'clock Express for town.[3]

This is our danger : this the secret foe
That aims at Oxford such a deadly blow.
What champion can we find to save the State,
To crush the plot ?   We darkly whisper " Wait ! " [4]

My scheme is this : remove the votes of all
The residents that are not Liberal— [5]
Leave the young Tutors uncontrolled and free,
And Oxford then shall see—what it shall see.
What next ?   Why then, I say, let Convocation
Be shorn of all her powers of legislation.[6]

[1] " Not to mention that, as we cannot promise Paradise to our supporters they are very apt to take the train for London just before the election."

[2] It is not known to what the word " Paradise " was intended to allude, and therefore the hint, here thrown out, that the writer meant to recall the case of the late Chairman of Mr. Gladstone's committee, who had been recently collated to the See of Chester, is wholly wanton and gratuitous.

[3] A case of this kind had actually occurred on the occasion of the division just alluded to.

[4] Mr. Wayte, now President of Trinity, then put forward as the Liberal candidate for election to Council.

[5] " You and others suggest, as the only effective remedy, that the Constituency should be reformed, by the exclusion of the non-academical elements which form a main part of the strength of this party domination."

[6] " I confess that, having included all the really academical elements in Congregation, I would go boldly on, and put an end to the legislative functions of Convocation."

But why stop there?   Let us go boldly on—
Sweep everything beginning with a "Con"
Into oblivion!   Convocation first,
Conservatism next, and, last and worst,
" *Concilium Hebdomadale* " must,
Consumed and conquered, be consigned to dust! [1]
    And here I must relate a little fable
I heard last Saturday at our high table :—
The cats, it seems, were masters of the house,
And held their own against the rat and mouse :
Of course the others couldn't stand it long,
So held a caucus, (not, in their case, wrong ;)
And, when they were assembled to a man,
Uprose an aged rat, and thus began :—
    "Brothers in bondage!   Shall we bear to be
For ever left in a minority?
With what "fell unity of purpose" cats
Oppose the trusting innocence of rats !
So unsuspicious are we of disguise,
Their machinations take us by surprise— [2]
Insulting and tyrannical absurdities! [3]
It is too bad by half—upon my word it is !
For, now that these Con——, cats, I should say, (frizzle
    'em !)
Are masters, they exterminate like Islam ! [4]
How shall we deal with them?   I'll tell you how :—
Let none but kittens be allowed to miaow !

[1] " This conviction, that while we have Elections to Council we shall not entirely get rid of party organisation and its evils, leads me to venture a step further, and to raise the question whether it is really necessary that we should have an Elective Council for legislative purposes at all."

[2] " Sometimes, indeed, not being informed that the wires are at work, we are completely taken by surprise."

[3] " We are without protection against this most insulting and tyrannical absurdity."

[4] " It is as exterminating as Islam."

The Liberal kittens seize us but in play,
And, while they frolic, we can run away :
But older cats are not so generous,
Their claws are too Conservative for us !
Then let *them* keep the stable and the oats,
While kittens, rats, and mice have all the votes.

"Yes ; banish cats ! The kittens would not use
Their powers for blind obstruction,[1] nor refuse
To let us sip the cream and gnaw the cheese—
How glorious then would be our destinies ![2]
Kittens and rats would occupy the throne,
And rule the larder for itself alone ! "[3]

So rhymed my friend, and asked me what I thought of it
I told him that so much as I had caught of it
Appeared to me (as I need hardly mention)
Entirely undeserving of attention.

But now, to guide the Congregation, when
It numbers none but really " able " men,
A " *Vice-Cacellarius* " will be needed
Of every kind of human weakness weeded !
Is such the president that we have got ?
He ought no doubt to be ; why should he not ?[4]
I do not hint that Liberals should dare

[1] " Their powers would scarcely be exercised for the purposes of fanaticism, or in a spirit of blind obstruction."

[2] " These narrow local bounds, within which our thoughts and schemes have hitherto been pent, will begin to disappear, and a far wider sphere of action will open on the view."

[3] " Those councils must be freely opened to all who can serve her well and who will serve her for herself."

[4] " To preside over a Congregation with full legislative powers, the Vice-Chancellor ought no doubt to be a man of real capacity ; but why should he not ? His mind ought also, for this as well as for his other high functions, to be clear of petty details, and devoted to the great matters of University business ; but why should not this condition also be fulfilled ? "

To oust the present holder of the chair—
But surely he would not object to be
Gently examined by a Board of three ?
Their duty being just to ascertain
That he's " all there " (I mean, of course, in brain,)
And that his mind, from " petty details " clear,
Is fitted for the duties of his sphere.

All this is merely moonshine, till we get
The seal of Parliament upon it set.
A word then, Senior Censor, in your ear :
The Government is in a state of fear—
Like some old gentleman, abroad at night,
Seized with a sudden shiver of affright,
Who offers money, on his bended knees,
To the first skulking vagabond he sees—
Now is the lucky moment for our task ;
They daren't refuse us anything we ask ! [1]

And then our Fellowships shall open be
To Intellect, no meaner quality !
No moral excellence, no social fitness
Shall ever be admissible as witness.
" Avaunt, dull Virtue ! " is Oxonia's cry :
" Come to my arms, ingenious Villainy ! "

For Classic Fellowships, an honour high,
Simonides and Co. will then apply—
Our Mathematics will to Oxford bring
The 'cutest members of the betting-ring—
Law Fellowships will start upon their journeys
A myriad of unscrupulous attorneys—

---

[1] " If you apply now to Parliament for this or any other University reform, you will find the House of Commons in a propitious mood. . . . Even the Conservative Government, as it looks for the support of moderate Liberals on the one great subject, is very unwilling to present itself in such an aspect that these men may not be able decently to give it their support."

While poisoners, doomed till now to toil unknown,
Shall mount the Physical Professor's throne !
And thus would Oxford educate, indeed,
Men far beyond a merely local need—
With no career before them, I may say,[1]
Unless they're wise enough to go away,
And seek far West, or in the distant East,
Another flock of pigeons to be fleeced.

I might go on, and trace the destiny
Of Oxford in an age which, though it be
Thus breaking with tradition, owns a new
Allegiance to the intellectual few—
(I mean, of course, the—pshaw ! no matter who !)
But, were I to pursue the boundless theme,
I fear that I should seem to you to dream.[2]

This to fulfil, or even—humbler far—
To shun Conservatism's noxious star
And all the evils that it brings behind,
These pestilential coils must be untwined—
The party-coils, that clog the march of Mind—
Choked in whose meshes Oxford, slowly wise,
Has lain for three disastrous centuries.[3]
Away with them ! (It is for this I yearn !)
Each twist untwist, each Turner overturn !
Disfranchise each Conservative, and cancel

[1] " With open Fellowships, Oxford will soon produce a supply of men fit for the work of high education far beyond her own local demands, and in fact with no career before them unless a career can be opened elsewhere."

[2] " I should seem to you to dream if I were to say what I think the destiny of the University may be in an age which, though it is breaking with tradition, is, from the same causes, owning a new allegiance to intellectual authority."

[3] " But to fulfil this, or even a far humbler destiny—to escape the opposite lot—the pestilential coils of party, in which the University has lain for three disastrous centuries choked, must be untwined."

The votes of Michell, Liddon, Wall, and Mansel!
Then, then shall Oxford be herself again,
Neglect the heart, and cultivate the brain—
Then this shall be the burden of our song,
" All change is good—whatever is, is wrong—'
Then Intellect's proud flag shall be unfurled,
And Brain, and Brain alone, shall rule the world !

THE OFFER OF THE CLARENDON TRUSTEES.

"Accommodated : that is, when a man is, as they say, accommodated ; or when a man is—being—whereby—he may be thought to be accommodated ; which is an excellent thing."

DEAR SENIOR CENSOR,—In a desultory conversation on a point connected with the dinner at our high table, you incidentally remarked to me that lobster-sauce, "though a necessary adjunct to turbot, was not entirely wholesome."

It is entirely unwholesome. I never ask for it without reluctance : I never take a second spoonful without a feeling of apprehension on the subject of possible nightmare.[1] This naturally brings me to the subject of Mathematics, and of the accommodation provided by the Uni-

[1] See page 82, Notes 1, 2.

versity for carrying on the calculations necessary in that important branch of Science.

As Members of Convocation are called upon (whether personally, or, as is less exasperating, by letter) to consider the offer of the Clarendon Trustees, as well as every other subject of human, or inhuman, interest, capable of consideration, it has occurred to me to suggest for your consideration how desirable roofed buildings are for carrying on mathematical calculations : in fact, the variable character of the weather in Oxford renders it highly inexpedient to attempt much occupation, of a sedentary nature, in the open air.

Again, it is often impossible for students to carry on accurate mathematical calculations in close contiguity to one another, owing to their mutual interference, and a tendency to general conversation : consequently these processes require different rooms in which irrepressible conversationists, who are found to occur in every branch of Society, might be carefully and permanently fixed.

It may be sufficient for the present to enumerate the following requisites ; others might be added as funds permitted.

A.   A very large room for calculating Greatest

Common Measure. To this a small one might be attached for Least Common Multiple : this, however, might be dispensed with.

B. A piece of open ground for keeping Roots and practising their extraction : it would be advisable to keep Square Roots by themselves, as their corners are apt to damage others.

C. A room for reducing Fractions to their Lowest Terms. This should be provided with a cellar for keeping the Lowest Terms when found, which might also be available to the general body of Undergraduates, for the purpose of " keeping Terms."

D. A large room, which might be darkened, and fitted up with a magic lantern for the purpose of exhibiting Circulating Decimals in the act of circulation. This might also contain cupboards, fitted with glass-doors, for keeping the various Scales of Notation.

E. A narrow strip of ground, railed off and carefully levelled, for investigating the properties of Asymptotes, and testing practically whether Parallel Lines meet or not : for this purpose it should reach, to use the expressive language of Euclid, " ever so far."

This last process, of " continually producing the

Lines," may require centuries or more : but such a period, though long in the life of an individual, is as nothing in the life of the University.

As Photography is now very much employed in recording human expressions, and might possibly be adapted to Algebraical Expressions, a small photographic room would be desirable, both for general use and for representing the various phenomena of Gravity, Disturbance of Equilibrium, Resolution, &c., which affect the features during severe mathematical operations.

May I trust that you will give your immediate attention to this most important subject?

Believe me,

Sincerely yours,

Feb. 6, 1868.   MATHEMATICUS

THE DESERTED PARKS.

"SOLITUDINUM FACIUNT : *PARCUM* APPELLANT."

Museum ! loveliest building of the plain
Where Cherwell winds towards the distant main ;
How often have I loitered o'er thy green,
Where humble happiness endeared the scene !
How often have I paused on every charm,
The rustic couple walking arm in arm—
The groups of trees, with seats beneath the shade

For prattling babes and whisp'ring lovers made—·
The never-failing brawl, the busy mill
Where tiny urchins vied in fistic skill—
(Two phrases only have that dusky race
Caught from the learned influence of the place ;
Phrases in their simplicity sublime,
" Scramble a copper ! "   " Please, Sir, what's the time ? "
These round thy walks their cheerful influence shed ;
These were thy charms—but all these charms are fled.

    Amidst thy bowers the tyrant's hand is seen,
And rude pavilions sadden all thy green ;
One selfish pastime grasps the whole domain,
And half a faction swallows up the plain ;
Adown thy glades, all sacrificed to cricket,
The hollow-sounding bat now guards the wicket ;
Sunk are thy mounds in shapeless level all,
Lest aught impede the swiftly rolling ball ;
And trembling, shrinking from the fatal blow,
Far, far away thy hapless children go.

    Ill fares the place, to luxury a prey,
Where wealth accumulates, and minds decay ;
Athletic sports may flourish or may fade,
Fashion may make them, even as it has made ;
But the broad Parks, the city's joy and pride,
When once destroyed can never be supplied !

    Ye friends to truth, ye statesmen, who survey
The rich man's joys increase, the poor's decay,
'Tis yours to judge, how wide the limits stand
Between a splendid and a happy land.
Proud swells go by with laugh of hollow joy,
And shouting Folly hails them with " Ahoy ! "
Funds even beyond the miser's wish abound,
And rich men flock from all the world around.
Yet count our gains.   This wealth is but a name,

That leaves our useful products still the same.
Not so the loss.   The man of wealth and pride
Takes up a space that many poor supplied ;
Space for the game, and all its instruments,
Space for pavilions and for scorers' tents ;
The ball, that raps his shins in padding cased,
Has worn the verdure to an arid waste ;
His Park, where these exclusive sports are seen,
Indignant spurns the rustic from the green ;
While through the plain, consigned to silence all,
In barren splendour flits the russet ball.

In peaceful converse with his brother Don,
Here oft the calm Professor wandered on ;
Strange words he used—men drank with wondering ears
The languages called "dead," the tongues of other years.
(Fnough of Heber !   Let me once again
Attune my verse to Goldsmith's liquid strain.)
A man he was to undergraduates dear,
And passing rich with forty pounds a year.
And so, I ween, he would have been till now,
Had not his friends ('twere long to tell you how)
Prevailed on him, Jack-Horner-like, to try
Some method to evaluate his pie,
And win from those dark depths, with skilful thumb,
Five times a hundredweight of luscious plum—
Yet for no thirst of wealth, no love of praise,
In learned labour he consumed his days !

O Luxury ! thou cursed by Heaven's decree,
How ill exchanged are things like these for thee !
How do thy potions, with insidious joy,
Diffuse their pleasures only to destroy ;
Iced cobbler, Badminton, and shandy-gaff,
Rouse the loud jest and idiotic laugh ;
Inspired by them, to tipsy greatness grown,

Men boast a florid vigour not their own ;
At every draught more wild and wild they grow ;
While pitying friends observe " I told you so ! "
Till, summoned to their post, at the first ball,
A feeble under-hand, their wickets fall.

   Even now the devastation is begun,
And half the business of destruction done ;
Even now, methinks while pondering here in pity,
I see the rural Virtues leave the city.
Contented Toil, and calm scholastic Care,
And frugal Moderation, all are there ;
Resolute Industry that scorns the lure
Of careless mirth—that dwells apart secure—
To science gives her days, her midnight oil,
Cheered by the sympathy of others' toil—
Courtly Refinement, and that Taste in dress
That brooks no meanness, yet avoids excess—
All these I see, with slow reluctant pace
Desert the long-beloved and honoured place !

   While yet 'tis time, Oxonia, rise and fling
The spoiler from thee : grant no parleying !
Teach him that eloquence, against the wrong,
Though very poor, may still be very strong ;
That party-interests we must forego,
When hostile to " pro bono publico " ;
That faction's empire hastens to its end,
When once mankind to common sense attend ;
While independent votes may win the day
Even against the potent spell of " Play ! "

May, 1867.

THE END.

THE NEW BELFRY.

[Oxford has always been sensitive in respect of her new buildings; in proportion as she has a right to be proud of what is old, she assumes the privilege of being hypercritical over anything in the nature of an innovation. The grandest of the modern architects have had to run the gauntlet of ridicule when they laid their hands on the University buildings; but perhaps there was never better ground for ridicule than that which Mr. Dodgson discovered in "the three T's" at Christ Church.

In or about the year 1871, one of the old canons' houses, which stood between the cathedral and the "Tom" Quadrangle, was vacated, and the authorities agreed that it should be demolished, in order to make space for a direct approach to the cathedral from the quadrangle. Dean Liddell called in the aid of Mr. Bodley, who constructed a double archway, running under the solid masonry, and of sufficient length to warrant the critics in describing it as the Tunnel. About the same time it was decided to remove the bells from the tower of the cathedral, and make a new belfry over the staircase of the Hall. The arcade of the tower was cut through for the purpose of liberating the bells, and the gap in the stonework is referred to by Mr. Dodgson as the Trench. From lack of funds, or some other reason, Bodley's idea of a campanile of wood and copper was not proceeded with, and the bells were ensconced in a plain wooden case, of which the author of " The New Belfry "—first printed in 1872, and hurried by the Oxford public through five editions—made merciless fun. He likens it to a meat-safe, a box, a Greek Lexicon, a parallelopiped, a bathing-machine, a piece of bar soap, a tea-caddy, a clothes-horse ; but his favourite name for it is the Tea-chest. The Tunnel, the Trench, and the Tea-chest are the " three T's " immortalised in the "Monograph by D.C.L." and the "Threnody" published in 1873—of which there were three editions. Between these two skits, it may be mentioned, Mr. Dodgson printed for private circulation a four-page pamphlet in a more serious vein : " Objections submitted to the Governing Body of Christ Church, Oxford, against certain proposed alterations in the Great Quadrangle."

In justice to Mr. Bodley it should be stated that he lost no time in concealing his wooden case by a low tower with four corner turrets, at the north-east corner of the quadrangle. The Tea-chest, I need hardly say, is a thing of the past; only its memory survives in the "Notes by an Oxford Chiel."

"D.C.L.," of course, is a transposition of Mr. Dodgson's initials. His playful humour often sparkles in a word, even in a single letter, and may escape the notice of present-day readers, though contemporaries would be quick enough to seize on every suggestion of fun, however far-fetched or recondite. It may not be possible in all instances to explain an allusion, where it is evident that an allusion was made. One ought to know why the motto of the "Vision" is: "Call you this *baching* of your friends?" and why Venator, in the same piece, sings a "*Bach*analian Ode." Who was Bache, for instance? But attention may be called to a few of the allusions in these two "Notes," at the risk of its being entirely superfluous for many readers.

The Treasurer, who (it is suggested) "strove to force" the belfry on an unwilling House, was

Canon John Bull, a notable figure in his day, and a member of the Chapter of Christ Church. The Professor who, as some imagined, "designed this box, which, whether with a *lid on* or not, equally offends the eye," was the Ireland Professor of Exegesis, Mr. Dodgson's close friend Dr. Liddon. "The head of the House and the architect," who wished to embody their names among the alterations then in progress, and conceived the idea of representing in the belfry a gigantic copy of a Greek Lexicon," were Liddell and Scott—Sir George Gilbert Scott, who had originally undertaken the work, and then handed it over to his pupil, G. F. Bodley. "Jeeby," I am afraid, is Mr. George Bodley without any doubt. He is severely handled as the offender in chief. The apostrophe to the new feature of the "great educational establishment"—"Thou tea-chest"—is to be read in schoolboy fashion as "Tu doces."

References to passing events are frequent enough in these two pieces. The "bread and butter question," towards the end of "The New Belfry," was one of the recurring disputes on the quality of the battels, which every college periodically experiences. The "Indirect Claims" and the "anything but indirect Claimants" recall the Geneva Arbitration and the Tichborne case, both of which were the subject of much "prating" in 1872. The "short-comings in the payment of the Greek Professor" takes us back to the story of the Jowett persecution.

"The Wandering Burgess," in "The Vision of the Three T's," is Mr. Gladstone, who had been defeated at Oxford in 1865, elected for South Lancashire in the same year, and for Greenwich in 1868. The reference in the ballad to Ayrton and Lowe, Odger and Beales, was natural enough to a satirist in 1873. Mr. Lowe's abortive match-tax is elsewhere commemorated. The Lunatic's speech in Chapter II. ("Lo you, said our Rulers,") brings before us Gladstone and Cardwell by name, the proposal to make Oxford a military centre, and the disestablishment of the Irish Church in 1870. The professor with his *humerus*, and his gag on the necessity of German, reflects two controversies which ere now have counted for a good deal in the conversation of Oxford common rooms.]

THE NEW BELFRY

OF

CHRIST CHURCH, OXFORD.

A MONOGRAPH

BY

D. C. L.

" A thing of beauty is a joy for ever."

East view of the new Belfry, Ch. Ch., as seen from the Meadow.

SECOND THOUSAND.

Oxford :

JAMES PARKER AND CO.

1872.

CONTENTS.

———

§ 1. *On the etymological significance of the new Belfry, Ch. Ch.*

The word "Belfry" is derived from the French *bel*, "beautiful, becoming, meet," and from the German *frei*, "free, unfettered, secure, safe." Thus the word is strictly equivalent to "meat-safe," to which the new belfry bears a resemblance so perfect as almost to amount to coincidence.

§ 2. *On the style of the new Belfry, Ch. Ch.*

The style is that which is usually known as "Early Debased": very early, and remarkably debased.

§ 3. *On the origin of the new Belfry, Ch. Ch.*

Outsiders have enquired, with a persistence verging on personality, and with a recklessness scarcely distinguishable from insanity, to *whom* we are to attribute the first grand conception of the work. Was it the Treasurer, say they, who thus strove to force it on an unwilling House? Was it a Professor who designed this box, which, whether with a lid on or not, equally offends the eye? Or was it a Censor whose weird spells evoked the horrid thing, the bane of this and of succeeding generations? Until some reply is given to these and similar questions, they must and will remain—for ever—unanswered!

On this point Rumour has been unusually busy. Some say that the Governing Body evolved the idea in solemn conclave—the original motion being to adopt the Tower of St. Mark's at Venice as a model; and that by a series of amendments it was reduced at last to a simple cube. Others say that the Reader in Chemistry suggested it as a form of crystal. There are others who affirm that the Mathematical Lecturer found it in the Eleventh Book of Euclid. In fact, there is no end to the various myths afloat on the subject. Most fortunately, we are in possession of the real story.

The true origin of the design is as follows : we have it on the very best authority.

The head of the House, and the architect, feeling a natural wish that their names should be embodied, in some conspicuous way, among the alterations then in progress, conceived the beautiful and unique idea of representing, by means of the new Belfry, a gigantic copy of a Greek Lexicon.[1]   But, before the idea had been reduced to a working form, business took them both to London for a few days, and during their absence, somehow (*this* part of the business has never been satisfactorily explained) the whole thing was put into the hands of a wandering architect, who gave the name of Jeeby.   As the poor man is now incarcerated at Hanwell, we will not be too hard upon his memory, but will only say that he professed to have originated the idea in a moment of inspiration, when idly contemplating one of those high coloured, and mysteriously decorated chests which, filled with dried leaves from gooseberry bushes and quick-set hedges, profess to supply the market with tea of genuine Chinese growth.   Was there not something prophetic in the choice?   What traveller is there, to whose lips, when first he enters that great educational establishment and gazes on this its newest decoration, the words do not rise unbidden—" Thou tea-chest "?

---

[1] The Editor confesses to a difficulty here.   No sufficient reason has been adduced why a model of a Greek Lexicon should in any way " embody " the names of the above illustrious individuals.

It is plain then that Scott, the great architect to whom the work of restoration has been entrusted, is not responsible for this. He is *said* to have pronounced it a "casus belli," which (with all deference to the Classical Tutors of the House, who insist that he meant merely "a case for a bell") we believe to have been intended as a term of reproach.

The following lines are attributed to Scott :—

> " If thou wouldst view the Belfry aright,
> Go visit it at the mirk midnight—
> For the least hint of open day
> Scares the beholder quite away.
> When wall and window are black as pitch,
> And there's no deciding which is which ;
> When the dark Hall's uncertain roof
> In horror seems to stand aloof ;
> When corner and corner, alternately,
> Is wrought to an odious symmetry :
> When distant Thames is heard to sigh
> And shudder as he hurries by ;
> Then go, if it be worth the while,
> Then view the Belfry's monstrous pile,
> And, home returning, soothly swear,
> ' 'Tis more than Job himself could bear ! ' "

§ 4. *On the chief architectural merit of the new Belfry, Ch. Ch.*

Its chief merit is its simplicity—a simplicity so

pure, so profound, in a word, so *simple*, that no other word will fitly describe it. The meagre outline, and baldness of detail, of the present Chapter, are adopted in humble imitation of this great feature.

§ 5. *On the other architectural merits of the new Belfry, Ch. Ch.*

The Belfry has no other architectural merits.

§ 6. *On the means of obtaining the best views of the new Belfry, Ch. Ch.*

The visitor may place himself, in the first instance, at the opposite corner of the Great Quadrangle, and so combine, in one grand spectacle, the beauties of the North and West sides of the edifice. He will find that the converging lines forcibly suggest a vanishing point, and if that vanishing point should in its turn suggest the thought, " Would that *it* were on the point of vanishing ! " he may perchance, like the soldier in the ballad, " lean upon his sword " (if he has one : they are not commonly worn by modern tourists), " and wipe away a tear."

He may then make the circuit of the Quadrangle, drinking in new visions of beauty at every step—

> " Ever charming, ever new,
> When will the Belfry tire the view? "

as Dyer sings in his well-known poem, " Grongar Hill "—and as he walks along from the Deanery towards the Hall staircase, and breathes more and more freely as the Belfry lessens on the view, the delicious sensation of relief, which he will experience when it has finally disappeared, will amply repay him for all he will have endured.

The *best* view of the Belfry is that selected by our artist for the admirable frontispiece which he has furnished for the first volume of the present work.[1]   This view may be seen, in all its beauty, from the far end of Merton Meadow.   From that point the imposing position (or, more briefly, the imposition) of the whole structure is thrillingly apparent.   There the thoughtful passer-by, with four right angles on one side of him, and four anglers, who have no right to be there, on the other, may ponder on the mutability of human things, or recall the names of Euclid and Isaak

[1] On further consideration, it was deemed inexpedient to extend this work beyond the compass of one Volume.

Walton, or smoke, or ride a bicycle, or do anything that the local authorities will permit.

§ 7. *On the impetus given to Art in England by
the new Belfry, Ch. Ch.*

The idea has spread far and wide, and is rapidly
pervading all branches of manufacture. Already
an enterprising maker of bonnet-boxes is ad-
vertising "the Belfry pattern": two builders of
bathing machines at Ramsgate have followed
his example : one of the great London houses is
supplying "bar-soap" cut in the same striking
and symmetrical form : and we are credibly
informed that Borwick's Baking Powder and
Thorley's Food for Cattle are now sold in no
other shape.

§ 8. *On the feelings with which old Ch. Ch. men
regard the new Belfry.*

Bitterly, bitterly do all old Ch. Ch. men lament
this latest lowest development of native taste.
" We see the Governing Body," say they : " where
is the Governing *Mind ?* " and Echo (exercising a
judicious " natural selection," for which even
Darwin would give her credit) answers "where ? '

At the approaching " Gaudy," when a number of old Ch. Ch. men will gather together, it is proposed, at the conclusion of the banquet, to present to each guest a portable model of the new Belfry, tastefully executed in cheese.

§ 9. *On the feelings with which resident Ch. Ch. men regard the new Belfry.*

Who that has seen a Ch. Ch. man conducting his troop of "lionesses" (so called from the savage and pitiless greed with which they devour the various sights of Oxford) through its ancient precincts, that has noticed the convulsive start and ghastly stare that always affect new-comers, when first they come into view of the new Belfry, that has heard the eager questions with which they assail their guide as to the how, the why, the what for, and the how long, of this astounding phenomenon, can have failed to mark the manly glow which immediately suffuses the cheek of the hapless cicerone ?

> " Is it the glow of conscious pride—
> Of pure ambition gratified—
> That seeks to read in other eye
> Something of its own ecstasy ?
> Or wrath, that worldlings should make fun

Of anything 'the House' has done ?
Or puzzlement, that seeks in vain
The rigid mystery to explain ?
Or is it shame that, knowing not
How to defend or cloak the blot—
The foulest blot on fairest face
That ever marred a noble place—
Burns with the pangs it will not own,
Pangs felt by loyal sons alone ? "

§ 10. *On the logical treatment of the new Belfry, Ch. Ch.*

The subject has been reduced to three Syllogisms.

The first is in " Barbara." It is attributed to the enemies of the Belfry.

Wooden buildings in the midst of stone-work are barbarous ;
Plain rectangular forms in the midst of arches and decorations are barbarous ;
Ergo, the whole thing is ridiculous and revolting.

The second is in " Celarent," and has been most carefully composed by the friends of the Belfry.

The Governing Body would conceal this appalling structure, if they could ;
The Governing Body would conceal the feelings of chagrin with which they now regard it, if they could ;
Ergo . . . (*MS. unfinished*).

The third Syllogism is in " Festino," and is

the joint composition of the friends and the
enemies of the Belfry.

> To restore the character of Ch. Ch., a tower must be built;
> To build a tower, ten thousand pounds must be raised;
> *Ergo*, no time must be lost.

These three Syllogisms have been submitted to
the criticism of the Professor of Logic, who writes
that "he fancies he can detect some slight want
of logical sequence in the Conclusion of the
third." He adds that, according to *his* experience
of life, when people thus commit a fatal blunder in
child-like confidence that money will be forthcoming to enable them to set it right, in ten cases
out of nine the money is *not* forthcoming. This is
a large percentage.

§ 11. *On the dramatic treatment of the new
Belfry, Ch. Ch.*

Curtain rises, discovering the DEAN, CANONS, *and*
STUDENTS *seated round a table, on which the
mad* ARCHITECT, *fantastically dressed, and
wearing a Fool's cap and bells, is placing a
square block of deal.*

DEAN (*As* HAMLET). Methinks I see a Bell-
tower!

CANONS (*Looking wildly in all directions*). Where, my good Sir?

DEAN. In my mind's eye —— (*Knocking heard*) Who's there?

FOOL. A spirit, a spirit; he says his name's poor Tom.

(*Enter* THE GREAT BELL, *disguised as a mushroom.*)

GREAT BELL. Who gives anything to poor Tom, whom the foul fiend hath led through bricks and through mortar, through rope and windlass, through plank and scaffold; that hath torn down his balustrades, and torn up his terraces; that hath made him go as a common pedlar, with a wooden box upon his back. Do poor Tom some charity. Tom's a-cold.

> Rafters and planks, and such small deer,
> Shall be Tom's food for many a year.

CENSOR. I feared it would come to this.

DEAN (*As* KING LEAR). The little Dons and all, Tutor, Reader, Lecturer—see, they bark at me!

CENSOR. His wits begin to unsettle.

DEAN (*As* HAMLET). Do you see yonder box that's almost in shape of a tea-caddy?

CENSOR. By its mass, it is like a tea-caddy, indeed.

DEAN. Methinks it is like a clothes-horse.

CENSOR. It is backed by a clothes-horse.

DEAN. Or like a tub.

CENSOR. Very like a tub.

DEAN. They fool me to the top of my bent.

(*Enter from opposite sides* THE BELFRY *as* BOX, *and* THE BODLEY LIBRARIAN *as* COX.)

LIBRARIAN. Who are you, Sir?

BELFRY. If it comes to that, Sir, who are you?
(*They exchange cards.*)

LIBRARIAN. I should feel obliged to you if you could accommodate me with a more protuberant Bell-tower, Mr. B. The one you have now seems to me to consist of corners only, with nothing whatever in the middle.

BELFRY. Anything to accommodate you, Mr. Cox. (*Places jauntily on his head a small model of the skeleton of an umbrella, upside down.*)

LIBRARIAN. Ah, tell me—in mercy tell me— have you such a thing as a redeeming feature, or the least mark of artistic design, about you?

BELFRY. No!

LIBRARIAN. Then you are my long-lost door scraper!

(*They rush into each other's arms.*)

(*Enter* TREASURER *as* ARIEL.   *Solemn music.*)

SONG AND CHORUS.

> Five fathom square the Belfry frowns ;
>   All its sides of timber made ;
> Painted all in greys and browns ;
>   Nothing of it that will fade.
> Christ Church may admire the change—
> Oxford thinks it sad and strange.
> Beauty's dead !   Let's ring her knell.
> Hark ! now I hear them—ding-dong, bell.

§ 12. *On the Future of the new Belfry, Ch. Ch.*

The Belfry has a great Future before it—at least, if it has not, it has very little to do with Time at all, its Past being (fortunately for our ancestors) a nonentity, and its Present a blank.   The advantage of having been born in the reign of Queen Anne, and of having died in that or the subsequent reign, has never been so painfully apparent as it is now.

Credible witnesses assert that, when the bells are rung, the Belfry must come down.   In that case considerable damage (the process technically described as " pulverisation ") must ensue to the beautiful pillar and roof which adorn the Hall staircase.   But the architect is prepared even for this emergency. " On the first symptom of deflection " (he writes from Hanwell) " let the pillar be carefully removed and placed, with its super-struent superstructure " (we cannot forbear calling attention to this beautiful phrase), " in the centre of ' Mercury.' *There* it will constitute a novel and most unique feature of the venerable House."

" Yes, and the Belfry shall serve to generations yet unborn as an ariel Ticket-office," so he cries with his eye in a fine frenzy rolling, " where the Oxford and London balloon shall call ere it launch forth on its celestial voyage—and where expectant passengers shall while away the time with the latest edition of *Bell's Life !*"

§ 13. *On the Moral of the new Belfry, Ch. Ch.*

The moral position of Christ Church is undoubtedly improved by it. " We have been attacked, and perhaps not without reason, on the Bread-and-Butter question," she remarks to an inattentive World (which heeds her not, but prates on of Indirect Claims and of anything but indirect Claimants), " we have been charged—and, it must be confessed, in a free and manly tone—with shortcomings in the payment of the Greek Professor, but who shall say that we are not all 'on the square' *now* ? "

This, however, is not *the* Moral of the matter. Everything has a moral, if you choose to look for it. In Wordsworth, a good half of every poem is devoted to the Moral : in Byron, a smaller pro portion : in Tupper, the whole. Perhaps the most graceful tribute we can pay to the genius of the last-named writer, is to entrust to him, as an old member of Christ Church, the conclusion of this Monograph.

" Look on the Quadrangle of Christ, squarely, for is it not a Square ?

And a Square recalleth a Cube ; and a Cube recalleth the Belfry ;

And the Belfry recalleth a Die, shaken by the hand of the gambler ;

Yet, once thrown, it may not be recalled, being, so to speak, irrevocable.

There it shall endure for ages, treading hard on the heels of the Sublime—

For it is but a step, saith the wise man, from the Sublime unto the Ridiculous :

And the Simple dwelleth midway between, and shareth the qualities of either."

FINIS.

THE VISION

OF

THE THREE T'S.

A THRENODY

BY

THE AUTHOR OF

THE NEW BELFRY."

" Cal you this, baching of your friends ? "

West view of the new Tunnel.

SECOND EDITION.

𝕺𝖗𝖋𝖔𝖗𝖉 :

JAMES PARKER AND CO.

1873.

CONTENTS.

CHAPTER I.

CHAPTER II.

CHAPTER III.

CHAPTER I.

A Conference betwixt an Angler, *a* Hunter, *and a* Professor *concerning angling, and the beautifying of Thomas his Quadrangle. The Ballad of " The Wandering Burgess."*

PISCATOR, VENATOR.

PISCATOR. My honest Scholar, we are now arrived at the place whereof I spake, and trust me, we shall have good sport. How say you? Is not this a noble Quadrangle we see around us? And be not these lawns trimly kept, and this lake marvellous clear?

VENATOR. So marvellous clear, good Master, and withal so brief in compass, that methinks, if any fish of a reasonable bigness were therein, we must perforce espy it. I fear me there is none.

PISC. The less the fish, dear Scholar, the greater the skill in catching of it. Come, let's sit down, and while we unpack the fishing gear, I'll deliver a few remarks, both as to the fish to be met with hereabouts, and the properest method of fishing.

But you are to note first (for, as you are pleased to be my Scholar, it is but fitting you should imitate my habits of close observation) that the margin of this lake is so deftly fashioned that each portion thereof is at one and the same distance from that tumulus which rises in the centre.

VEN. O' my word 'tis so! You have indeed a quick eye, dear Master, and a wondrous readiness of observing.

PISC. Both may be yours in time, my Scholar, if with humility and patience you follow me as your model.

VEN. I thank you for that hope, great Master! But ere you begin your discourse, let me enquire of you one thing touching this noble Quadrangle— Is all we see of a like antiquity? To be brief, think you that those two tall archways, that excavation in the parapet, and that quaint wooden box, belong to the ancient design of the building, or have men of our day thus sadly disfigured the place?

PISC. I doubt not they are new, dear Scholar. For indeed I was here but a few years since, and saw naught of these things. But what book is that I see lying by the water's edge?

VEN. A book of ancient ballads, and truly I

am glad to see it, as we may herewith beguile the tediousness of the day, if our sport be poor, or if we grow aweary.

PISC. This is well thought of.   But now to business.   And first I'll tell you somewhat of the fish proper to these waters.   The Commoner kinds we may let pass : for though some of them be easily Plucked forth from the water, yet are they so slow, and withal have so little in them, that they are good for nothing, unless they be crammed up to the very eyes with such stuffing as comes readiest to hand.   Of these the Stickle-back, a mighty slow fish, is chiefest, and along with him you may reckon the Fluke, and divers others : all these belong to the " Mullet " genus, and be good to play, though scarcely worth examination.

I will say somewhat of the Nobler kinds, and chiefly of the Gold-fish, which is a species highly thought of, and much sought after in these parts, not only by men, but by divers birds, as for example the King-fishers : and note that wheresoever you shall see those birds assemble, and but few insects about, there shall you ever find the Gold-fish most lively and richest in flavour ; but wheresoever you perceive swarms of a certain gray fly, called the Dun-fly, there the Gold-fish are ever poorer in quality, and the King-fishers seldom seen.

A good Perch may sometimes be found here-abouts : but for a good fat Plaice (which is indeed but a magnified Perch) you may search these waters in vain. They that love such dainties must needs betake them to some distant Sea.

But for the manner of fishing, I would have you note first that your line be not thicker than an ordinary bell-rope ; for look you, to flog the water, as though you laid on with a flail, is most pre-posterous, and will surely scare the fish. And note further, that your rod must by no means exceed ten, or at the most twenty, pounds in weight, for——

VEN. Pardon me, my Master, that I thus break in on so excellent a discourse, but there now approaches us a Collegian, as I guess him to be, from whom we may haply learn the cause of these novelties we see around us. Is not that a bone which, ever as he goes, he so cautiously waves before him ?

Enter PROFESSOR.

PISC. By his reverend aspect and white hair, I guess him to be some learned Professor. I give you good day, reverend Sir ! If it be not ill manners to ask it, what bone is that you bear about with you ? It is, methinks, a humerous whimsy to chuse so strange a companion.

PROF. Your observation, Sir, is both anthropolitically and ambidexterously opportune : for this is indeed a *Humerus* I carry with me. You are, I doubt not, strangers in these parts, for else you would surely know that a Professor doth ever carry that which most aptly sets forth his Profession. Thus, the Professor of Uniform Rotation carries with him a wheelbarrow—the Professor of Graduated Scansion a ladder—and so of the rest.

VEN. It is an inconvenient and, methinks, an ill-advised custom.

PROF. Trust me, Sir, you are absolutely and amorphologically mistaken : yet time would fail me to show you wherein lies your error, for indeed I must now leave you, being bound for this great performance of music, which even at this distance salutes your ears.

PISC. Yet, I pray you, do us one courtesy before you go ; and that shall be to resolve a question, whereby my friend and I are sorely exercised.

Prof. Say on, Sir, and I will e'en answer you to the best of my poor ability.

Pisc. Briefly, then, we would ask the cause for piercing the very heart of this fair building with that uncomely tunnel, which is at once so ill-shaped, so ill-sized, and so ill-lighted.

Prof. Sir, do you know German?

Pisc. It is my grief, Sir, that I know no other tongue than mine own.

Prof. Then, Sir, my answer is this, *Warum nicht?*

Pisc. Alas, Sir, I understand you not.

Prof. The more the pity. For now-a-days all that is good comes from the German. Ask our men of science: they will tell you that any German book must needs surpass an English one. Aye, and even an English book, worth naught in this its native dress, shall become, when rendered into German, a valuable contribution to Science.

Ven. Sir, you much amaze me.

Prof. Nay, Sir, I'll amaze you yet more. No learned man doth now talk, or even so much as cough, save only in German. The time has been, I doubt not, when an honest English "Hem!" was held enough, both to clear the voice and rouse the attention of the company, but now-a-days no man of Science, that setteth any store by his good name, will cough otherwise than thus, *Ach! Euch! Auch!*

VEN. 'Tis wondrous. But, not to stay you further, wherefore do we see that ghastly gash above us, hacked, as though by some wanton schoolboy, in the parapet adjoining the Hall?

PROF. Sir, do *you* know German?

VEN. Believe me, No.

PROF. Then, Sir, I need but ask you this, *Wie befinden Sie Sich?*

VEN. I doubt not, Sir, but you are in the right on't.

PISC. But, Sir, I will by your favour ask you one other thing, as to that unseemly box that blots the fair heavens above. Wherefore, in this grand old City, and in so conspicuous a place, do men set so hideous a thing?

PROF. Be you mad, Sir? Why this is the very climacteric and coronal of all our architectural aspirations! In all Oxford there is naught like it!

PISC. It joys me much to hear you say so.

PROF. And, trust me, to an earnest mind,

the categorical evolution of the Abstract, ideologically considered, must infallibly develope itself in the parallelopipedisation of the Concrete! And so Farewell.

[*Exit* PROFESSOR.

PISC. He is a learned man, and methinks there is much that is sound in his reasoning.

VEN. It is *all* sound, as it seems to me. But how say you? Shall I read you one of these ballads? Here is one called "The Wandering Burgess," which (being forsooth a dumpish ditty) may well suit the ears of us whose eyes are oppressed with so dire a spectacle.

PISC. Read on, good Scholar, and I will bait our hooks the while.

[VENATOR *readeth.*

THE WANDERING BURGESS.

Our Willie had been sae lang awa',
   Frae bonnie Oxford toon,
The townsfolk they were greeting a'
   As they went up and doon.

He hadna been gane a year, a year,
   A year but barely ten,
When word cam unto Oxford toon,
   Our Willie wad come agen.

Willie he stude at Thomas his Gate,
    And made a lustie din ;
And who so blithe as the gate-porter
    To rise and let him in ?

" Now enter Willie, now enter Willie,
    And look around the place,
And see the pain that we have ta'en
    Thomas his Quad to grace."

The first look that our Willie cast,
    He leuch loud laughters three,
The neist look that our Willie cast,
    The tear blindit his e'e.

Sae square and stark the Tea-chest frowned
    Athwart the upper air,
But when the Trench our Willie saw,
    He thoucht the Tea-chest fair.

Sae murderous-deep the Trench did gape
    The parapet aboon,
But when the Tunnel Willie saw,
    He loved the Trench eftsoon.

'Twas mirk beneath the tane archway,
    'Twas mirk beneath the tither ;
Ye wadna ken a man therein,
    Though it were your ain dear brither.

He turned him round and round about,
    And looked upon the Three ;
And dismal grew his countenance,
    And drumlie grew his e'e.

"What cheer, what cheer, my gallant knight?"
    The gate-porter 'gan say.
"Saw ever ye sae fair a sight
    As ye have seen this day?"

"Now haud your tongue of your prating, man:
    Of your prating now let me be.
For, as I'm true knight, a fouler sight
    I'll never live to see.

"Before I'd be the ruffian dark
    Who planned this ghastly show,
I'd serve as secretary's clerk
    To Ayrton or to Lowe.

"Before I'd own the loathly thing
    That Christ Church Quad reveals,
I'd serve as shoeblack's underling
    To Odger and to Beales!"

————

CHAPTER II.

*A Conference with one distraught: who discourseth
strangely of many things.*

PISCATOR, VENATOR.

PISCATOR. 'Tis a marvellous pleasant ballad.
But look you, another Collegian draws near. I
wot not of what station he is, for indeed his
apparel is new to me.

VENATOR. It is compounded, as I take it, of

the diverse dresses of a jockey, a judge, and a North American Indian.

Enter LUNATIC.

PISC. Sir, may I make bold to ask your name?

LUN. With all my heart. It is Jeeby, at your service.

PISC. And wherefore (if I may further trouble you, being, as you see, a stranger) do you wear so gaudy, but withal so ill-assorted, a garb?

LUN. Why, Sir, I'll tell you. Do you read the *Morning Post*?

PISC. Alas, Sir, I do not.

LUN. 'Tis pity of your life you do not. For, look you, not to read the *Post*, and not to know the newest and most commended fashions, are but one and the same thing. And yet this raiment, that I wear, is *not* the newest fashion. No, nor has it ever been, nor will it ever be, the fashion.

VEN. I can well believe it.

LUN. And therefore 'tis, Sir, that I wear it. 'Tis but a badge of greatness. My deeds you see around you. *Si monumentum quæris, circumspice!* You know Latin?

VEN. Not I, Sir! It shames me to say it.

LUN. You are then (let me roundly tell you)

monstrum horrendum, informe, ingens, cui lumen ademptum !

VEN. Sir, you may tell it me roundly—or, if you list, squarely—or again, triangularly. But if, as you affirm, I see your deeds around me, I would fain know which they be.

LUN. Aloft, Sir, stands the first and chiefest ! That soaring minaret ! That gorgeous cupola ! That dreamlike effulgence of——

VEN. That wooden box ?

LUN. The same, Sir ! 'Tis mine !

VEN. (*After a pause*). Sir, it is worthy of you.

LUN. Lower now your eyes by a hairsbreadth, and straight you light upon my *second* deed. Oh, Sir, what toil of brain, what cudgelling of forehead, what rending of locks, went to the fashioning of it !

VEN. Mean you that newly-made gap ?

LUN. I do, Sir. 'Tis mine !

VEN. (*After a long pause*). What else, Sir ? I would fain know the worst.

LUN. (*Wildly*). It comes, it comes. My *third* great deed ! Lend, lend your ears—your nose—any feature you can least conveniently spare ! See you those twin doorways ? Tall and narrow they loom upon you—severely simple

their outline—massive the masonry between—
black as midnight the darkness within! Sir, of
what do they mind you?

VEN. Of vaults, Sir, and of charnel-houses.

LUN. This is a goodly fancy, and yet they are
not vaults. No, Sir, you see before you a Railway Tunnel!

VEN. 'Tis very strange.

LUN. But no less true than strange. Mark
me. 'Tis love, 'tis love, that makes the world go
round! Society goes round of itself. In circles.
Military society in military circles. Circles must
needs have centres. Military circles military
centres.

VEN. Sir, I fail to see——

LUN. Lo you, said our Rulers, Oxford shall
be a military centre! Then the chiefest of them
(glad in countenance, yet stony, I wot, in heart)
so ordered it by his underling (I remember me
not his name, yet is he one that can play a card
well, and so serveth meetly the behests of that
mighty one, who played of late in Ireland a game
of cribbage such as no man, who saw it, may
lightly forget); and then, Sir, this great College,
ever loyal and generous, gave this Quadrangle as
a Railway Terminus, whereby the troops might

come and go. By that Tunnel, Sir, the line will enter.

PISC. But, Sir, I see no rails.

LUN. Patience, good Sir! For railing we look to the Public. The College doth but furnish sleepers.

PISC. And the design of that Tunnel is——

LUN. Is mine, Sir! Oh, the fancy! Oh, the wit! Oh, the rich vein of humour! When came the idea? I' the mirk midnight. Whence came the idea? From a cheese-scoop! How came the idea? In a wild dream. Hearken, and I will tell. Form square, and prepare to receive a canonry! All the evening long I had seen lobsters marching around the table in unbroken order. Something sputtered in the candle— something hopped among the tea-things—something pulsated, with an ineffable yearning, beneath the enraptured hearthrug! My heart told me something was coming—and something came. A voice cried "Cheese-scoop!" and the Great Thought of my life flashed upon me! Placing an ancient Stilton cheese, to represent this venerable Quadrangle, on the chimney-piece, I retired to the further end of the room, armed only with a cheese-scoop, and with a dauntless courage awaited the word of command. Charge, Cheesetaster, charge! On, Stilton, on! With a yell and a bound I crossed the room, and plunged my scoop into the very heart of the foe! Once more! Another yell—another bound—another cavity scooped out! The deed was done!

VEN. And yet, Sir, if a cheese-scoop were your guide, these cavities must needs be circular.

LUN. They were so at the first—but, like the fickle Moon, my guardian satellite, I change as I go on. Oh, the rapture, Sir, of that wild moment! And did I reveal the Mighty Secret! Never, never! Day by day, week by week, behind a wooden screen, I wrought out that vision of beauty. The world came and went, and knew not of it. Oh, the ecstasy, when yesterday the Screen was swept away, and the Vision was a Reality! I stood by Tom-Gate, in that triumphal hour, and watched the passers-by. They stopped! They stared!! They started!!! A thrill of envy paled their cheeks! Hoarse inarticulate words of delirious rapture rose to their lips. What withheld me—what, I ask you candidly, withheld me from leaping upon them, holding them in a frantic clutch, and yelling in their ears " 'Tis mine, 'tis mine!"

Pisc. Perchance, the thought that——

Lun. You are right, Sir. The thought that there is a lunatic asylum in the neighbourhood, and that two medical certificates—but I will be calm. The deed is done. Let us change the subject. Even now a great musical performance is going on within. Wilt hear it? The Chapter give it—ha, ha! They give it!

Pisc. Sir, I will very gladly be their guest.

Lun. Then, guest, you have not guessed all! You shall be bled, Sir, ere you go! 'Tis love, 'tis love, that makes the hat go round! Stand and deliver! Vivat Regina! No money returned!

Pisc. How mean you, Sir?

Lun. I said, Sir, " No money returned!"

Pisc. And *I* said, Sir, " How mean——"

Lun. Sir, I am with you. You have heard of Bishops' Charges. Sir, what are Bishops to Chapters? Oh, it goes to my heart to see these quaint devices! First, sixpence for use of a door-scraper. Then, fivepence for right of choosing by which archway to approach the door. Then, a poor threepence for turning of the handle. Then, a shilling a head for admission, and half-a-crown for every two-headed man. Now this, Sir, is manifestly unjust, for you are to note that the double of a shilling——

Pisc. I do surmise, Sir, that the case is rare.

Lun. And then, Sir, five shillings each for care of your umbrella! Hence comes it that each visitor of ready wit hides his umbrella, ere he enter, either by swallowing it (which is perilous to the health of the inner man), or by running it down within his coat, even from the nape of the neck, which indeed is the cause of that which you may have observed in me, namely, a certain stiffness in mine outward demeanour. Farewell, gentlemen, I go to hear the music.

[*Exit* Lunatic.

CHAPTER III.

A Conference of the Hunter *with a* Tutor, *whilom the* Angler *his eyes be closed in sleep. The* Angler *awaking relateth his Vision. The* Hunter *chaunteth "A Bachanalian Ode."*

Piscator, Venator, Tutor.

Venator. He has left us, but methinks we are not to lack company, for look you, another is even now at hand, gravely apparelled, and bearing upon his head Hoffmann's Lexicon in four volumes folio.

PISCATOR. Trust me, this doth symbolise his craft. Good morrow, Sir. If I rightly interpret these that you bear with you, you are a teacher in this learned place ?

TUTOR. I am, Sir, a Tutor, and profess the teaching of divers unknown tongues.

PISC. Sir, we are happy to have your company, and, if it trouble you not too much, we would gladly ask (as indeed we did ask another of your learned body, but understood not his reply) the cause of these new things we see around us, which indeed are as strange as they are new, and as unsightly as they are strange.

TUTOR. Sir, I will tell you with all my heart. You must know then (for herein lies the pith of the matter) that the motto of the Governing Body is this :—

" *Diruit, ædificat, mutat quadrata rotundis* "; which I thus briefly expound.

Diruit. " *It teareth down.*" Witness that fair opening which, like a glade in an ancient forest, we have made in the parapet at the sinistral extremity of the Hall. Even as a tree is the more admirable when the hewer's axe hath all but severed its trunk—or as a row of pearly teeth, enshrined in ruby lips, are yet the more lovely for the loss of one—so, believe me, this our fair Quadrangle is but enhanced by that which foolish men in mockery call the " Trench."

Ædificat. "*It buildeth up.*" Witness that beauteous Belfry which, in its ethereal grace, seems ready to soar away even as we gaze upon it! Even as a railway porter moves with an unwonted majesty when bearing a portmanteau on his head—or as I myself (to speak modestly) gain a new beauty from these massive tomes— or as ocean charms us most when the rectangular bathing-machine breaks the monotony of its curving marge—so are we blessed by the presence of that which an envious world hath dubbed "the Tea-chest."

Mutat quadrata rotundis. "*It exchangeth square things for round.*" Witness that series of square-headed doors and windows, so beautifully broken in upon by that double archway! For indeed, though simple ("*simplex munditiis,*" as the poet saith), it is matchless in its beauty. Had those twin archways been greater, they would but have matched those at the corners of the Quadrangle—had they been less, they would but have copied, with an abject servility, the doorways around them. In such things, it is only a vulgar mind that thinks of a *match*. The subject is lowe. *We* seek the Unique, the Eccentric! *We* glory in this twofold excavation, which scoffers speak of as "the Tunnel."

VEN. Come, Sir, let me ask you a pleasant question. Why doth the Governing Body chuse for motto so trite a saying? It is, if I remember me aright, an example of a rule in the Latin Grammar.

TUTOR. Sir, if we are not grammatical, we are nothing!

VEN. But for the Belfry, Sir. Sure none can look on it without an inward shudder?

TUTOR. I will not gainsay it. But you are to note that it is not permanent. This shall serve its time, and a fairer edifice shall succeed it.

VEN. In good sooth I hope it. Yet for the time being it doth not, in that it is not permanent, the less disgrace the place. Drunkenness, Sir, is not permanent, and yet is held in no good esteem.

TUTOR. 'Tis an apt simile.

VEN. And for these matchless arches, as you

do most truly call them, would it not savour of more wholesome Art, had they matched the doorways, or the gateways?

TUTOR. Sir, do you study the Mathematics?

VEN. I trust, Sir, I can do the Rule of Three as well as another; and for Long Division——

TUTOR. You must know, then, that there be three Means treated of in Mathematics. For there is the Arithmetic Mean, the Geometric, and the Harmonic. And note further that a Mean is that which falleth between two magnitudes. Thus it is, that the entrance you here behold falleth between the magnitudes of the doorways and the gateways, and is in truth the Non-harmonic Mean, the Mean Absolute. But that the Mean, or Middle, is ever the safer course, we have a notable ensample in Egyptian history, in which land (as travellers tell us) the Ibis standeth ever in the midst of the river Nile, so best to avoid the onslaught of the ravenous alligators, which infest the banks on either side; from which habit of that wise bird is derived the ancient maxim, "*Medio tutissimus Ibis.*"

VEN. But wherefore be they *two?* Surely *one* arch were at once more comely and more convenient?

TUTOR. Sir, so long as public approval be won, what matter for the arch? But that they are two, take this as sufficient explication—that they are too tall for doorways, too narrow for gateways ; too light without, too dark within ; too plain to be ornamental, and withal too fantastic to be useful. And if this be not enough, you are to note further that, were it all one arch, it must needs cut short one of those shafts which grace the Quadrangle on all sides—and that were a monstrous and unheard-of thing, in good sooth, look you.

VEN. In good sooth, Sir, if I look I cannot miss seeing that there be three such shafts already cut short by doorways : so that it hath fair ensample to follow.

TUTOR. Then will I take other ground, Sir, and affirm (for I trust I have not learned Logic in vain) that to cut short the shaft were a common and vulgar thing to do. But indeed a single arch, where folk might smoothly enter in, were wholly adverse to Nature, who formeth never a mouth without setting a tongue as an obstacle in the midst thereof.

VEN. Sir, do you tell me that the block of masonry, between the gateways, was left there of set purpose, to hinder those that would enter in?

TUTOR. Trust me, it was even so; for firstly, we may thereby more easily control the entering crowds (" *divide et impera,*" say the Ancients), and secondly, in this matter a wise man will ever follow Nature. Thus, in the centre of a hall-door we usually place an umbrella stand—in the midst of a wicket-gate, a milestone, what place so suited for a watchbox as the centre of a narrow bridge?——Yea, and in the most crowded thoroughfare, where the living tide flows thickest, there, in the midst of all, the true *ideal* architect doth ever plant an obelisk! You may have observed this?

VEN. (*Much bewildered*). I *may* have done so, worthy Sir; and yet, methinks——

TUTOR. I must now bid you farewell; for the music, which I would fain hear, is even now beginning.

VEN. Trust me, Sir, your discourse hath interested me hugely.

TUTOR. Yet it hath, I fear me, somewhat wearied your friend, who is, as I perceive, in a deep slumber.

VEN. I had partly guessed it, by his loud and continuous snoring.

Tutor. You had best let him sleep on. He hath, I take it, a dull fancy, that cannot grasp the Great and the Sublime. And so farewell: I am bound for the music. [*Exit* Tutor.

Ven. I give you good day, good Sir. Awake, my Master! For the day weareth on, and we have catched no fish.

Pisc. Think not of fish, dear Scholar, but hearken! Trust me, I have seen such things in my dreams as words may hardly compass! Come, Sir, sit down, and I'll unfold to you, in such poor language as may best suit both my capacity and the briefness of our time.

THE VISION OF THE THREE T's.

Methought that, in some bygone Age, I stood beside the waters of Mercury, and saw, reflected on its placid face, the grand old buildings of the Great Quadrangle: near me stood one of portly form and courtly mien, with scarlet gown, and broad-brimmed hat whose strings, wide-fluttering in the breezeless air, at once defied the laws of gravity and marked the reverend Cardinal! 'Twas Wolsey's self! I would have spoken, but he raised his hand and pointed to the cloudless sky, from whence deep-muttering thunders now began to roll. I listened in wild terror.

Darkness gathered overhead, and through the gloom sobbingly down-floated a gigantic Box! With a fearful crash it settled upon the ancient College, which groaned beneath it, while a mocking voice cried, " Ha! Ha!" I looked for Wolsey: he was gone. Down in those glassy depths lay the stalwart form, with

*scarlet mantle grandly wrapped around it : the broad-brimmed
hat floated, boatlike, on the lake, while the strings with their
complex tassels, still defying the laws of gravity, quivered in the
air, and seemed to point a hundred fingers at the horrid Belfry !
Around, on every side, spirits howled in the howling blast,
blatant, stridulous !*

*A darker vision yet ! A black gash appeared in the shud-
dering parapet ! Spirits flitted hither and thither with averted
face, and warning finger pressed to quivering lips !*

*Then a wild shriek rang through the air, as, with volcanic
roar, two murky chasms burst upon the view, and the ancient
College reeled giddily around me !*

*Spirits in patent-leather boots stole by on tiptoe, with hushed
breath and eyes of ghastly terror ! Spirits with cheap um-
brellas, and unnecessary goloshes, hovered over me, sublimely
pendant ! Spirits with carpet bags, dressed in complete suits
of dittos, sped by me, shrieking "Away ! Away ! To the
arrowy Rhine ! To the rushing Guadalquiver ! To Bath !
To Jericho ! To anywhere !"*

*Stand here with me and gaze. From this thrice-favoured
spot, in one rapturous glance gather in, and brand for ever on
the tablets of memory, the Vision of the Three T's ! To your
left frowns the abysmal blackness of the tenebrous Tunnel. To
your right yawns the terrible Trench. While far above, away
from the sordid aims of Earth and the petty criticisms of Art,
soars, tetragonal and tremendous, the tintinabulatory Tea-
chest ! Scholar, the Vision is complete !*

VEN. I am glad on't ; for in good sooth I am
a-hungered. How say you, my Master? Shall
we not leave fishing, and fall to eating presently ?
And look you, here is a song, which I have

chanced on in this book of ballads, and which methinks suits well the present time and this most ancient place.

Pisc. Nay, then, let's sit down. We shall, I warrant you, make a good, honest, wholesome, hungry nuncheon with a piece of powdered beef and a radish or two that I have in my fish-bag. And you shall sing us this same song as we eat.

Ven. Well, then, I will sing; and I trust it may content you as well as your excellent discourse hath oft profited me.

VENATOR *chaunteth*

A BACHANALIAN ODE.

Here's to the Freshman of bashful eighteen !
  Here's to the Senior of twenty !
Here's to the youth whose moustache can't be seen !
  And here's to the man who has plenty !
      Let the men Pass !
      Out of the mass
I'll warrant we'll find you some fit for a Class !

Here's to the Censors, who symbolise Sense,
  Just as Mitres incorporate Might, Sir !
To the Bursar, who never expands the expense
  And the Readers, who always do right, Sir
      Tutor and Don,
      Let them jog on !
I warrant they'll rival the centuries gone !

Here's to the Chapter, melodious crew !
 Whose harmony surely *intends* well :
For, though it commences with " harm," it is true
 Yet its motto is " All's well that ends well ! "
 'Tis love, I'll be bound,
 That makes it go round !
For " In for a penny is in for a pound ! "

Here's to the Governing Body, whose Art
 (For they're Masters of Arts to a man, Sir !)
Seeks to beautify Christ Church in every part,
 Though the method seems hardly to answer !
 With three T's it is graced—
 Which letters are placed
To stand for the names of Tact, Talent, and Taste !

Pisc. I thank you, good Scholar, for this piece of merriment, and this Song, which was well humoured by the maker, and well rendered by you.

Ven. Oh, me ! Look you, Master ! A fish ! a fish !

Pisc. Then let us hook it. [*They hook it.*

Finis.

THE BLANK CHEQUE, A FABLE.

[The explanation of this skit is conveyed in the "Moral" at the end. It was a fact that the building of the New Schools was decided on in principle, and that arrangements were made for putting the work in hand, without precisely counting the cost.

"Mrs. Nivers" is the U-nivers-ity. The name which the author gives himself, "Mr. De Ciel," is an easy cryptogram for "D.C.L.," that is for C.L.D., and would not for a moment puzzle the Oxford man of 1874. "Mr. Prior Burgess" and his "three courses," and the "next boarder," who had to be more "hardy" in his notions, is a reflection from 1865. "Susan," who was entrusted with the blank cheque, and empowered to find "a New School for Angela," was the committee appointed to select a plan and submit an estimate. The "boys" are not difficult to recognise : "Harry-Parry" (Liddon), who had been trying to make "Pussy" stand on one leg ; "a Chase in the Hall" (Dr. Chase of St. Mary's); "Sam," the heavy-"weight" (Dr. Wayte of

Trinity) ; " Freddy . . . something of a Bully at times" (Dr. Bulley of Magdalen) ; " Benjy . . . oh the work we had with that boy till we raised his allowance" (Dr. Jowett, recently elected Master of Balliol) ; and " Arthur," who had gone to Westminster (Dean Stanley), "a set of dear good boys on the whole : they've only one real Vice among them."]

THE BLANK CHEQUE,

A FABLE.

THE AUTHOR OF

"THE NEW BELFRY

AND

"THE VISION OF THE THREE T'S.'

"Vell, perhaps," said Sam, "you bought houses, vich is delicate English for goin' mad; or took to buildin', vich is a medical term for being incurable."

𝕺𝔁𝔣𝔬𝔯𝔡:

JAMES PARKER AND CO.

1874

"Five o'clock tea" is a phrase that our "rude forefathers," even of the last generation, would scarcely have understood, so completely is it a thing of to-day; and yet, so rapid is the March of Mind, it has already risen into a national institution, and rivals, in its universal application to all ranks and ages, and as a specific for "all the ills that flesh is heir to," the glorious Magna Charta.

Thus it came to pass that, one chilly day in March, which only made the shelter indoors seem by contrast the more delicious, I found myself in the cosy little parlour of my old friend, kind, hospitable Mrs. Nivers. Her broad, good-humoured face wreathed itself into a sunny smile as I entered, and we were soon embarked on that wayward smooth-flowing current of chat about nothing in particular, which is perhaps the most enjoyable of all forms of conversation. John (I beg his pardon, "Mr. Nivers," I should say: but he was so constantly talked *of*, and *at*, by his better half, as "John," that his friends were apt to forget he had a surname at all) sat in a distant corner with his feet tucked well under his chair, in an attitude rather too upright for comfort, and rather too suggestive of general collapse for anything like dignity, and sipped his tea in silence. From some distant region came a sound like the roar of the sea, rising and falling, suggesting the presence of many boys; and indeed I knew that the house was full to overflowing of noisy urchins, overflowing with high spirits and mischief, but on the whole a very creditable set of little folk.

"And where are you going for your sea-side trip this summer, Mrs. Nivers?"

My old friend pursed up her lips with a mysterious smile and nodded.

"Can't understand you," I said.

"You understand me, Mr. De Ciel, just as well as I understand myself, and *that's* not saying much. *I* don't know where we're going: *John* doesn't know where we're going—but we're certainly going *somewhere;* and we shan't even know the name of the place till we find ourselves there! *Now* are you satisfied?"

I was more hopelessly bewildered than ever. "One of us is dreaming, no doubt," I faltered; "or—or perhaps I'm going mad, or——"

The good lady laughed merrily at my discomfiture.

"Well, well! It's a shame to puzzle you so," she said. "I'll tell you all about it. You see, last year we *couldn't* settle it, do what we would. *John* said 'Herne Bay,' and *I* said 'Brighton,' and the *boys* said 'somewhere where there's a circus,' not that we gave much weight to *that*, you know; well, and Angela (she's a growing girl, and we've got to find a new school for her this year); *she* said 'Portsmouth, because of the soldiers'; and Susan (she's my maid, you know), *she* said 'Ramsgate.' Well, with all those contrary opinions, somehow it ended in our going *nowhere*; and John and I put our heads together last week, and we settled that it should never happen again. And now, how do you think we've managed it?"

"Quite impossible to guess," I said dreamily, as I handed back my empty cup.

"In the first place," said the good lady, "we need change sadly. Housekeeping worries me more every year, particularly with boarders—and John *will* have a couple of gentlemen-boarders always on hand; he says it looks respectable, and that they talk so well, they make the House quite lively. As if *I* couldn't talk enough for him!

"It isn't that!" muttered John. "It's——"

"They're well enough sometimes," the lady went on (she never seemed to hear her husband's remarks), "but I'm sure when Mr. Prior Burgess was here, it was enough to turn one's hair grey! He was an open-handed gentleman enough—as liberal as could be—but *far* too particular about his meals. Why, if you'll believe me, he wouldn't sit down to dinner without there were three courses. We couldn't go on in *that* style, you know. I had to tell the next boarder he must be more hardy in his notions, or I could warrant him we shouldn't suit each other."

"Quite right," I said. "Might I trouble you for another half cup?"

"Seaside air we *must* have, you see," Mrs. Nivers went on, mechanically taking up the tea-pot, but too much engrossed in the subject to do more, "and as we can't agree where to go, and yet we must go *somewhere*—did you say half a cup?"

"Thanks," said I. "You were going to tell me what it was you settled."

"We settled," said the good lady, pouring out

the tea without a moment's pause in her flow of talk, "that the only course was (cream I think you take, but no sugar?   Just so) was to put the whole matter—but stop, John shall read it all out to you. We've drawn up the agreement in writing —quite ship-shape, isn't it, John?   Here's the document: John shall read it you—and mind your stops, there's a dear!"

John put on his spectacles, and in a tone of gloomy satisfaction (it was evidently his own composition) read the following :—

" *Be it hereby enacted and decreed,*
" *That Susan be appointed for the business of choosing a watering-place for this season, and finding a New School for Angela.*
" *That Susan be empowered not only to procure plans, but to select a plan, to submit the estimate for the execution of such plan to the Housekeeper, and, if the Housekeeper sanction the proposed expenditure, to proceed with the execution of such plan, and to fill up the Blank Cheque for the whole expense incurred.*"

Before I could say another word the door burst open, and a whole army of boys tumbled into the room, headed by little Harry, the pet of the family, who hugged in his arms the much-enduring parlour cat, which, as he eagerly explained in his broken English, he had been trying to teach to stand on one leg.

" Harry-Parry Ridy-Pidy Coachy-Poachy!" said the fond mother, as she lifted the little fellow to her knee and treated him to a jog-trot. " Harry's very fond of Pussy, he is, but he mustn't tease it, he mustn't! Now go and play on the stairs, there's dear children. Mr. De Ciel and I want to have a quiet talk." And the boys tumbled out of the room again, as eagerly as they had tumbled in, shouting, " Let's have a Chase in the Hall!"

" A good set of heads, are they not, Mr. De Ciel?" my friend continued, with a wave of her fat hand towards the retreating army. " Phreno-logists admire them much. Look at little Sam, there. He's one of the latest arrivals, you know, but he grows—mercy on us, how that boy does grow! You've no idea what a Weight he is! Then there's Freddy, that tall boy in the corner : he's rather too big for the others, that's a fact— and he's something of a Bully at times, but the boy has a tender heart, too ; give him a bit of poetry, now, and he's as maudlin as a girl! Then there's Benjy, again: a nice boy, but I daren't tell you what he costs us in pocket money! Oh, the work we had with that boy till we raised his allowance! Hadn't we, John?" ("John" grunted in acquiescence). "It was Arthur took up his cause so much, and worried poor John and me nearly into our graves. Arthur was a very nice boy, Mr. De Ciel, and as great a favourite with the other boys as Harry is now, before he went to Westminster. He used to tell them stories, and draw them the prettiest pictures you ever saw! Houses that were all windows and chimnies— what they call 'High Art,' I believe. We tried a conservatory once on the High-Art principle, and (would you believe it?) the man stuck the roof up on a lot of rods like so many knitting needles! Of course it soon came down about our ears, and we had to do it all over again. As I said to John at the time, 'If this is High Art, give me a little more of the Art next time, and a little less of the High!' He's doing very well at West-minster, I hear, but his tutor writes that he's very asthmatic, poor fellow——"

"Æsthetic, my dear, æsthetic!" remonstrated John.

"Ah, well, my love," said the good lady, "all those long medical words are one and the same thing to *me*. And they come to the same thing in the Christmas bills, too ; they both mean ' Draught as before ' ! Well, well ! They're a set of dear good boys on the whole : they've only one real Vice among them—but I shall tire you, talking about the boys so much. What do you think of that agreement of ours ? "

I had been turning the paper over and over in my hands, quite at a loss to know what to say to so strange a scheme. " Surely I've misunderstood you ? " I said. " You don't mean to say that you've left the whole thing to your maid to settle for you ? "

" But that's exactly what I *do* mean, Mr. De Ciel," the lady replied a little testily. " She's a very sensible young person, I can assure you. So now, wherever Susan chooses to take us, *there* we go ! " (" There we go ! There we go ! " echoed her husband in a dismal sort of chant, rocking himself backwards and forwards in his chair.) " You've no idea what a comfort it is to feel that the whole thing's in Susan's hands ! "

" Go where Susan takes thee," I remarked, with a vague idea that I was quoting an old song.

" Well, no doubt Susan has very correct taste, and all that — but still, if I might advise, I wouldn't leave all to her. She may need a little check——"

" That's the very word, dear Mr. De Ciel! " cried my old friend, clapping her hands. " And that's the very thing we've done, isn't it, John? " (" The very thing we've done," echoed John). " I made him do it only this morning. He has signed her a Blank Cheque, so that she can go to any cost she likes. It's such a comfort to get things settled and off one's hands, you know! John's been grumbling about it ever since, but now that I can tell him it's *your* advice——"

" But, my dear Madame," I exclaimed, " I don't mean cheque with a ' Q '! "

" ——your advice," repeated Mrs. N., not heeding my interruption, " why, of course he'll see the reasonableness of it, like a sensible creature as he is! " Here she looked approvingly at her husband, who tried to smile a " slow wise smile," like Tennyson's " wealthy miller," but I fear the result was more remarkable for slowness than for wisdom.

I saw that it would be waste of words to argue the matter further, so took my leave, and did not see my old friends again before their departure for the sea-side. I quote the following from a letter which I received yesterday from Mrs. Nivers :—

"Margate, *April* 1.

"Dear Friend,—*You know the old story of the dinner-party, where there was nothing hot but the ices, and nothing cold but the soup? Of this place I may safely say that there is nothing high but the prices, the staircases, and the eggs ; nothing low but the sea and the company ; nothing strong but the butter, and nothing weak but the tea !*"

From the general tenour of her letter I gather that they are not enjoying it.

Moral.

Is it really seriously proposed—in the University of Oxford, and towards the close of the nineteenth century (never yet reckoned by historians as part of the Dark Ages)—to sign a Blank Cheque for the expenses of building New Schools, before any estimate has been made of those expenses—before any plan has been laid before the University, from which such an estimate could be made—before any architect has been found to design such a plan— before any Committee has been elected to find such an architect ?

Finis.

B. TERRY, ESQ., AND MRS. TERRY.
(*From a photograph by Lewis Carroll.*)

AN ALBUM OF
PHOTOGRAPHIC PORTRAITS
BY LEWIS CARROLL

Lewis Carroll's achievements as a pioneer of amateur photography have been well documented by Helmut Gernsheim in his book, *Lewis Carroll, Photographer,* published by the Chanticleer Press, Inc., in 1950. Mr. Gernsheim's excellent study of Carroll's chief hobby contains much previously unpublished material from Carroll's personal notebooks and diaries. The sixty-four photographs which Mr. Gernsheim selected from Carroll's scrapbooks are excellent examples of Carroll's best work.

The photographs on the following thirty-four pages and others included in this edition are from the Morris L. Parrish Collection of the Princeton University Library. The Parrish Collection owns four of the twelve known scrapbooks which Carroll compiled and which consisted primarily of his own work. None of the originals in the Parrish Collection were reproduced in *Lewis Carroll, Photographer,* although a few are identical to duplicates in that collection. Dover Publications, Inc. is pleased to present a selection of photographs from the fine collection at Princeton, and is grateful to Mr. Alexander D. Wainwright, Curator, for his willing cooperation on this project.

THE EDITORS

DOVER PUBLICATIONS, INC.

1. ARCHDEACON DODGSON, LEWIS CARROLL'S FATHER

2. HENRIETTA DODGSON

3. EDWIN DODGSON

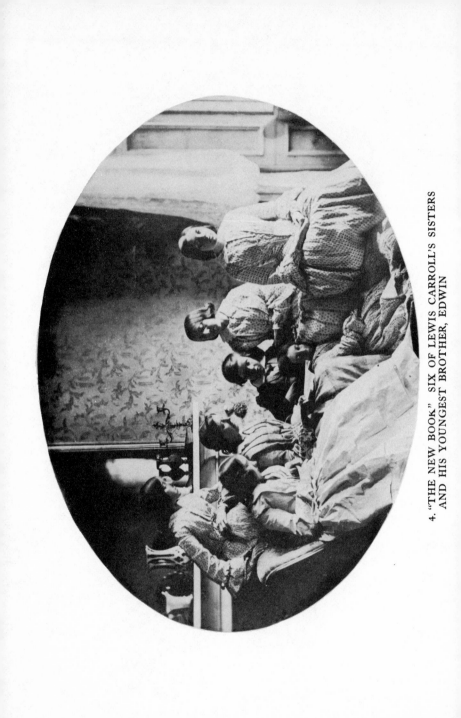

4. "THE NEW BOOK" SIX OF LEWIS CARROLL'S SISTERS
AND HIS YOUNGEST BROTHER, EDWIN

5. WILFRED L. DODGSON AND DIDO

6. "TIM," THE FAMILY DOLL

7. FLORENCE HILDA BAINBRIDGE

8. MRS. BARRY AND LOUIE

9. ALICE JANE DONKIN POSING FOR "THE ELOPEMENT"

10. "TIRED OF PLAY"   CONSTANCE AND MARY ELLISON

11. ETHEL AND LILIAN BRODIE

12. ALICE PLEASANCE LIDDELL

13. CAROLINE AND ROSAMUND LONGLEY

14. ALICE PLEASANCE LIDDELL AND LORINA
CHARLOTTE LIDDELL

15. MARGARET GATEY WITH MARY AND CHARLOTTE WEBSTER

16. ALICE PLEASANCE LIDDELL AS "THE BEGGAR MAID"

17. AGNES GRACE WELD (MRS. TENNYSON'S NIECE) AS
"LITTLE RED RIDING-HOOD"

18. ALFRED, LORD TENNYSON

19. HALLAM TENNYSON, ALFRED'S OLDEST SON

20. JOHN E. MILLAIS

21. GEORGE MACDONALD

22. W. HOLMAN HUNT

23. THOMAS WOOLNER

24. JOHN RUSKIN

25. AUBREY DE VERE

26. CHARLOTTE M. YONGE

27. BISHOP LONGLEY

28. MICHAEL FARADAY

29. BISHOP OF LINCOLN

30. HENRY W. ACLAND

31. PROFESSOR WILLIAM DINDORF

32. ALEXANDER MUNRO

33. PROFESSOR W. F. DONKIN

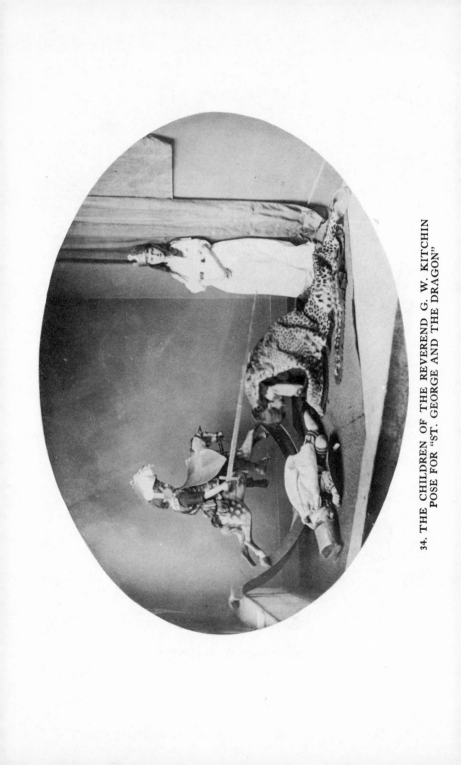

34. THE CHILDREN OF THE REVEREND G. W. KITCHIN
POSE FOR "ST. GEORGE AND THE DRAGON"

CHAPTER III

"ALICE" ON THE STAGE

THE only serious contributions to dramatic criticism which Lewis Carroll made are contained in two papers which appeared in *The Theatre*, and which are reproduced here by Mr. Clement Scott's kind permission. A short appreciation of him, by one of his oldest theatrical friends, Mr. A. W. Dubourg, will serve as an introduction to them :

" I gathered from my intercourse with Lewis Carroll that, subject to rigid limits as to the moral character of the play, he had considerable sympathy with the drama, believing that within those limits the stage might have a valuable and elevating influence upon all classes of playgoers and upon the public generally ; but with regard to the slightest transgression of those limits he was greatly sensitive, perhaps super-sensitive to the mind of a layman, and I have known him leave a theatre in the midst of a performance for a very small deviation from the line he had marked out.

" He was particularly sensitive as to the use of oaths on the stage—he strongly protested against it, and I know that he once entered into a serious controversy with a leading manager on the subject. The stage will always be a potent factor in social life, and the support accorded by seriously minded persons like Lewis Carroll will always tend to wholesomeness and moral elevation, because this support will make *good* things *pay*, and managers must look for profit from what they give to the public.

" Lewis Carroll took a kindly interest in child-life on the stage. I always think that any little girl of ten or twelve was potentially an 'Alice' in his eyes ; and I know that many a kind and generous act has he done for those stage-children and their parents—persons oftentimes greatly in want of substantial assistance.

" In conclusion, I should like to say these few words about my personal intercourse with Lewis Carroll.

" I knew well and greatly valued Charles Dodgson in the friendly intercourse of life ; but

the friend of the fireside and the family dinner-
table was totally unlike the Lewis Carroll that
popular imagination would picture — a quiet
retiring, scholarlike person, full of interesting
and pleasant conversation, oftentimes with an
undercurrent of humour, and certainly with a
sense of great sensitiveness with regard to the
serious side of life. The very thought of being
lionised was utterly distasteful and abhorrent,
and I never heard him utter in conversation a
single telling sentence on the lines of 'Alice' or
the 'Snark.' I may truthfully say that throughout much friendly intercourse with Charles
Dodgson, the remembrance of which I value
greatly, I never met that exquisite humorist,
Lewis Carroll."

"ALICE" ON THE STAGE.

BY LEWIS CARROLL.

("The Theatre," April, 1887.)

"Look here; here's all this Judy's clothes
falling to pieces again." Such were the pensive
words of Mr. Thomas Codlin; and they may

fitly serve as a motto for a writer who has set himself the unusual task of passing in review a set of puppets that are virtually his own—the stage embodiments of his own dream-children.

Not that the play itself is in any sense mine. The arrangements, in dramatic form, of a story written without the slightest idea that it would be so adapted, was a task that demanded powers denied to me, but possessed in an eminent degree, so far as I can judge, by Mr. Savile Clarke. I do not feel myself qualified to criticise his play, as a play ; nor shall I venture on any criticism of the players as players.

What is it, then, I have set myself to do ? And what possible claim have I to be heard ? My answer must be that, as the writer of the two stories thus adapted, and the originator (as I believe, for at least I have not *consciously* borrowed them) of the "airy nothings" for which Mr. Saville Clarke has so skilfully provided, if not a name, at least, a "local habitation," I may without boastfulness claim to have a special knowledge of what it was I meant them to be, and so a special understanding of how far that intention has been realised. And I fancied there might be some readers of *The Theatre* who would be inte-

rested in sharing that knowledge and that understanding.

Many a day had we rowed together on that
quiet stream—the three little maidens and I—and
many a fairy tale had been extemporised for their
benefit—whether it were at times when the nar-
rator was " i' the vein," and fancies unsought came
crowding thick upon him, or at times when the
jaded Muse was goaded into action, and plodded
meekly on, more because she had to say something than that she had something to say—yet
none of these many tales got written down : they
lived and died, like summer midges, each in its
own golden afternoon until there came a day
when, as it chanced, one of my little listeners
petitioned that the tale might be written out for
her. That was many a year ago, but I distinctly
remember, now as I write, how, in a desperate
attempt to strike out some new line of fairy-lore,
I had sent my heroine straight down a rabbit-hole,
to begin with, without the least idea what was to
happen afterwards. And so, to please a child I
loved (I don't remember any other motive), I
printed in manuscript, and illustrated with my
own crude designs—designs that rebelled against
every law of Anatomy or Art (for I had never had

a lesson in drawing)—the book which I have just had published in facsimile. In writing it out, I added many fresh ideas, which seemed to grow of themselves upon the original stock ; and many more added themselves when, years afterwards, I wrote it all over again for publication : but (this may interest some readers of " Alice" to know) every such idea and nearly every word of the dialogue, *came of itself.* Sometimes an idea comes at night, when I have had to get up and strike a light to note it down—sometimes when out on a lonely winter walk, when I have had to stop, and with half-frozen fingers jot down a few words which should keep the new-born idea from perishing—but whenever or however it comes, *it comes of itself.* I cannot set invention going like a clock, by any voluntary winding up : nor do I believe that any *original* writing (and what other writing is worth preserving ?) was ever so produced. If you sit down, unimpassioned and un-inspired, and *tell* yourself to write for so many hours, you will merely produce (at least I am sure *I* should merely produce) some of that article which fills, so far as I can judge, two-thirds of most magazines—most easy to write most weary to read—men call it "padding," and it is to my mind one of the most detestable things in modern literature. "Alice" and the "Looking-Glass" are made up almost wholly of bits and scraps, single ideas which came of themselves. Poor they may have been; but at least they were the best I had to offer: and I can desire no higher praise to be written of me than the words of a Poet, written of a Poet,

> " He gave the people of his best :
> The worst he kept, the best he gave."

I have wandered from my subject, I know: yet grant me another minute to relate a little incident of my own experience. I was walking on a hillside, alone, one bright summer day, when suddenly there came into my head one line of verse—one solitary line—"For the Snark *was* a Boojum, you see." I knew not what it meant, then: I know not what it means, now; but I wrote it down: and, some time afterwards, the rest of the stanza occurred to me, that being its last line: and so by degrees, at odd moments during the next year or two, the rest of the poem pieced itself together, that being its last stanza. And since then, periodically I have received courteous letters from strangers, begging to know whether "The Hunting of the Snark" is an allegory, or contains some hidden moral, or is a political satire : and for all such questions I have but one answer, "*I don't know !*" And now I return to my text, and will wander no more.

Stand forth, then, from the shadowy past, "Alice," the child of my dreams. Full many a year has slipped away, since that "golden after-noon" that gave thee birth, but I can call it up almost as clearly as if it were yesterday — the cloudless blue above, the watery mirror below, the boat drifting idly on its way, the tinkle of the drops that fell from the oars, as they waved so sleepily to and fro, and (the one bright gleam of life in all the slumberous scene) the three eager faces, hungry for news of fairy-land, and who would not be said "nay" to : from whose lips "Tell us a story, please," had all the stern im-mutability of Fate!

What wert thou, dream-Alice, in thy foster-father's eyes? How shall he picture thee? Loving, first, loving and gentle : loving as a dog (forgive the prosaic simile, but I know no earthly love so pure and perfect), and gentle as a fawn : then courteous—courteous to *all*, high or low, grand or grotesque, King or Caterpillar, even as

MISS BEADEN AS "THE ROSE" IN "ALICE IN WONDERLAND" AT THE
ROYAL OPERA COMIQUE THEATRE, LONDON, 1898.

(*From a photograph by the London Stereoscopic Company.*)

though she were herself a King's daughter, and
her clothing of wrought gold : then trustful, ready
to accept the wildest impossibilities with all that
utter trust that only dreamers know ; and lastly,
curious—wildly curious, and with the eager enjoyment of Life that comes only in the happy hours
of childhood, when all is new and fair, and when
Sin and Sorrow are but names—empty words
signifying nothing !

And the White Rabbit, what of *him* ? Was *he*
framed on the " Alice " lines, or meant as a contrast ? As a contrast, distinctly. For *her* "youth,"
"audacity," "vigour," and "swift directness of
purpose," read "elderly," "timid," "feeble," and
"nervously shilly-shallying," and you will get
something of what I meant him to be. I *think*
the White Rabbit should wear spectacles. I am
sure his voice should quaver, and his knees
quiver, and his whole air suggest a total inability
to say " Bo " to a goose !

But I cannot hope to be allowed, even by the
courteous Editor of *The Theatre*, half the space I
should need (even if my *reader's* patience would
hold out) to discuss each of my puppets one by
one. Let me cull from the two books a Royal
Trio—the Queen of Hearts, the Red Queen, and

the White Queen. It was certainly hard on my
Muse, to expect her to sing of *three* Queens,
within such brief compass, and yet to give to
each her own individuality. Each, of course, had
to preserve, through all her eccentricities, a certain
queenly *dignity*. *That* was essential. And for
distinguishing traits, I pictured to myself the
Queen of Hearts as a sort of embodiment of
ungovernable passion—a blind and aimless Fury.
The Red Queen I pictured as a Fury, but of
another type ; *her* passion must be cold and calm ;
she must be formal and strict, yet not unkindly ;
pedantic to the tenth degree, the concentrated
essence of all governesses ! Lastly, the White
Queen seemed, to my dreaming fancy, gentle,
stupid, fat and pale ; helpless as an infant ; and
with a slow, maundering, bewildered air about
her just *suggesting* imbecility, but never quite
passing into it ; that would be, I think, fatal to
any comic effect she might otherwise produce.
There is a character strangely like her in Wilkie
Collins' novel "No Name" : by two different
converging paths we have somehow reached the
same ideal, and Mrs. Wragg and the White
Queen might have been twin-sisters.

As it is no part of my present purpose to find

fault with any of those who have striven so
zealously to make this " dream-play " a waking
success, I shall but name two or three who seemed
to me specially successful in realising the characters of the story.

None, I think, was better realised than the two
undertaken by Mr. Sydney Harcourt, "the
Hatter" and " Tweedledum." To see him
enact the Hatter was a weird and uncanny
thing, as though some grotesque monster, seen
last night in a dream, should walk into the
room in broad daylight, and quietly say " Good
morning!" I need not try to describe what I
meant the Hatter to be, since, so far as I can now
remember, it was exactly what Mr. Harcourt has
made him : and I may say nearly the same of
Tweedledum : but the Hatter surprised me most
—perhaps only because it came first in the play.

There were others who realised my ideas nearly
as well; but I am not attempting a complete
review : I will conclude with a few words about
the two children who played " Alice " and "the
Dormouse."

Of Miss Phœbe Carlo's performance it would
be difficult to speak too highly. As a mere effort
of memory, it was surely a marvellous feat for so

young a child, to learn no less than two hundred and fifteen speeches—nearly three times as many as Beatrice in "Much Ado About Nothing." But what I admired most, as realising most nearly my ideal heroine, was her perfect assumption of the high spirits, and readiness to enjoy *everything*, of a child out for a holiday. I doubt if any grown actress, however experienced, could have worn this air so perfectly ; *we* look before and after, and sigh for what is not ; a child never does *this :* and it is only a child that can utter from her heart the words poor Margaret Fuller Ossoli so longed to make her own, "I am all happy *now !* "

And last (I may for once omit the time-honoured addition "not least," for surely no tinier maiden ever yet achieved so genuine a theatrical success ?) comes our dainty Dormouse. "Dainty" is the only epithet that seems to me exactly to suit her : with her beaming baby-face, the delicious crispness of her speech, and the perfect realism with which she makes herself the embodied essence of Sleep, she is surely the daintiest Dormouse that ever yet told us "I sleep when I breathe!" With the first words of that her opening speech, a sudden silence falls upon the house (at least it has been so every time *I* have been there), and the baby tones sound strangely clear in the stillness. And yet I doubt if the charm is due only to the incisive clearness of her articulation ; to me there was an even greater charm in the utter self-abandonment and conscientious *thoroughness* of her acting. If Dorothy ever adopts a motto, it ought to be " thorough." I hope the time may soon come when she will have a better part than " Dormouse " to play—when some enterprising manager will revive the "Midsummer Night's Dream " and do his obvious duty to the public by securing Miss Dorothy d'Alcourt as " Puck " !

It would be well indeed for our churches if some of the clergy could take a lesson in enunciation from this little child ; and better still, for " our noble selves," if *we* would lay to heart some things that she could teach us, and would learn by her example to realise, rather more than we do, the spirit of a maxim I once came across in an old book, " Whatsoever thy hand findeth to do, *do it with thy might*."

THE STAGE AND THE SPIRIT OF REVERENCE.

By Lewis Carroll.

(" *The Theatre*," *June*, 1888.)

THIS article is *not* going to be a sermon in disguise.
This I protest, at the outset, knowing how entirely
usage—a mistaken usage, as I think—has limited
the word to *religious* topics only, and that the
reader is only too likely to turn this page hastily
over, muttering " *Chacun à son goût.* This is
meant for sectarians of *some* kind. *I* have no
such narrow sympathies. Talk to me as a *man*,
and I'll listen ! "

But that is exactly what I want to do. I want
to talk to the play-going or play-writing reader,
who may honour me with his attention, as a *man :*
not as a churchman, not as a Christian, not even
as a believer in God—but simply as a man who
recognises (*this*, I admit, is essential) that there is
a distinction between good and evil ; who honours
good men and good deeds, simple as being good ;
and who realises that from evil men and evil
deeds comes much, if not all, of the sorrow of
life.

And may not the word "good," also, have a broader meaning than usage has assigned to it? May it not fairly include all that is brave, and manly, and true in human nature? Surely a man may honour these qualities, even though he own to no *religious* beliefs whatever? A striking example of this kind of "reverence" is recorded of the robber-tribes of Upper Scinde, during Sir Charles Napier's campaign (I quote from a lecture by Robertson, of Brighton, on "The Influence of Poetry on the Working Classes") :—

"A detachment of troops was marching along a valley, the cliffs overhanging which were crested by the enemy. A sergeant, with eleven men, chanced to become separated from the rest by taking the wrong side of a ravine, which they expected soon to terminate, but which suddenly deepened into an impassable chasm. The officer in command signalled to the party an order to return. They mistook the signal for a command to charge; the brave fellows answered with a cheer, and charged. At the summit of the steep mountain was a triangular platform, defended by a breast-work, behind which were seventy of the foe. On they went, charging up one of these fearful paths, eleven against seventy. The contest could not long be doubtful with such odds. One after another they fell : six upon the spot, the remainder hurled backwards ; but not until they had slain nearly twice their own number.

" There is a custom, we are told, amongst the hillsmen, that when a great chieftain of their own falls in battle, his wrist is bound with a thread either of red or green, the red denoting the highest rank. According to custom, they stripped the dead, and threw their bodies over the precipice. When their comrades came, they found their corpses stark and gashed ; but round both wrists of every British hero was twined the red thread ! "

In " reverence " such as this I am happy to believe that the standard reached on the Stage is fully as high as in the literature of Fiction, and distinctly higher than what often passes without protest in Society.

Take, for instance, the treatment of *vice*. In Fiction and in many a social circle, vice is condoned, and sentiments utterly vile and selfish are freely expressed, in language that would be hissed off the stage of a respectable theatre, unless put into the mouth of the stage " villain." In the " Silver King," as I saw it some years

ago, when the gentlemanly scoundrel, splendidly
acted by Mr. Willard, sent the coarser scoundrel,
who served as his tool on the hateful mission of
turning out of doors the poor mother whose child
was dying, it was good to hear the low fierce hiss
that ran through the audience as the old wretch
went off. Any one who witnessed that fine drama
would, I think, believe with me that those who
thus hiss—evil as their own lives may be in
some cases—yet have their better moments, when
the veil is lifted, when they see Sin in all its
native hideousness, and shudder at the sight!

And, for an example of the sympathy shown by
play-goers for what is pure and good, I may
recall the experience of a few weeks back, when I
went to see "The Golden Ladder" (produced by
the same conscientious actor and manager—Mr.
Wilson Barrett—who gave us "The Silver
King"), and heard with delight the ripple of
applause which greeted the soliloquy of the
comical old greengrocer, Mr. George Barrett,
about his child, to whom he has given the
ambitious name "Victoria Alexandra."

"And I guv her them two names, because
they're the best two names as is!" That ripple
of applause seemed to me to say, "Yes, the very

sound of those names—names which recall a Queen whose spotless life has for many long years been a blessing to her people, and a Princess who will worthily follow in her steps—is sweet music to English ears!"

The reader can no doubt recall many occasions when Pit and Gallery have shown equally keen sympathy with self-denial, generosity, or any of the qualities that ennoble human nature. I will content myself with two more examples.

Years ago I saw Mr. Emery play the hero of "All is not Gold that Glitters"—a factory-owner, with a rough manner but a tender heart ; and I well remember how he "brought down the house," when speaking of the "hands" employed in his factory, with the words, "And a' couldn't lie down and sleep in peace, if a' thowt there was man, woman, or child among 'em as was going to bed cold and hungry!" What mattered it to us that all this was fiction ? That the "hands," so tenderly cared for, were creatures of a dream? We were not "reverencing" that actor only, but every man, in every age, that has ever taken loving thought for those around him, that ever "hath given his bread to the hungry, and hath covered the naked with a garment."

Irene Barnes
Aug. 29/87

MISS IRENE VANBRUGH.
(From a sketch by Lewis Carroll.)

My other example shall be a memory of the greatest actor our generation has seen — one whose every word and gesture seemed inspired, and made one feel " He has me in his power ; he can make me laugh and weep as he will!"—I mean Frederick Robson. Who, that ever saw him in " The Porter's Knot," can forget the delicious pathos of the scene where the old father, who has sacrificed the earnings of a lifetime to save his son's reputation and send him abroad, is in an innocent conspiracy, with the girl to whom his son is betrothed, to keep the old mother happy by reading her a letter they pretend to have come from her boy. Unknown to him, the loving girl has resolved on giving her last earnings to the old couple, and has added a postscript. " Dear Mother,—I am getting on so well that I send you this five-pound note," which the old man, reading the letter to his wife, comes upon so unexpectedly that he nearly betrays the whole plot. Then came the " aside " — with that humorous glance at the audience that none ever gave as he did—" Well! This here has growed since the morning!" And then, suddenly detecting the loving stratagem, and shaking his fist at the girl, " Oh, you little *rascal !* " As Borachio would say, " I tell this story vilely." Would that any words of mine *could* convey to the reader the infinite tenderness that breathed in those whispered " words of unmeant bitterness ! "

And now, before narrowing the field of discussion and considering how " reverence " is due to subjects connected with religion, I wish to give to this word also a broader sense than the conventional one. I mean by it simply a belief in *some* good and unseen being, above and outside human life as we see it, to whom we feel ourselves responsible. And I hold that " reverence " is due, even to the most degraded type of " religion," as embodying in a concrete form a principle which the most absolute Atheist professes to revere in the abstract.

These subjects may be classed under two headings, according as they are connected with the principle of good or with that of evil. Under the first heading we may name the Deity, and good spirits, the act of prayer, places of worship, and ministers : under the second, evil spirits and future punishment.

The " irreverence " with which such topics are sometimes handled, both on and off the Stage, may be partly explained by the fact (not unlikely to be overlooked) that no word has a meaning *inseparably* attached to it ; a word means what the speaker intends by it, and what the hearer understands by it, and that is all.

I meet a friend and say " Good morning!" Harmless words enough, one would think. Yet possibly, in some language he and I have never heard, these words may convey utterly horrid and loathsome ideas. But are *we* responsible for this? This thought may serve to lessen the horror of some of the language used by the lower classes, which, it is a comfort to remember, is often a mere collection of unmeaning *sounds*, so far as speaker and hearer are concerned.

And even where profane language seems really blameworthy, as being consciously and deliberately used, I do not think the worst instances occur on the stage ; you must turn for such to fashionable Society and popular Literature.

No type of anecdote seems so sure to amuse the social circle as that which turns some familiar Bible-phrase into a grotesque parody. Sometimes the wretched jest is retailed, half-apologetically, as said by a child, " and, of course," it is added, " the *child* meant no harm!" Possibly : but does the *grown man* mean no harm, who thus degrades what he ought to treat with reverence, just to raise a laugh?

Again, can such jesting as that of the "Ingoldsby Legends," where evil spirits are treated as subjects for uproarious merriment, be tolerated by any one who realises what "evil" means, whether in disembodied spirits (whose existence he may possibly doubt) or in living men and women? Shall the curse of all the race, the misery of all the ages, serve us for a passing *jest?*

But the lowest depths of conscious and deliberate irreverence that my memory recalls, have been, I am sorry to say, the utterances of *reverend* jesters. I have heard, from the lips of clergymen, anecdotes whose horrid blasphemy outdid anything that would be even *possible* on the Stage. Whether it be that long familiarity with sacred phrases deadens one's sense of their meaning, I cannot tell : it is the only excuse I can think of : and such a theory is partly supported by the curious phenomenon (which the reader can easily test for himself) that if you repeat a word a great many times in succession, however suggestive it may have been when you began, you will end by divesting it of every shred of meaning, and almost

wondering how you could ever have meant anything by it!

How far can the Stage use of oaths, or phrases
introducing the name of the Deity, be justified?
To me it is only when lightly and jestingly
uttered that they seem profane. Used gravely,
and for a worthy purpose, they are at any rate not
to be condemned by any appeal to the *Bible :* one
of the loveliest pieces of its prose-poetry, the well-
known " Entreat me not to leave thee," &c., ends
with an undeniable oath, " The Lord do so to me,
and more also, if aught but death part thee and
me." And it is on Society, rather than on the
Stage, that we should lay the blame of the light
use of such language, common in the last generation, when such phrases as " My God ! " " Good
Lord ! " were constantly used as mere *badinage,*
and when so refined a writer as Miss Austen
could make a young lady say (in " Pride and
Prejudice ") " Lord, how ashamed I should be
of not being married before three-and-twenty ! "
When quite common, such words possibly conveyed no meaning either to speaker or hearer :
in these days they jar on the ear, for their
strangeness forces us to realise their meaning.
When Shakespeare wrote " Much Ado," Beatrice's

" O God, that I were a man ! I would eat his heart in the market-place," and Benedick's " O God, sir, here's a dish I love not ; I cannot endure my lady Tongue," no doubt fell with equally innocent effect on the ear : but in our day, though the first may well be retained, as gravely said and on a worthy occasion, the second comes as a false note, and I think Mr. Irving, instead of toning it down into " O Lord ! " would have done better by omitting it altogether.

The act of prayer is almost uniformly treated with reverence on the Stage. My experience furnishes only one instance to the contrary, where the heroine of a ballet, supposed to be in her chamber at night, and soon to be serenaded by her lover at the window, went through the horrid mockery of kneeling in semblance of prayer. But I see no objection to its introduction on the Stage, if reverently represented, as in the scene in " Hamlet," where Claudius is found praying : and I well remember the grand effect produced by Charles Kean (in " Henry V.," just before the battle of Agincourt), by kneeling, for a short passionate prayer, on the battle-field.

Places of worship, also, when made the sub-jects of stage representation, are usually treated with perfect propriety : one must turn to the orgies of the Salvation Army, or the ribaldry of the street preacher, to realise how far religion can be vulgarised, and with what loathsome familiarity the holiest themes can be insulted. We have lately been privileged to see an instance of exquisite taste and reverent handling in the church-scene in " Much Ado " at the Lyceum. Some objected, at the time, to any such scene being put on the Stage, yet probably none of its censors would condemn "sacred" pictures? And surely the distinction between a picture painted on canvas, and a picture formed by living figures on a stage is more fanciful than real? To me the solemn beauty of that scene suggested the hope that some might see it—some to whom the ideas of God, or heaven, or prayer, were strange—and might think " Is *this* what church is like? I'll go and see it for myself ! " Yet *one* false note there certainly was to mar the beauty of that scene. The dialogue between Beatrice and Benedick, with all its delicate banter and refined comedy, spoken amid such surroundings, must have given pain to many to whom the special scene had been a pure delight. I heartily wish Mr. Irving could see his way to transfer it to the *outside* of the church. Surely a manager, who could endure an interpolation so utterly alien to the spirit of the scene as " Kiss my hand again ! " can have no *very* strong feeling about keeping the text of Shakespeare inviolate !

As for ministers of religion, I would not seek to shield them from ridicule *when they deserve it ;* but is it not sometimes too indiscriminate ? Mr. Gilbert—to whom we owe a deep debt of gratitude for the pure and healthy fun he has given us in such comedies as " Patience "—seems to have a craze for making bishops and clergymen con-temptible. Yet are they behind other professions in such things as earnestness, and hard work, and devotion of life to the call of duty ? That clever song, " The pale young curate," with its charming music, is to me simply painful. I seem to see him as he goes home at night, pale and worn with the day's work, perhaps sick with the pestilent atmosphere of a noisome garret where, at the risk of his life, he has been comforting a dying man—and is your sense of humour, my reader, so keen that you can *laugh* at that man ? Then at least be consistent. Laugh also at that pale young doctor, whom you have summoned in such hot haste to your own dying child : ay, and laugh also at that pale young soldier, as he sinks on the trampled battlefield, and reddens the dust with his life-blood for the honour of Old England!

Still, the other side of this picture is now and again given us on the Stage, and one could not desire a more gentle and lovable type of old age than the "Vicar of Wakefield," as played by Mr. Irving, or a more manly and chivalrous hero than the young clergyman in "The Golden Ladder," played by Mr. Wilson Barrett.

The common treatment of such subjects as *evil spirits* must be regarded from a fresh standpoint. "What reverence," it might fairly be asked, "is due to the Devil, whether we believe that such a being exists or not?" My answer is, that *seriousness* at least is due in dealing with such subjects. The darkest deeds of lust or cruelty that have blasted human happiness have often seemed to the guilty wretch to be due to influences other than his own thoughts : but, even setting aside such evidence, the whole subject is too closely bound up with the deepest sorrows of life to be fit matter for jesting. Yet how often one hears in Society the ready laughter with which any sly allusion to the Devil is received—ay, even by clergymen themselves, who, if their whole life be not one continuous lie, do believe that such a being exists, and that his existence is one of the saddest facts of life.

In this respect I think the tone of the Stage not lower than—I doubt if it be so low as—that of Society. Such a picture as Irving gives us of " Mephistopheles " must surely have a healthy influence. Who can see it and not realise, with a vividness few preachers could rival, the utter *hatefulness* of sin ?

The same claim, for seriousness of treatment, may be made as to the subjects of Hell and future punishment. In the last generation the Stage, in its constant light use of words connected with " damnation," was simply following the lead of Society ; and it is satisfactory to notice that the idle curses, no longer heard in respectable Society, are fast vanishing from the Stage. Let me mention one instance of false treatment of this subject on the Stage, and conclude with two of the better kind.

I have never seen Mr. Gilbert's clever play " Pinafore " performed by grown-up actors : as played by *children*, one passage in it was to me sad beyond words. It occurs when the captain

utters the oath " Damn me!" and forthwith a
bevy of sweet innocent-looking little girls sing,
with bright, happy looks, the chorus "He said
' Damn me!' He said ' Damn me!'" I cannot
find words to convey to the reader the pain I felt
in seeing those dear children taught to utter such
words to amuse ears grown callous to their ghastly
meaning. Put the two ideas side by side—Hell
(no matter whether *you* believe in it or not :
millions do), and those pure young lips thus
sporting with its horrors—and then find what
fun in it you can! How Mr. Gilbert could have
stooped to write, or Sir Arthur Sullivan could
have prostituted his noble art to set to music such
vile trash, it passes my skill to understand.

But I am no such purist as to object to *all* such
allusions : when gravely made, and for a worthy
purpose, they are, I think, entirely healthy in
their effect. When the hero of " The Golden
Ladder," claimed as prisoner by a French officer
is taken under the protection of a British captain
(finely played by Mr. Bernage), and the French-
man's " He is my prison-erre!" is met by the
choleric captain's stentorian reply, " Then, damn
it, come on board my ship and take him!" the
oath did not sound " irreverent " in any degree.

Q. F. TWISS, ESQ. AS "THE ARTFUL DODGER."
Morris L. Parrish Collection, Princeton University Library

Here was no empty *jesting :* all was grim earnest !

One more example, and I have done. No dramatic version of " David Copperfield " would do justice to the story if it failed to give the scene after Steerforth has eloped with "little Em'ly," leaving her betrothed, Ham Peggotty, a broken-hearted man. Ham has brought the news to his father, and David is present.

" Mas'r Davy," implored Ham, " go out a bit, and let me tell him what I must. You doen't ought to hear it, sir."

" I want to know his name ! " I heard said, once more.

" For some time past," Ham faltered, " there's been a servant about here at odd times. There's been a gen'lm'n, too. . . . A strange chay and horses was outside town this morning. . . . When the servant went to it, Em'ly was nigh him. The t'other was inside. He's the man."

" For the Lord's love," said Mr. Peggotty, falling back, and putting out his hand, as if to keep off what he dreaded, " doen't tell me his name's Steerforth ! "

" Mas'r Davy," exclaimed Ham, in a broken voice, " it ain't no fault of yourn—and I am far from laying of it to you—but his name is Steer-forth, and he's a damned villain ! "

The critic who would exclaim, on witnessing such a scene, " Shocking irreverence! That oath ought to be cut out ! " attaches a meaning to the word " irreverence " with which I have no sympathy.

May I conclude with an allusion to the distinctly dramatic tone of much of the language of the Bible ? In doing so I make no special appeal to Christians : any one, who possesses any literary taste at all, will admit that, for poetry and simple pathos, it stands high in the literature of the world. Much of the vivid force of the parables depends on their dramatic character : one fancies, in reading the parable of the " Sower," that the recital was illustrated by the actual events of the moment : one pictures a neighbouring hill-side, with its sharp sky-line, along which slowly moves a figure, seen clear and black against the bright sky, and giving, by the regular swing of his arm, a sort of rhythmic cadence to the words of the speaker.

Whether the parable of " The Prodigal Son " has ever served as the basis of a drama I know not : the general idea has no doubt been so used again and again : but the story, as it stands, simply translated into modern life, would make a most effective play.

The First Act, with the splendour of the wealthy home, would be in picturesque contrast with the Second, where we should find the spendthrift in gaudy and ostentatious vulgarity, surrounded by unmanly men and unwomanly women, wasting his substance in the " far country." The Third might depict his downward career, ending in a deep despair—then the revulsion of feeling—then the pathetic words " I will arise, and go to my Father!" and when the Fourth Act took us back to the ancestral halls, and showed us the wretched outcast, pausing irresolute at the door, mocked by a troop of listless menials, who would fain drive the beggar back to starvation and death, and the old father rushing forth to clasp the wanderer to his breast—might not some eyes, even among the roughs of the Gallery, be " wet with most delicious tears," and some hearts be filled with new and noble thoughts, and a spirit of " reverence " be aroused, for " whatsoever things are just, whatsoever things are pure, whatsoever things are lovely," which would not lightly pass away ?

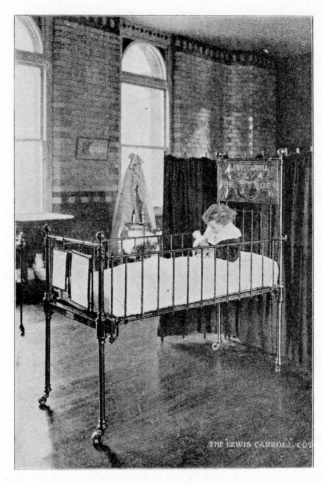

THE "LEWIS CARROLL" COT.
(From a photograph by Messrs. Bedford, Lemere & Co., 147, Strand, W.C.)

CHAPTER IV

I T is as a writer of children's stories that Lewis
Carroll is best known ; his mathematical and
logical works, the views which he expressed
with so much emphasis on the chief religious and
ethical questions of the day have made little
effect on the public compared with the adventures
of Alice. With this fact in view, it is not surprising that while all his letters are interesting,
and some even brilliant, it is those which he
wrote to children that have been most widely
read and appreciated. In " The Life and Letters
of Lewis Carroll " I included a considerable
number of these letters ; but, since the publication of that book, many more have come into my
hands, and the present seems a favourable opportunity to introduce them to a larger public than
that for which they were originally intended.

Lewis Carroll was one of those men who are blessed at times with moods too frivolous to admit of expression in the ordinary modes of speech and writing. It was at such times as these, when he was himself, in all but age and ignorance, a child, that he indited the letters which comprise the present chapter. I have arranged them in the most haphazard way, and without any attempt at logical or any other sequence ; written upon the impulse of the moment, in some splendid fit of midsummer madness, it would be a sacrilege to treat them *au grand sérieux.*

To Miss Henrietta, and Master Edwin Dodgson.

"CH. CH., *Jan.* 31*st.*

"MY DEAR HENRIETTA,

"MY DEAR EDWIN,

"I am very much obliged by your nice little birthday gift—it was much better than a cane would have been—I have got it on my watch-chain, but the Dean has not yet remarked it.

"My one pupil has begun his work with me, and I will give you a description how the lecture is conducted. It is the most important point, you know, that the tutor should be *dignified* and at a distance from the pupil, and that the pupil should be as much as possible *degraded.*

"Otherwise, you know, they are not humble enough.

"So I sit at the further end of the room ; outside the door (*which is shut*) sits the scout : outside the outer door (*also shut*) sits the sub-scout : half-way downstairs sits the sub-sub-scout ; and down in the yard sits the *pupil*.

"The questions are shouted from one to the other, and the answers come back in the same way—it is rather confusing till you are well used to it. The lecture goes on something like this :—

"*Tutor.* What is twice three ?

"*Scout.* What's a rice tree ?

"*Sub-Scout.* When is ice free ?

"*Sub-sub-Scout.* What's a nice fee ?

"*Pupil* (*timidly*). Half a guinea !

"*Sub-sub-Scout.* Can't forge any !

"*Sub-Scout.* Ho for Jinny !

"*Scout.* Don't be a ninny !

"*Tutor* (*looks offended, but tries another question*). Divide a hundred by twelve !

"*Scout.* Provide wonderful bells !

"*Sub-Scout.* Go ride under it yourself !

"*Sub-sub-Scout.* Deride the dunder-headed elf !

"*Pupil* (*surprised*). Who do you mean ?

"*Sub-sub-Scout.* Doings between !

"*Sub-Scout.* Blue is the screen !

"*Scout.* Soup-tureen !

"And so the lecture proceeds.

"Such is Life.

"from

"Your most affect. brother,

"CHARLES L. DODGSON.

The above letter was written by Lewis Carroll

shortly after he had obtained his studentship, to his youngest brother and sister. The Rev. Edwin Dodgson went afterwards to Twyford School ; Lewis Carroll used to say of him that he was " well-intentioned but vulgar," and, after his first term at school, his verdict was that he was " less well-intentioned and more vulgar."

The Misses Winifred and Enid Stevens were two of Mr. Dodgson's Oxford child friends. To the latter he dedicated " Sylvie and Bruno Concluded " ; the third letters of the lines at the beginning of the book spell her name.

" My friendship with Mr. Dodgson," writes Mrs. Hawke (Miss Winifred Stevens), " spread over about ten years of my child- and girlhood ; and my recollections of it are chiefly of long walks round Oxford, blissful days in town, and many pleasurable hours spent in the treasure-house of his rooms in Christ Church, where—no matter how often one went—there was always something fresh to be seen, something new and strange to hear. I shall not easily forget his showing me Mr. Furniss's original drawings for ' Sylvie and Bruno,' before that book was published, and his reading to me —as a secret—the now famous Gardener's rhymes!"

ONE OF THE ILLUSTRATIONS IN "THE TWO VOICES" (A POEM
REPUBLISHED IN "RHYME? AND REASON?").

(*From an etching by Lewis Carroll in "Misch-Masch."*)

"CH. CH., *May* 22, 1887.

"MY DEAR WINNIE,—But you will be getting tired of this long letter: so I will bring it to an end, and sign myself,

"Yours affectionately,

"C. L. DODGSON.

"P.S.—I enclose 2 copies of 'Castle Croquet.'

"P.P.S.—You have no idea what a struggle it was to me to put 'Winnie,' instead of 'Miss Stevens,' and 'Affectionately' instead of 'Yours truly!'

"P.P.P.S.—The year after next, or thereabouts, I *hope* to find an opportunity to take you for another walk. By that time, I fear, Time will have begun to write 'wrinkles on your azure brow'; however, *I* don't care! A really *venerable* companion makes one look youthful oneself, and I shall like to hear people whisper to each other, 'Who in the world is that *very* interesting-looking boy who is walking with that old lady with snowy tresses, and taking as much care of her as if she were his great-grandmother?'

"P.P.P.P.S.—No time for more."

"7, LUSHINGTON ROAD, EASTBOURNE.

"*Sept.* 13, 1893.

"DEAREST ENID,—I've had it in my mind for ever so long, Enid would like to hear about your adventures at Eastbourne,' and I've been meaning to write you a letter. But I *am* so busy, dear child! 'Sylvie and Bruno Concluded' takes up (when I'm in the humour for it, which I generally *am*, just now) six or eight hours a day. And there are letters that must be written. And a new thing has come to take up my time; last Sunday I preached the first sermon I ever preached in Eastbourne, though I have come here for seventeen summers (so my landlady says), and next Sunday I am to preach another; and these take up a lot of time, thinking them over.

"But the *great* difficulty is that *adventures don't happen!* Oh, how *am* I to make some happen, so as to have something to tell to my darling Enid? Shall I go out and knock down some man in the road? (I should choose a little weak one, you know.) *That* would indeed be an adventure, both for him and for me. And my share of it would be the being walked off by the policeman, and locked up in a cell at the police-station. Then my adventures *could* be written to you. Only *I* couldn't do it, you know—it would have to be done by the policeman. 'Honord Mis, you will be pleazed to no that Mr. Dodgson is now kicking at the dore of his sell— I tuk him sum bred and warter jus now; but he sed he woodnt have eny. He sed as how heed just had his diner.' How would you like *that* sort of thing, my Enid?

"Well, here is a little adventure. I was taking a walk the other day, and I came on a boy and girl about twelve and ten years old; and they seemed to be in some trouble; and they were carefully examining her finger. So I said, 'Is anything the matter?' And they told me she had just been stung by a wasp. So I told them to put some hartshorn to it as soon as they got home, and that would take away all the pain. And I gave them a tiny lesson in chemistry, and explained that, if you mix an acid and an alkali, they fizz up, and the acid loses its acidity; and that wasp's poison is an *acid*, and hartshorn is an *alkali*. When I got home I thought, 'Now I won't be so badly provided next time I come across a stung little girl' (or 'a little stung girl'—which is the best way to say it?). So I bought myself a little bottle of strong ammonia (which is better than hartshorn), and I put it in my pocket when I go a walk.

"And now, if it happens again, I can make the little girl

happy in a minute.   But *no* little girl has ever got stung since, that *I* have met with.   Isn't it a sad, sad pity ?

.   .   .   .   .

"Your very loving old friend,
"CHARLES L. DODGSON."

Mrs. Chivers Wilson (Miss Sarah Sinclair) sends me the following poem, an acrostic on her name, by Lewis Carroll, and two letters which he wrote to herself and to her sister :—

LOVE AMONG THE ROSES.

"Seek ye Love, ye fairy-sprites?
    And where reddest roses grow,
Rosy fancies he invites,
And in roses he delights,
    Have ye found him ? "   "No ! "

"Seek again, and find the boy
    In Childhood's heart, so pure and clear."
Now the fairies leap for joy,
    Crying, "Love is here ! "

"Love has found his proper nest ;
    And we guard him while he dozes
In a dream of peace and rest
    Rosier than roses."

LEWIS CARROLL.
Jan. 3, 1878.

" Address, CH. CH., OXFORD.
"*Jan.* 22, 1878.

"MY DEAR JESSIE,—I liked your letter better than anything I have had for some time. I may as well just tell you a few of the things I like, and then, whenever you want to give me a birthday present (my birthday comes once every seven years, on the fifth Tuesday in April) you will know what to give me. Well, I like, *very* much indeed, a little mustard with a bit of beef spread thinly under it ; and I like brown sugar—only it should have some apple pudding mixed with it to keep it from being too sweet ; but perhaps what I like best of all is salt, with some soup poured over it. The use of the soup is to hinder the salt from being too dry ; and it helps to melt it. Then there are other things I like; for instance, pins—only they should always have a cushion put round them to keep them warm. And I like two or three handfuls of hair ; only they should always have a little girl's head beneath them to grow on, or else whenever you open the door they get blown all over the room, and then they get lost, you know. Tell Sally it's all very well to say she can do the two thieves and the five apples, but can she do the fox and the goose and the bag of corn ? That the man was bringing from market, and he had to get them over a river, and the boat was so tiny he could only take *one* across at a time ; and he couldn't ever leave the fox and the goose together, for then the fox would eat the goose ; and if he left the goose and the corn together, the goose would eat the corn. So the only things he *could* leave safely together were the fox and the corn, for you never see a fox eating corn, and you hardly ever see corn eating a fox. Ask her if she can do *that* puzzle.

"I think I'll come and see you again—suppose we say once every two years; and in about ten years I really think we shall be good friends. Don't you think we shall ? I shall be very glad to hear from you whenever you feel inclined

"Be rather in the trumpet's mouth."   F Tennyson

"He gave it to his father."   Ossian

(From etchings by Lewis Carroll in "Misch-Masch.")

to write, and from Sally too, if *she* likes to try her hand at writing. If she can't write with her hand, let her try with her foot. Neat foot-writing is a very good thing. Give my love to her and Kate and Harry; only mind you keep a little for yourself.

"Your affectionate friend,

"LEWIS CARROLL.

"Thank your Mama for her letter which has just come."

"Thank Jessie   "CH. CH., OXFORD,
    for letter.   "*Feb.* 9, 1878.

"MY DEAR SALLIE,—Please tell Jessie I meant it *all* for nonsense, so I hope she won't give me a pincushion, for I've got three already. I've forgotten what I said in my letter to her, and *she* knows it all by heart; so you see this is what has happened—the letter has gone out of *my* mind into *her* mind; it is just like a person going into a new house. I wonder if it found Jessie's mind warm and comfortable, and if it liked it as well as its old house? I *think*, when it first got in, it looked round and said, 'Oh dear, oh dear! I shall *never* be comfortable in this new mind! I wish I was back in the old one! Why, here's a great awkward sofa, big enough to hold a dozen people! And it's got the word 'KINDNESS' marked on it. Why, I shan't be able to have it all to myself. Now, in my *old* house there was just *one* chair—a nice soft armchair that would just hold me; and it had the word 'SELFISHNESS' marked on the back; so other people couldn't come bothering in, because there were no chairs for them. And what a stupid little stool that is by the fire, marked 'HUMILITY'! Ah, you should have seen what a nice high stool there was in my old house! Why, if you sat on it you nearly knocked your head against the ceiling!

And it was marked 'CONCEIT,' of course ; that's a much nicer name than 'HUMILITY.'   Well, let's see what's in the cupboard. In my old house there was just *one* large bottle of vinegar, with a label on it, 'SOUR TEMPER,' but *this* cupboard is stuffed full of jars !   Let's see what the names are.   Oh dear, oh dear !   Why, they're all full of sugar, and the labels are ' LOVE OF SALLIE,' ' LOVE OF KATE,' ' LOVE OF HARRY ! '   Oh, I can't have all this rubbish here !   I shall throw them all out of the window ! '

"I wonder what *this* letter will say when it gets into *your* mind !   And what will it find there, do you think ?   I send my love for Jessie and Kate and Harry and you, and four kisses : that's just one a-piece.   I hope they won't get broken on the way.

" Yours affectionately,
"LEWIS CARROLL."

There must be many children whose recollections of summer holidays spent at Sandown and Eastbourne bring back to them the quaint and charming personality of Lewis Carroll, to whom these places were " happy hunting grounds " in his quest for " child friends."   Miss Laura Plomer (now Mrs. Horniman) was one of these, and I believe there is somewhere a water-colour sketch which Mr. Dodgson made of her on Sandown beach, while the following poem was written by him in a copy of " The Hunting of the Snark," which he gave her in 1876 :—

" Love-lighted eyes, that will not start
 At frown of rage or malice !
Uplifted brow, undaunted heart
Ready to dine on raspberry-tart
 Along with fairy Alice !

In scenes as wonderful as if
 She'd flitted in a magic skiff
Across the sea to Calais :
Be sure this night, in Fancy's feast,
Even till Morning gilds the east,
 Laura will dream of Alice !

Perchance, as long years onward haste,
 Laura will weary of the taste
Of Life's embittered chalice :
May she, in such a woeful hour,
Endued with Memory's mystic power,
 Recall the dreams of Alice !
     " LEWIS CARROLL,
       "June 17, 1876."

Another Sandown friend was Miss Florence
Balfour (Mrs. Collier Foster), to whom the two
following letters were written :—

     " CH. CH., OXFORD.
      " *April* 6, 1876.
 " MY DEAR BIRDIE,—When you have read the ' Snark,'
I hope you will write me a little note and tell me how
you like it, and if you can *quite* understand it. Some
children are puzzled with it. Of course you know what a

MISS ALICE LIDDELL (MRS. HARGREAVES).
(*From a photograph by Lewis Carroll.*)

Snark is? If you do, please tell *me:* for I haven't an idea what it is like. And tell me which of the pictures you like best.

" Your affectionate friend,

" LEWIS CARROLL."

" CH. CH., OXFORD,

" *Feb.* 10, 1882.

" MY DEAR BIRDIE,—As are the feelings of the old lady who, after feeding her canary and going out for a walk, finds the cage entirely filled on her return, with a live turkey—or of the old gentleman who, after chaining up a small terrier overnight, finds a hippopotamus raging around the kennel in the morning—such are my feelings when, trying to recall the memory of a small child who went to wade in the sea at Sandown, I meet with the astonishing photograph of the same microcosm suddenly expanded into a tall young person, whom I should be too shy to look at, even with the telescope which would no doubt be necessary to get any distinct idea of her smile, or at any rate to satisfy oneself whether she had eyebrows or not !

" There ! that long sentence has exhausted me, and I have only strength to say, ' Thank you very sincerely for the two photographs.'—They are terribly lifelike ! Are you going to be at Sandown next summer ? It is just *possible* I may be running over there for two or three days ; but Eastbourne is always my headquarters now.

" Believe me yours affectionately,

" C. L. DODGSON."

The next four letters are addressed to Miss Helen Feilden (now Mrs. Paul Mason), a " child friend" to begin with, but one of those whose friendship with Mr. Dodgson outlasted childhood.

"CH. CH., OXFORD,
"*March* 15, 1873.

"MY DEAR HELEN,—Your Mamma gave me such a sad description of your lonely life down at Torquay (if it *is* lonely, at least : she didn't use that word, I think—but that was the kind of impression I had of it) and added that you liked receiving letters there, to comfort you a *little* in the misery of your existence (you know she didn't exactly *say* 'misery of existence,' but I think she must have meant it) that I said I would try and write you a letter—it was very prudent of me to say that, because I never *could write* a letter in my life (my letters always end at the foot of the first page) but anybody can *try*. This is my first trial, in your case ; but I'm afraid it will fail—for what is there to write about ? You don't know much about Oxford, I'm afraid, so that you wouldn't care to hear what happens here —and it's a good thing you don't, for nothing *ever* happens here, I believe ! There never *was* such a place for things not happening. And *I* don't know much about Torquay— though I should like to know a little what your life is like there. When you've any time for writing, tell me what sort of life it is. I was down near Torquay two years ago, at Babbacombe (or Mary Church : I'm not sure which it was —perhaps they're the same place)—at all events it was at Mr. Argles' house, at the side of the most lovely bay you ever saw, with very steep rocky sides—I wonder if you ever were there ? We walked into Torquay sometimes. I don't think it can be more than two miles from you. Very likely I may be going there again next July, or August—but I

MARY MILLAIS.
Morris L. Parrish Collection, Princeton University Library

suppose I shouldn't find you there then, should I?—But
this is wandering from the point. I'm very glad you like
the volume of 'Phantasmagoria,' and one thing I am writing
this for is, to ask you if you ever read my little fairy-story
called 'Bruno's Revenge,' which came out in *Aunt Judy's
Magazine*, some years ago. If you haven't, and would like
to see it (though it is quite a baby-story) I will lend you a
copy to read; I'm afraid I've got none at present for giving
away.

"I don't care much about fairies, as a general rule: and
that is the only time I ever tried to write about them: and
they've come out much more like children than fairies, after
all!

" I don't know if you are fond of puzzles, or not. If you
are, try this. If not, never mind. A gentleman (a noble-
man let us say, to make it more interesting) had a sitting-
room with only one window in it—a square window, 3 feet
high and 3 feet wide. Now he had weak eyes, and the
window gave too much light, *so* (don't you like '*so*' in a
story?) he sent for the builder, and told him to alter it, so
as only to give half the light. Only, he was to keep it
square—he was to keep it 3 feet high— and he was to keep
it 3 feet wide. How did he do it? Remember, he wasn't
allowed to use curtains, or shutters, or coloured glass, or
anything of that sort.

" I must tell you an awful story of my trying to set a
puzzle to a little girl the other day. It was at a dinner-
party, at dessert. I had never seen her before, but, as she
was sitting next me, I rashly proposed to her to try the
puzzle (I daresay you know it) of 'the fox, and goose, and
bag of corn.' And I got some biscuits to represent the fox
and the other things. Her mother was sitting on the other
side, and said, 'Now mind you take pains, my dear, and do
it right!' The consequences were awful! She *shrieked* out

" I can't do it ! I can't do it ! Oh, Mamma ! Mamma ! " threw herself into her mother's lap, and went off into a fit of sobbing which lasted several minutes ! That was a lesson to me about trying children with puzzles. I do hope the square window won't produce any awful effects on *you !*

> " I am,
>> " Your very affectionate friend,
>>> " C. L. DODGSON."

> "CH. CH., *May* 14, 1876.

" MY DEAR HELEN,—I am going to give myself the pleasure of copying for you (what I hope will also give *you* some pleasure to read) a letter written by Dr. Newman to a young lady [1] thanking her for sending him a copy of the 'Snark.' I do not copy it for what he says about the book, but about the Easter Letter—I value *very* much more any appreciation of *it* than of the book—and I think it will interest you, as you are one of the few who have taken any notice of the Letter. The name of the young lady is Helen, which gives you an additional claim to have a copy of her letter.

" ' MY DEAR HELEN,—Let me thank you and your sisters without delay, for the amusing specimen of imaginative nonsense which came to me from you and them this morning. Also, as being your gift, it shows that you have not forgotten me, though a considerable portion of your lives has passed since you saw me. And, in thanking you, I send you also my warmest Easter greetings and good wishes.

" ' The little book is not all of it nonsense, though amusing nonsense ; it has two pleasant prefixes of another sort. One

---

[1] Miss Helen Church.

of them is the 'Inscription to a Dear Child;' the style of which, in words and manner, is so entirely of the School of Keble, that I think it could not have been written, had the 'Christian Year' never made its appearance.

" ' The other, " The Easter Greeting to Every Child, &c.," s likely to touch the hearts of old men more than those for whom it is intended.   I recollect well my own thoughts and feelings, such as the author describes, as I lay in my crib in the early spring, with outdoor scents, sounds, and sights wakening me up, and especially the cheerful ring of the mower's scythe on the lawn, which Milton long before me had noted;—and how, in coming downstairs slowly, for I brought down both feet on each step, I said to myself, " This is June !" though what my particular experience of June was, and how it was broad enough to be a matter of reflection I really cannot tell.

" ' Can't you, Mary, and Edith, recollect something of the same kind, though you may not think so much of it as I do now ?

" ' May the day come for all of us, of which Easter is the promise, when that first spring may return to us, and a sweetness which cannot die may gladden our garden.

" ' Ever yours affectionately,
" ' JOHN H. NEWMAN.'

" Is it not beautiful ?

" Give my kindest regards to your Mother.   I have thought many times of her letter, but feel no hope of writing such a book as she suggests.   And now, humbly imitating Dr. Newman, I will sign myself to my ' Helen,' as he does to his,

" Ever yours affectionately,
" C. L. DODGSON."

"CH. CH., OXFORD,
"*Dec.* 1, 1878.

" MY DEAR HELEN,—As Mrs. Lewis gives no hint that she expects me to send back to *her* the enclosed letter from Mrs. Bancroft, I venture to send it on to *you*, thinking that even apart from your own personal interest in its contents, you may like to have it as an autograph of one of the chief stars of the dramatic profession. The other autograph, which (as you know) I have been trying to get for you, has *not* appeared—why, I know not. Whether it is that Marion Terry merely dislikes giving autographs as a general rule, or whether she has (as is dimly possible) seen (and disliked) you in some casual meeting in the street, or even (as is remotely probable) has met you in society before you knew her by sight, and there (as is easily credible) has been introduced to you, preserving her own *incognito* under some fictitious name, and having (as is reasonably likely) analysed, as far as time allowed, your temper and character, has decided (as is hardly doubtful) that it is not such as *she* could approve or even tolerate, and has finally (as is morally certain) formed a rooted repugnance to you and all connected with you—in either case her conduct is sufficiently accounted for. Yet I must admit that the latter explanation is founded, to a great extent, on conjecture. In all this uncertainty one thing only is certain, that I am, as ever,

" Affectionately yours,
"C. L. DODGSON."

" CH. CH., *April* 12, 1881.

" MY DEAR HELEN,—I have behaved very badly to you in leaving your two interesting (they are always *that*) letters, the first of them dated Dec. 4, 1880, so long unanswered. So, before saying anything out of my own head, I will try to make some appropriate remarks on them.

" And first, many thanks for your history of the 'Ober-Ammergau Passion-Play'—I am very much interested in reading accounts of that play; and I thoroughly believe in the deep religious feeling with which the actors go through it; but would not like to see it myself. I should fear that for the rest of one's life the Gospel History and the accessories of a theatre would be associated in the most uncomfortable way. I am very fond of the theatre, but I had rather keep my ideas and recollections of it *quite* distinct from those about the Gospels.

" Next in your letter come many questions about the Terrys. I have not seen any of them, to speak to, for a long time; but I went to the Haymarket and the Lyceum last vacation. At the Haymarket I saw 'School,' in which Marion plays charmingly. It was the 18th of January, the day of that fearful storm in London, and the streets were all snow; but I had got tickets for three, so we braved it, two young ladies (I hardly care to go to a theatre alone now) and self. The theatre was nearly empty: about 100 stalls being empty out of (116 I think it was.) Besides the 16 or so in the stalls, there were 20 or 30 other people dotted about. I never saw so curious a sight. The company seemed to think it rather fun than otherwise; or perhaps they wanted to reward the few who had been brave enough to come. At any rate they seemed to act their best.

" At the Lyceum (to which I took one of the loveliest children in London—aged thirteen—I wish I could show her to you) we saw 'The Cup' and 'The Corsican Brothers.' 'The Cup' is a lovely poem, and the scenery, grouping, &c., are beyond all praise; but really as a *play* there is nothing in it. There are just *two* events in it. The villain (Mr. Irving) tries to carry off Camma and kills her husband—and afterwards wants her to marry him and share his throne. Whereupon she does the (dramatically) obvious thing, accepts him,

MISS KATE TERRY AS "ANDROMEDA."
(*From a photograph by Lewis Carroll.*)

and makes a poisoned cup a very early ingredient of the
marriage ceremony. Both drink it, so *both* die. Why *she*
should die, Mr. Tennyson only knows! I suppose he would
say, 'It gives a roundness and finish to the thing.' So it
may; but a heroine who would poison herself for *that* must
have an almost morbid fondness for roundness and finish. I
must tell you, I think, of a graceful act of kindness on the
part of Miss Ellen Terry. I had happened to be writing to
her a few days before, and told her I was going to bring a
child who was an enthusiastic admirer of hers—('She is like
the washerwoman in the Bab Ballads,' I said; 'she long has
loved you from afar')—and that we should be in the centre
of the stalls. So, after the 1st Act of the 'Corsican Brothers'
the box-keeper came along our row of stalls, and presented,
'With Miss Ellen Terry's compliments,' a roll of paper and
a lovely bouquet of violets. The roll we found contained one
of the illustrated books of the 'Corsican Brothers' inscribed
in some such words as these—'Camma would have sent the
words of the "Cup," but they are not printed. So she begs
Agnes to accept this with her love. Given at our Temple
of Artemis—signed, Camma.' Wasn't it pretty of her? The
child was in ecstasies of delight, and nursed the bouquet all
the way home. 'And you must send her *heaps* of love!' she
said; 'you know she sent me *her* love!' I don't think I
ever saw her look so graceful as she does in the long
trailing silk robe (a light sea-green) which she wears as
'Camma.'

"I haven't even seen Mdme Modjeska; but every one,
that *has*, praises her. I am charmed with your neighbours in
the theatre, who supposed her to be playing Marie Stuart
ex tempore! ('Gagging the part,' to use stage-slang.)

"And now what can I say on my own account? Shall I
send you a Dutch version of 'Alice' with about eight of the
pictures done large in colours? It would do well to show to

little children.   I think of trying a coloured ' Alice' myself—
a ' Nursery edition.'   What do you think of it ?

"If you won't think me very vain, I will add the verses I
sent Agnes to commemorate our visit to the Lyceum.   I told
her they had been found on a torn piece of paper, of which
I sent a facsimile.

" Kindest regards to your Mother.

" Always your affectionately,

" C. L. Dodgson."

" It is the lawyer's daughter,
　　And she is grown so dear, so dear,
She costs me, in one evening,
　　The income of a year !
' You can't have children's love,' she cried,
　　' Unless you choose to fee 'em !'
' And what's your fee, child ?' I replied.
　　She simply said——

' We saw " The Cup." ' 　I *hoped* she'd say,
　　' I'm grateful to you, very.'
She murmured, as she turned away,
　　' That lovely——
' Compared with her, the rest,' she cried,
　　' Are just like to or three um-
' -berellas standing side by side !
　　' Oh, gem of——

' We saw Two Brothers.   I confess
　　To *me* they seemed one man.
' Now which is which, child ?   Can you guess
　　She cried, ' A-course I can !'
Bad puns like this I *always* dread,
　　And am resolved to flee 'em.
And so I left her there, and fled ;
　　She *lives* at——"

Some reminiscences from the pen of Mrs. Samuel Bickersteth (Miss Ella Monier Williams) follow; the elaborate practical joke which she describes must have afforded both her and Mr. Dodgson a great deal of amusement, mixed at first, no doubt, in her case, with some not unreasonable disappointment.

"It is difficult to add anything to what has already been written about Lewis Carroll, but as one of the 'children' whose love for him endured beyond childhood, I should like to tell something of the fascination of his friendship. As a child he gave one the sense of such *perfect understanding*, and this knowledge of child nature was the same whether the child was only seven years of age, or in her teens. A 'grown-up' child was his horror. He called one day just after I had 'put my hair up,' and I, with girlish pride, was pleased he should be there to see. My satisfaction received a blow when he said, 'I will take you for a walk if you let your hair down your back, but not unless.' What girl could refuse the attraction of a walk with him? I speedily complied with his request, and was rewarded by an hour of happy companionship, mainly occupied as we walked along by playing a game of croquet in our

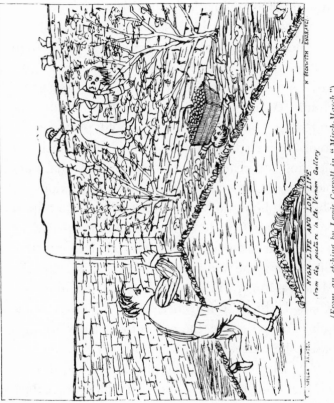

HIGH LIFE AND LOW LIFE
From the picture in the Vernon Gallery

(From an etching by Lewis Carroll in "Misch-Masch.")

heads. How it was done I cannot recollect, but his clever original brain planned it out by some system of mathematical calculation.

" A visit to Mr. Dodgson's rooms to be photographed was always full of surprises. Although he had quaint fancies in the way he dressed his little sitters, he never could bear a dressed-up child. A ' natural child ' with ruffled untidy hair suited him far better, and he would place her in some ordinary position of daily life, such as sleeping, or reading, and so produce charming pictures. On one occasion he was anxious to obtain a photograph of me as a child sitting up in bed in a fright, with her hair standing on end as if she had seen a ghost. He tried to get this effect with the aid of my father's (the late Sir Monier Monier Williams) electrical machine, but it failed, chiefly I fear because I was too young quite to appreciate the current of electricity that had to be passed through me.

" In 1873 Lewis Carroll played a practical joke on me which, however, ended quite amicably. I had spent the summer of that year on the Continent, and he had done the same. He called at our house in Oxford early that November, and in the course of conversation promised to lend me the journal of his travels, if I would allow him to have mine. I consented on the condition that he showed it to no one, as the chance of reading his journal was too good to miss.

" At the end of a fortnight he returned my journal with this amusing letter :—

" ' *Saturday.*

" ' My dear Ella,—I send you Vol. II. of my Journal, and am much obliged to you for lending me yours. So far, I have come upon very little that you need be unwilling for the public to read. For I consider such sentences as : " July 10.— Fractious all the evening, and went to bed in the sulks," and again : " July 14.—Bought a new parasol, and sat out on the balcony to be admired. A little girl passing by told me I looked 'as stuck up as a peacock in its Sunday best.' I would have broken the parasol over her head, only I couldn't reach her," as quite natural and childlike.

" ' I suppose the passage that made you at first unwilling to lend me the book was this one : " July 21.—At breakfast Mamma objected to my taking more marmalade, saying I had already helped myself three times ' profusely.' I was so vexed that I got hold of the tablecloth, and jerked all the plates and things down upon the floor. Of course some were broken. It wasn't *my* fault. As I told Mamma, my temper's as good as gold, unless you provoke me. And then I'm a little queer sometimes——" But even *this* is a little incident that might happen to *any* one. I don't think the worse of you for it (because that would be impossible).

" ' Your affect. friend,

" ' C. L. Dodgson.'

" A few days after I received the following :—

" ' *November* 17*th*.

" ' My dear Ella,—I return your book with many thanks; you will be wondering why I kept it so long.   I understand, from what you said about it, that you have no idea of publishing any of it yourself, and hope you will not be annoyed at my sending three short chapters of extracts from it, to be published in *The Monthly Packet*.   I have not given any names in full, nor put any more definite title to it than simply " Ella's Diary, or The Experiences of an Oxford Professor's Daughter, during a Month of Foreign Travel."

" ' I will faithfully hand over to you any money I may receive on account of it, from Miss Yonge, the editor of *The Monthly Packet*.

" ' Your affect. friend,

" ' C. L. Dodgson.'

" I treated the whole matter as a hoax, and wrote to tell him so, receiving this letter in reply :—

" ' My dear Ella,—I grieve to tell you that *every word of my letter was strictly true*.   I will now tell you more—that Miss Yonge *has not declined* the MS., but she will not give more than a guinea a chapter.   Will that be enough ?

" ' Yours affectionately,

" ' C. L. Dodgson.'

" This second letter succeeded in taking me in, and with childish pleasure I wrote and said I did

THE DUETT.
from the picture in the Kenner Gallery

(From an etching by Lewis Carroll in "Misch-Masch.")

not quite understand how it was my journal could be worth printing, but expressed my pleasure. I then received this letter :—

"'My dear Ella,—I'm afraid I have hoaxed you too much. But it really was true. I "hoped you wouldn't be annoyed at my &c.," for the very good reason that I hadn't done it. And I gave no *other* title than "Ella's Diary," nor did I give *that* title. Miss Yonge hasn't declined it—because she hasn't seen it. And I need hardly explain that she hasn't given more than three guineas!

"' Not for three hundred guineas would I have shown it to *any* one—after I had promised you I wouldn't.

"' In haste,

"'Yours affectionately,

"'C. L. D.'

"I confess to having been rather disappointed, but my love for Mr. Dodgson soon led me to his rooms in Christ Church, where we laughed together over the joke; though I told him that I had not forgiven him, and should not have gone to see him, had I not wanted to see his pictures!

"When I married in 1881, he was then full of his amusing game of Doublets, and wrote in his congratulatory letter to my husband (the Rev. Samuel Bickersteth) :—

"' Do not make *Ella weep*.

" On his replying that he did not know how to do so, he showed him how to turn the first word into the second in wondrous few changes.

" I last saw Mr. Dodgson about two years ago, when we had a long talk in the library of the Indian Institute at Oxford, and as he explained to me at length his elaborate scheme for teaching children logic and mathematics, there appeared to me to be no diminution in his physical or mental vigour, or in his love for children. Full of mischievous teasing, as usual, he tried to prove to me—the mother of six sons—how infinitely superior he considered girls to boys. I little thought it would be the last time I should meet the man of so gentle and kindly a nature, whose friendship enriched my childhood."

Of the remaining letters it is only necessary for me to say that the first four were written by Mr. Dodgson to his cousin, Miss Menella Wilcox, for whom he wrote the song " Matilda Jane," which readers of " Sylvie and Bruno" will remember; the next three to Miss Lucy Walters, a Guildford friend; the three following to Miss Dora Abdy, and the last, a most characteristic specimen of his more frivolous style of correspondence, to Miss Evelyn Dubourg.

"FAIRY COOKS"   EVELYN DUBOURG AND KATHLEEN O'REILLY.
Morris L. Parrish Collection, Princeton University Library

"7, LUSHINGTON ROAD, EASTBOURNE,
"*July* 20, 1886.

"MY DEAR NELLA,—Many years ago, when you were quite young, and before your hair had even *begun* to turn grey (do you remember the time?), I wrote for you (or rather for your doll) a little song called ' Matilda Jane '—if you happen still to have it, or if you can remember it, I should be glad to have the words. There were only four verses of it, so it ought not to take you long to copy it out.

" I'm down here all alone, but as happy as a king—at least, as happy as *some* kings—at any rate I should think I'm about as happy as King Charles the First when he was in prison.

"C. L. DODGSON."

"CH. CH., OXFORD,
" *October* 20, 1878.

"MY DEAR NELLA,—Thank you very much for the napkin ring, but do you know I never use anything of the sort, so I hope you won't mind giving it to somebody else instead, and if you really want to make something for me, make me a little bag (say a square bag about the size of this note sheet): *that* would be really useful, and I should be really glad to have it. And work your initials on it, and then I shall always remember who made it for me. Now I'll tell you something. The other day, at Eastbourne, I saw—what do you think? Of course you guess 'a Snark.' Well, no ; it wasn't quite that, but it was very near it. I went to see a lady who was taking care of a little girl called ' Bibby ' (she comes from India and is seven years old. I wish they would send her to your Mama to take care of ; I am sure you would love her), and her little brother came into the room, and I suppose he began doing some mischief or other, for the lady called out suddenly, ' Oh, Boojum ! you mustn't touch that.' Wasn't it a grand thing to see a live

Boojum at last ?   I am happy to say I didn't vanish away ; but then, you see, I'm not a Baker.   I don't know what Boojum's real name is.   Bibby's real name is ' Clare ' (isn't that a pretty name ?)—' Clare Turton.'

"It's the middle of the night, so good-night.   I must go to bed.   I send you my best love and fourteen kisses, which ought to last you a week.

"Ever your affectionate cousin,

"LEWIS CARROLL."

" *November* 19*th.*

"MY DEAR NELLA,—What a darling little bag it is !   And it will be very useful to me ; it'll hold anything I want to take with me—buttercups, or live mice, or anything.   And I thank you very much for it.   I shall always think of you when I use it.

"Your loving cousin,

"C. L. DODGSON."

"MY DEAR NELLA,—If Eastbourne was only a mile off from Scarborough, I would come and see you to morrow ; but it *is* such a long way to come !   There was a little girl running up and down on the parade yesterday, and she always ended her run exactly where I was sitting ; she just looked up in my face, and then off she went again.   So when she had been about six times, I smiled at her, and she smiled at me and ran away again ; and the next time I held out my hand, and she shook hands directly ; and I said, ' Will you give me that piece of seaweed ? ' and she said ' No ! ' and ran away again.   And the next time I said, ' Will you cut off a little bit of the sea-weed for me ? '   And she said, ' But I haven't got a pair of scissors ! '   So I lent her that folding pair of scissors, and she cut off a little bit very carefully, and gave it to me and ran away again.   But in a moment she came back and said, ' I'm frightened that my Mother won't like you to keep it!' so I gave it back again, and I told her to ask her Mother to get a needle and thread, and sew the two bits of seaweed together again; and she laughed, and said she would keep the two bits in her pocket. Wasn't she a queer little vegetable? I'm glad you don't keep running away all the time while we are talking. Is Matilda Jane quite well? And has she been running out in the rain again without her shoes on!

"Give my love to your Mamma, and to your Aunt Lucy; not my Aunt Lucy, because she is at Guildford.

"Charles L. Dodgson."

"*July* 14, 1877,
"Grosvenor House, 44, Grand Parade, Eastbourne."

"The Chestnuts,
"5 min. to spare.

"My dear Lucy,—I want to explain our ungrateful behaviour in going off just as the banquet appeared. I knew my cousin had a letter to write, and, when I had given her her choice whether we should call on you at tea-time, or go earlier and come back for tea, she chose the latter. So I had to play the part of the old lady's confidential maid (I daresay you know the story?) whose duty it was, *when there was any friend present*, to urge the lady to drink brandy and water, the lady showing an aristocratic reluctance to taking so vulgar a fluid.

"*Please* don't think we were unfriendly, or anxious to get away!"

.   .   .   .

"Ch. Ch., Oxford,
"*March* 17, 1888.

"My dear Lucy,—When I ask myself, 'What can have caused this sudden revulsion of feeling? How can I have given such deep offence as to produce the sudden drop, from the letter dated February 8th, signed "Ever yours affectionately," to the one dated March 15th, and signed "Yours very sin-

THE FIREPLACE IN LEWIS CARROLL'S STUDY AT CHRIST CHURCH.[1]

cerely"?' The subject seems at first buried in mystery. Still, it is of vital importance to find it out, and, if possible, to make amends for my misdeeds, for it needs a very slight acquaintance with Rule of Three to see how such a correspondence will go on

[1] See page 369.

through ' Yours truly,' and ' Yours faithfully,' till you write in the third person (' Miss Lucy Walters presents her compliments, &c.').

" Ten hours of anxious meditation have opened my eyes— I now see that my (almost) irremediable error was that, after getting a very nice letter from *you*, inviting me to the Bushey Theatricals, I was ill-advised enough to answer it *to my cousin Annie*.

" Well, it was very wicked and heartless, I must admit. And the only way I can see, which will *really* remedy it, is to choose a number of letters, received from *other* people, and answer them all to *you*.

" Do not then be surprised, my dear Lucy, if you hear from me to this effect :—

" ' MY DEAR LUCY,—So the poor wax doll has had a fall and broken its nose? Well, I'm very sorry to hear it, &c., &c.'

"or

" ' MY DEAR LUCY,—Sample of wine to hand, and approved of. Please forward six dozen, and advise despatch of goods, &c., &c.'

" or

" ' MY DEAR LUCY,—Unless the clock, entrusted to you for repair, is delivered before the end of this month I shall instruct my solicitor to &c., &c.'

" But understand that I have received letters—from a little girl, from my wine-merchant, and from my watchmaker, and am answering them all to *you*.

" May I hope that, when you have received a dozen or so of these letters, you will regard them as sufficient atonement for my crime, and will gradually return to the friendly relations which have so long existed between us ?

" Yours always affectionately,

"C. L. DODGSON."

"Ch. Ch., *June* 21, 1889.

"So you don't consider ' I can easily get the name for you ' as at all implying 'and will '? Then I greatly fear, Lucy, that, next time I have the pleasure of sharing some meal with you, and venture to say, "Can you give me a potato?' you will reply, ' Yes, I can, *easily !* ' and will then fold your hands in your lap, and gaze abstractedly at the ceiling. Such results are strictly logical, and within the limits of the British Constitution ; but they do not tend to the progress of a banquet.

"And now you fear that I shall 'cut' you ! I *can* do so, my dear Lucy, *easily !*

"Yours affectionately,
"C. L. D.,
"With many thanks. '

"Ch. Ch., *May* 13, 1895.

"Dear Miss Dora Abdy,—May I have the pleasure of fetching you, for a *tête-à-tête* dinner, some day soon?   And, if so, will you name the day ?

"Yours respectfully,
"(That's a good *safe* beginning, *isn't it ?*)
"C. L. Dodgson."

"P.S.—Now *please* don't go and tell all your friends, in the strictest confidence, ' I've just had a letter from a gentleman, and he asks me to *name the day !* ' "

"Ch. Ch., Oxford,
"*May* 25, 1895.

"Dear Miss Abdy,—My suggestion was that you should name a day *after* the Eights were over (the last night of them is the 29th), as you *might* wish to go to them any one of the six nights.

"If you dine with me on Tuesday, it will have to be at our

High Table in Hall, along with another friend, who comes into Oxford that day for the purpose. You would not find him at all formidable or disagreeable to meet : he is quite worthy of your regard, if not esteem. Nor need the mere *novelty* of the situation deter you. Novelty, *by itself*, is no drawback to a scheme ; in some cases (as with milk, eggs, and jokes) it is a positive advantage. Also, if accepted as an obstacle, it would have the same effect on the scheme of your dining in my *rooms*, which also is a thing outside your experience.

"If, however, you still feel some unaccountable reluctance to this arrangement, it would be well to propose some other day. Whatever the day, you will be welcome.

"Yours very sincerely,
"C. L. DODGSON."

CH. CH., OXFORD,
"*June* 16, 1895.

"MY DEAR DORA,—Among the host of virtues which, as you are no doubt aware, form the background of my character (a few trifling faults being thrown in as foreground ornaments, merely by way of contrast), *a readiness to adopt suggestions* (when they happen to coincide with my own inclinations) is one of the most marked—so prominent, in fact, that my biographer will fail to do justice to it unless he devotes a whole chapter to the subject.

"Please let me know whether, if I were going up from here, or from Eastbourne, to town for the day, you would have the physical courage and the metaphysical audacity to travel alone between Guildford and Waterloo, where I would meet you and whence I would see you off. Without affirming that there is any *high* degree of probability of my going to see 'Much Ado' on the 6th, I will go so far as to admit that *more* wonderful things have happened !

"Yours affectionately,
"C. L. DODGSON."

"July 3, 1880.

"So E. D. is *de rigeur ?* Very good. It is not the *only* E. D. I have met with possessing this character. But why 'of course'? Are there *no* exceptions? Surely, if you go to morning parties in evening dress (which you *do*, you know), why not to evening parties in morning dress?

"Anyhow, I have been invited to *three* evening parties in London this year, in each of which 'Morning Dress' was specified.

"Again, doctors (not that *I* am a real one—only an amateur) must always be in trim for an instant summons to a patient. And when you invite a doctor to dinner (say), do you not always add 'Morning Dress'? (I grant you it is done by initials in *this* case. And perhaps you will say you don't understand M.D. to stand for 'Morning Dress'? Then take a few lessons in elementary spelling.)

"Aye, and many and many a time have I received invitations to evening parties wherein the actual colours of the Morning Dress expected were stated!

"For instance, 'Red Scarf: Vest, Pink.' That is a *very* common form, though it is usually (I grant you) expressed by initials.

"But I spare you. No doubt you are by this time duly ashamed of your too-sweeping assertion, and anxious to apologise. Will you plead that you know not how to apologise, and that ladies never *do* apologise to gentlemen? Then take a few lessons in elementary manners.

"Yours affect.,

"LEWIS CARROLL.

"P.S.—You will say 'What morning parties do I go to in evening dress?' I reply 'Balls.' You will say again, '*What* balls ever go on in the morning?' I reply '*Most* balls.'"

CHAPTER V

IN 1888 appeared "Curiosa Mathematica. Part I. A New Theory of Parallels," by C. L. Dodgson; the second Part, entitled "Pillow Problems, thought out during wakeful hours," was published in 1893. Lewis Carroll had intended to complete the series with a third Part, which was to be of a more miscellaneous character, but he was never able to carry this out. A small portion of it is in proof, and this is reproduced here, together with a few other mathematical problems, &c., which would probably have found their way into the projected volume if Mr. Dodgson had lived long enough to finish his task.

FRAGMENT OF "CURIOSA MATHEMATICA PART III."

BOOK II.

BRIEF METHODS OF PERFORMING SOME PROCESSES IN ARITHMETIC.

CHAPTER I.

LONG MULTIPLICATION.

THE principle of this Method occurred to me on the 19th of September, 1879. I had been thinking of the great inconvenience arising, in the ordinary process of Long Multiplication, from the distance which often separates the two digits that are to be multiplied together, and what an advantage it would be if the sum could be so arranged that they should be close together. Then came the lucky thought that, by writing the lesser Number *backwards*, and moving it along above the other Number, we should have, at each stage of its progress, visible all at once, the set of pairs of digits, whose products have to be added together to make one column of working in the ordinary way.

The Method, which I evolved from this idea, may be enunciated as follows :—

Write down the 2 given Numbers, placing the lesser, if they are of unequal lengths, above the other, and bringing their units-digits into a vertical line. Draw a line below. On a separate slip of paper write the upper Number *backwards*, putting a mark over the units-digit. With this slip cover up the upper given Number, bringing the two units-digits into a vertical line. Looking at this pair of digits, write the units-digit of their product just below the line and vertically below the mark, and its tens-digit further down and one place to the left. Shift the slips one place to the left. Looking at the 2 pairs of digits, which now stand in vertical lines, sum their products, beginning with the right-hand pair, and write the units-digit of the result just below the line and vertically below the mark, and its tens-digit further down and one place to the left. Shift the slip again, and proceed as before.

An example will make this clear. Let the given Numbers be 574, 3819. Write them as here shown, drawing a line below, and write the 574, backwards, on a separate slip, with a mark above the 4.

$$\begin{array}{|c|} \hline \overline{4}75 \\ \hline \end{array}$$
$$574$$
$$3^819$$

With this slip cover the upper Number, so that the mark stands vertically above the units-digit of the lower Number.

$$\begin{array}{|c|} \hline \overline{4}75 \\ \hline \end{array}$$
$$3^819$$

Looking at the pair of digits, which stand in a vertical line, say " 36," and write the 6 just below the line and vertically below the mark, and the 3 further down and one place to the left.

$$\begin{array}{|c|} \hline \overline{4}75 \\ \hline \end{array}$$
$$3^819$$
$$6$$
$$3$$

Shift the slip one place to the left.

$$475$$

3819

6

3

Looking at the 2 vertical pairs of digits, say " 63 and 4, 67." Enter it.

$$475$$

3819

76

63

Shift the slip one place to the left.

$$475$$

3819

76

63

Looking at the 3 vertical pairs of digits, say "45 and 7, 52 ; and 32, 84." Enter it.

$$475$$

3819

476

863

Shift the slip as before.

$$\begin{array}{c} \overline{475} \\ \hline 3819 \\ \hline 476 \\ 863 \end{array}$$

Looking at the 3 vertical pairs of digits, say " 5 and 56, 61 ; and 12, 73." Enter it.

$$\begin{array}{c} \overline{475} \\ \hline 3819 \\ \hline 3476 \\ 7863 \end{array}$$

Shift the slip as before.

$$\begin{array}{c} \overline{475} \\ \hline 3819 \\ \hline 3476 \\ 7863 \end{array}$$

Looking at the 2 vertical pairs of digits, say " 40 and 21, 61." Enter it.

$$\begin{array}{c} \overline{475} \\ \hline 3819 \\ \hline 13476 \\ 67863 \end{array}$$

Shift the slip as before.

$$\overline{475}$$

$$3819$$

$$\overline{}$$

$$13476$$
$$67863$$

Looking at the vertical pair of digits, say " 15." Enter it.

$$\overline{475}$$

$$3819$$

$$\overline{}$$

$$513476$$
$$167863$$

Now remove the slip, draw a line below, and add together the 2 lines of working.

$$574$$
$$3819$$

$$\overline{}$$

$$513476$$
$$167863$$

$$\overline{2192106}$$

The Reader will notice that the working, for each position of the slip, is a distinct thing, and can be done *by itself*, without reference to the rest of the work.   Hence, if there is a doubt as to any particular digit in the answer, the digits, whose sum it is, can be tested *by themselves*, *e.g.*, if it were suspected that the 9 was wrong, we might test the 7, which stands vertically above it, by placing the slip in the position of the 8th diagram ; and then the 1, which stands above the 7, by placing it in the position of the 10th diagram.

When the upper given Number does not contain more than 4 or 5 digits, the above Rule can be easily worked ; but, with a really *large* upper given Number, it will be found convenient to go along each series of products *twice*—first summing their *units*-digits, and entering the units-digit of the result in the upper line of the working, and then summing their *tens*-digits. Thus, the Mental Process for the 6th diagram might be as follows : " 5 and 7, 12 ; and 2, 14." Enter the 4, and carry the 1. " 5 and 3, 8." Enter it.

In working this form of the Method, the following Rules should be borne in mind :—

In collecting the *units*-digits of a set of products of pairs of digits, remember that, if *one* member of a pair is 1, the units-digit is the *other :* if *one* is 5, the units-digit is 5 or 0, according as the *other* is odd or even : if *one* is 9, the units-digit is 10 *minus* the *other*.

In collecting the *tens*-digits, remember that, if *one* member of a pair is 1, or if the sum of the two members is less than 7, there is *no* tens-digit ; if *one* is 5, the tens-digit is the number of 2's contained in the *other* : if *one* is 9, the tens-digit is the *other minus* 1.

Many of these Long Multiplication sums will need only *two* lines of working : when a set of products occurs, whose sum contains 3 digits, a *third* line will be needed : when it contains 4, a *fourth*—but this can only happen when the lesser Number contains at least 13 digits : and, when it contains 5, a *fifth* will be needed—but *this* can only happen when the lesser Number contains at least 124 digits, and therefore exceeds a trillion of sextillions !

This Method can easily be applied to the Multiplication of Decimals : all that is needed is to place the slip, to begin with, so that the mark comes vertically above that decimal place to which we wish to carry the working. I will give two examples, exhibiting, in each, first, the sum as set, ready for working ;

secondly, the state of things just before the slip is shifted for the first time ; thirdly, the final state, just before the slip is removed ; fourthly, the sum added up.

| 730·0 | 341·$\overline{8}$6 |

·037
·2156

68·143
2379·5

| 730·0 | 341·$\overline{8}$6 |

·2156

2379·5

3
5

5
1

| 730·$\overline{0}$ | 341·$\overline{8}$6 |

·2156

2379·5

·006723
125

24817·6275
136228·641
11

·037
·2156

63·143
2379·5

·006723
125

24817·6275
136228·641

·007976

11

162146·2685

Hence the Answer to the first sum, correct to 4 places, is ·0080 ; and the Answer to the second, correct to 2 places, is 162146·27.

CHAPTER II.

§ 1.

Divisors of the form $(10^n \pm 1)$.

YEARS ago I had discovered the curious fact that, if you put a " o " over the unit-digit of a given Number, which happens to be a multiple of 9, and subtract all along, always putting the remainder over the next digit, the final subtraction gives remainder " o," and the upper line, omitting its final " o," is the " 9-Quotient " of the given Number (*i.e.*, the Quotient pro duced by dividing it by 9).

Having discovered this, I was at once led, by analogy, to the discovery that, if you put a " o " *under* the unit-digit of a given Number, which happens to be a multiple of 11, and proceed in the same way, you get an analogous result.

In each case I obtained the Quotient of a Division-sum by the shorter and simpler process of *subtraction:* but, as this result was only obtainable in the (comparatively rare) case of the given Number being an exact multiple of 9, or of 11, the discovery seemed to be more curious than useful.

Lately, it occurred to me to examine cases where the given Number was *not* an exact multiple. I found that, in these cases, the final subtraction yielded a Number which was sometimes the actual Remainder produced by Division, and which always gave materials from which that Remainder could be found. But, as it did not yield the Quotient (or only by a very " bizarre " process, which was decidedly longer and harder than actual Division), the discovery still seemed to be of no practical use.

But, quite lately, it occurred to me to try what would happen if, after discovering the Remainder, I were to put it, instead of a " o," over or under the unit-digit, and then subtract as before. And I was charmed to find that the old result followed : the final subtraction yielded remainder " o," and the new line, omitting its units-digit, was the required Quotient.

Now, there are shorter processes for obtaining the 9-Remainder or the 11-Remainder of a given Number, than my subtraction-rule (the process for finding the 11-Remainder is another discovery of mine). Adopting these, I brought my rule to completion on September 28, 1897.

(1) Rule for finding the Quotient and Remainder produced by dividing a given Number by 9.

To find the 9-Remainder, sum the digits ; then sum the digits of the result : and so on till you get a single digit. If this be less than 9, it is the required Remainder : if it be 9, the required Remainder is o. Throughout this process, 9's may be " cast out " *ad libitum*.

To find the 9-Quotient, draw a line below the given Number and put its 9-Remainder under its unit-digit ; then subtract downwards, putting the remainder under the next digit, and so on. If the left-hand end-digit of the given Number be less than 9, its subtraction ought to give remainder " o " : if it be 9, it ought to give remainder " 1," to be put in the lower line, and " 1 " to be carried, whose subtraction will give remainder " o." Now mark off the 9-Remainder at the right-hand end of the lower line, and the rest of it will be the 9-Quotient.

Examples :—

$$9//753096 \qquad 9//946138 \qquad 9//583173$$

$$83677//3 \qquad 105126//4 \qquad 64797//0$$

(2) Rule for finding the Quotient and Remainder produced by dividing a given Number by 11.

To find the 11-Remainder, begin at the units-end, and sum the 1st, 3rd, &c., digits, and also the 2nd, 4th, &c, digits; and find the 11-Remainder of the difference of these sums. If the former sum be the greater, the required Remainder is the number so found: if the former sum be the lesser, it is the difference between this number and 11 : if the sums be equal, it is " 0."

To find the 11-Quotient, draw a line below the given Number and put its 11-Remainder under its units-digit: then subtract, putting the remainder under the next digit, and so on. The final subtraction ought to give remainder " 0." Now mark off the 11-Remainder at the right-hand end of the lower line, and the rest of it will be the 11-Quotient.

Examples :—

$$11//732108 \qquad 11//853471$$

$$66555//3 \qquad 77588//3$$

$$11//594263 \qquad 11//475684$$

$$54023//10 \qquad 43244//0$$

These new Rules have yet another advantage over the Rule of actual Division, viz., that the final subtraction supplies a *test* of the correctness of the result: if it does not give remainder " 0," the sum has been done wrong : if it does, then either it has been done right, or there have been *two* mistakes—a rare event.

Mathematicians will not need to be told that rules, analogous to the above, will necessarily hold good for the divisors 99, 101, 999, 1001, &c. The only modification needed would be to mark off the given Number in periods of 2 or more digits, and to treat each period in the same way as the above rules have treated single digits. Here, for example, is the whole of the working needed for dividing 2 given Numbers by 999 and by 10001 :—

$$
\begin{array}{r|r}
2 & 437 \\
999//73 \mid 210 \mid 584 \mid 668 & 902 \\
\hline
73 \mid 283 \mid 868 \mid 537 // 439 &
\end{array}
$$

$$
\begin{array}{r|r}
& 1383 \\
1 & 2269 \\
10001//547 \mid 2915 \mid 0836 & 9354 \\
\hline
547 \mid 2367 \mid 8469 // \ 885 &
\end{array}
$$

In the first of these examples, the 2 | 437, written above, is the sum of the periods. As this contains 2 periods, it is treated in the same way; and the final result, 439, is the 999-Remainder.

In the second, the 1 | 2269, written above, is the sum of the 1st and 3rd periods: the 1383 is the sum of the 2nd and 4th. The difference of these sums is 10886, whose 10001-Remainder is 885.

§ 2.

Divisors of the form (h $10^{n} \pm$ k), where at least one of the two numbers, h and k, is greater than 1.

The Method, now to be described, is applicable to three distinct cases :—

(1) Where $h > 1, k = 1$;
(2) Where $h = 1, k > 1$;
(3) Where $h > 1, k > 1$.

With certain limitations of the values of h, k, and n, this Method will be found to be a shorter and safer process than that of ordinary Long Division. These limitations are that neither h nor k should exceed 12, and that, when $k > 1$, n

should not be less than 3; outside these limits, it involves difficulties which make the ordinary process preferable.

In this Method, two distinct processes are required—one, for dealing with cases where $h > 1$, the other, for cases where $k > 1$. The former of these processes was, I believe, first discovered by myself, the latter by my nephew, Mr. Bertram J. Collingwood, who communicated to me his Method of dealing with Divisors of the form $(10^n - k)$.

In what follows, I shall represent 10 by t.

Mr. Collingwood's Method, for Divisors of the form $(t^n - k)$, may be enunciated as follows :—

"To divide a given Number by $(t^n - k)$, mark off from it a period of n digits, at the units-end, and under it write k-times what would be left of it if its last period were erased. If this number contains more than n digits, treat it in the same way; and so on, till a number is reached which does not contain more than n digits. Then add up. If the last period of the result, *plus* k-times whatever was carried out of it, in the adding up, be less than the Divisor, it is the required Remainder; and the rest of the result is the required Quotient. If it be not less, find what number of times it contains the Divisor, and add that number to the Quotient, and subtract that multiple of the Divisor from the Remainder."

For example, to divide 86781592485703152764092 by 9993 (*i.e.*, by $t^4 - 7$), he would proceed thus :—

```
9993//867 8159 2485 7031 5276 4092
      6074 7114 7399 9220 6932
         4 2522 9803 1799 4540
          29 7660 8622 2593
             208 3626 0354
                1458 5382
                   1 0206
                        7
```

Quot. 868 4238 2153 2104 0004//4106 + 14 = 4120 Rem.

This new Method will be best explained by beginning with case (3) : it will be easily seen what changes have to be made in it when dealing with cases (1) and (2).

The Rule for case (3), when the sign is " – ," may be enunciated thus :—

Mark off the Dividend, beginning at its units-end, in periods of n digits. If there be an overplus, at the left-hand end, less than h, do not mark it off, but reckon it and the next n digits as one period.

To set the sum, write the Divisor, followed by a double vertical; then the Dividend, divided into its periods by single verticals, with width allowed in each space for $(n + 2)$ digits. Below the Dividend draw a single line, and, further down, a double one, leaving a space between, in which to enter the Quotient, having its units-digit below that of the last period but one of the Dividend, and also the Remainder, having its units-digit below that of the last period of the Dividend. In this space, and in the space below the double line, draw verticals, corresponding to those in the Dividend ; and make the last in the upper space double, to separate the Quotient from the Remainder.

For example, if we had to divide 5984407103826 by 6997 (*i.e.*, 7. t^3 – 3), the sum, as set for working, would stand thus :—

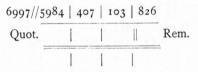

$$6997//5984 \mid 407 \mid 103 \mid 826$$
Quot. | | ‖ Rem.

To work the sum, divide the 1st period by h ; enter its quotient in the 1st Column below the double line, and place its remainder above the 2nd period, where it is to be regarded as *prefixed* to that period. To the 2nd period, with its prefix, add k-times the number in the 1st Column, and enter the result at the top of the 2nd Column. If this number *is not* less than the Divisor, find what number of times it contains the Divisor, and enter that number in the 1st Column, and k-times it in the 2nd, and then draw a line below the 2nd Column, and add in this new item, deducting from the result t''-times the number just entered in the 1st Column; and then add up the 1st Column, entering the result in the Quotient. If the number at the top of the 2nd Column *is* less than the Divisor, the number in the 1st Column may be at once entered in the Quotient. The number entered in the Quotient, and the number at the foot of the 2nd Column, are the Quotient and Remainder that would result if the Dividend ended with its 2nd period. Now take the number at the foot of the 2nd Column as a new 1st period, and the 3rd period as a new 2nd period, and proceed as before.

The above example, worked according to this Rule, would stand thus :—

$$
\begin{array}{r|c|c|c|c}
 & & 6 & 5 & 3 \\
6997 \parallel 5984 & 407 & 103 & 826 & \\
\end{array}
$$

Quot. 855 | 281 | 849 ‖ 6373 Rem.

854 | 8969 | 5946 |

1 | 3 |
1972 |
281 |

849

The Mental Process being as follows : —

Divide the 5984 by 7, entering its Quotient, 854, in the 1st

Column, and placing its Remainder, 6, above the 2nd period. Then add, to the 6407, 3-times the 854, entering the result in the 2nd Column, thus : " 7 and 12, 19." Enter the 9, and carry the 1. " 1 and 15, 16." Enter the 6, and carry the 1. " 5 and 24, 29." Enter the 9, and carry the 2, which, added to the prefix 6, makes 8, which also you enter. Observing that this 8969 *is not* less than the Divisor, and that it contains the Divisor *once*, enter 1 in the 1st Column, and 3-times 1 in the 2nd, and then draw a line below, and add in this new item, remembering to deduct from the result 7-times t^3, *i.e.*, 7000: the result is 1972. Then add up the 1st Column, as far as the double line, and enter the result, 855, in the Quotient. Now take the 1972 as a new 1st period, and the 3rd period, 103, as a new 2nd period, and proceed as before, thus : Draw a double line below the 1972, and divide it by 7, entering its Quotient, 281, below it, and its Remainder, 5, above the 3rd period. Then add, to the 5103, 3-times the 281, entering the result, 5946, in the 3rd column ; and observe that this *is* less than the Divisor. Then add up the 2nd Column, as far as its lowest double line, and enter the result, 281, in the Quotient. Now take the 5946 as a new 1st period, and the final period, 826, as a new 2nd period, and proceed as before, thus : Draw a double line below the 5946, and divide it by 7, entering the Quotient, 849, below it, and the Remainder, 3, above the final period. Now add, to the 3826, 3-times the 849, entering the result, 6373, which you can foresee *will be* less than the Divisor, as the Remainder. Then add up the 3rd Column, as far as its lowest double line, and enter the result, 849, as the final period of the Quotient.

It may be well to explain the real effect of the three processes described in the 5th sentence of the preceding paragraph, viz., (1) "enter 1 in the 1st Column " ; (2) " enter 3-times 1 in the 2nd Column " ; (3) " add in this new item,

remembering to deduct from the result 7000." The effect of
(2) and (3), combined, is to *increase* the 2nd Column by 3
and to *diminish* it by 7000; *i.e.*, to *diminish* it by (7000–3),
which is 6997. And the effect of (1) is to account for this
6997, which has been thus deducted from the Remainder
(thus reducing it to the *true* Remainder), by adding 1 to the
Quotient (thus raising it to the *true* Quotient).

The Rule for case (3), when the sign is " $+$," may be
deduced from the above Rule by simply changing the sign
of k. This will, however, introduce a new phenomenon,
which must be provided for by the following additional
clause :—

When you add to the 2nd period with its prefix $(-k)$-times
the number in the 1st Column, *i.e.*, when you *subtract* k-times
this number *from* the 2nd period with its prefix, it will sometimes happen that the subtrahend exceeds the minuend. In
this case the subtraction will end with a *minus* digit, which
may be indicated by an asterisk. Now find what number of
Divisors must be added to the 2nd Column to cancel this
minus digit, and enter that number, marked with an asterisk,
in the 1st Column, and that multiple of the Divisor in the 2nd;
and then draw a line below the 2nd Column, and add in this
new item.

As an example, let us take a new Dividend, but retain the
previous Divisor, changing the sign of k, so that it will become
7003 (*i.e.*, 7. $t^3 + 3$). The sum, as set for working, would
stand thus :—

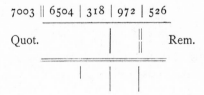

7003 ‖ 6504 | 318 | 972 | 526

Quot.   Rem.

After working, it would stand thus :—

$$
\begin{array}{c|c|c|c}
 & 1 & 4 & 5 \\
7003 \parallel 6504 & 3{\scriptstyle 1}8 & 972 & 526
\end{array}
$$

Quot.   928 | 790 | 371   ‖   4413   Rem.

$$
\begin{array}{c|c|c}
929 & 2^*531 & 2602 \\
1^* & 7\ 003 & \\
\hline
 & 5\ 534 & 371 \\
\hline
 & 790 &
\end{array}
$$

the Mental Process being as follows :—

Divide the 6504 by 7, and enter the Quotient, 929, in the
1st Column, and the Remainder, 1, above the 2nd period.
Then subtract, from the 1318, 3-times the 929, entering the
result in the 2nd Column, thus : " 27 from 8 I can't, but 27
from 28, 1." Enter the 1, and carry the borrowed 2. " 8
from 1 I can't, but 8 from 11, 3." Enter the 3, and carry the
borrowed 1. " 28 from 3 I can't, but 28 from 33, 5." Enter
the 5, and carry the borrowed 3. "3 from 1, *minus* 2." Enter
it, with an asterisk. Observing that, to cancel this *minus* 2, it
will suffice to add *once* the Divisor, enter a (− 1) in the 1st
Column, and 7003 in the 2nd ; and then draw a line below
the 2nd Column, and add in this new item : the result is
5534. Then add up the 1st Column, and enter the result,
928, in the Quotient. Now take the 5534 as a new 1st period,
and the third period, 972, as a new 2nd period, and proceed
as before, thus : Draw a double line below the 5534, and
divide it by 7, entering the Quotient, 790, below it, and the
Remainder, 4, above the 3rd period. Then subtract, from the
4972, 3-times the 790, entering the result, 2602, in the 3rd
Column ; and observe that this *does not* contain a *minus* digit.
Then add up the 2nd Column, as far as its lowest double line,

and enter the result, 790, in the Quotient. Now take the
2602 as a new 1st period, and the final period, 526, as a new
2nd period, and proceed as before, thus. Draw a double line
below the 2602, and divide it by 7, entering the Quotient, 371,
below it, and the Remainder, 5, above the final period. Then
subtract, from the 5526, 3-times the 371, entering the result,
4413, which you can foresee will be *less* than the Divisor, as
the Remainder. Then add up the 3rd Column, as far as its
lowest double line, and enter the result, 371, as the final period
of the Quotient.

The Rules for case (2) may be derived, from the above, by
making $k=1$; and those for case (3) by making $h=1$. I will
give worked examples of these; but it will not be necessary to
give the Mental Processes.

By making $k=1$, we get Divisors of the form $(h.\,t''\pm1)$: let
us take $(11t^4-1)$ and $(6t^5+1)$

$$
\begin{array}{ccccc}
 & & 9 & 10 & 4 \\
109999\parallel 107523\mid & 8168\mid & 9662\mid & 0985 \\
\text{Quot.}\quad 9774\mid & 9813\mid & 0861\parallel 41846 \text{ Rem.}
\end{array}
$$

$$
\begin{array}{c|c|c}
9774\mid & 107942 & 119474 \\
 & & 1 \\
 & 9812 & 9475 \\
 & 1 & \\
 & 861 &
\end{array}
$$

$$
\begin{array}{ccccc}
 & 3 & & & 3 \\
600001\parallel 7239\mid & 51798\mid & 2\ 6004\mid & 13825 \\
\text{Quot.}\quad 1206\mid & 58431\mid & 9\ 4595\parallel 219230 \text{ Rem.}
\end{array}
$$

$$
\begin{array}{c|c}
\mid 350592 & 47572 \\
 & 60\ 0001 \\
58432 & \\
1^{*}\mid & 56\ 7573 \\
 & 9\ 4595
\end{array}
$$

In this last example there is no need to enter the Quotient, produced by dividing the 7239 by 7, in the 1st Column; we easily foresee that the number at the top of the 2nd Column *will be* less than the Divisor, so that there will be no new item in the 1st: hence we at once enter the 1206 in the Quotient.

By making $h = 1$, we get Divisors of the form $(t^n \pm k)$: let us take $(t^4 - 7)$ and $(l^5 + 12)$.

9993 ‖ 867 | 8159 | 2485 | 7031 | 5276 | 4092

Quot. 867 | 4238 | 2153 | 2104 | 0004 ‖ 4120 Rem.

867	14228	32130	22088	19990
1	7	21	14	14
	4235	2151	2102	4
	3	2	2	

100012 ‖ 7185 | 6 2039 | 10327 | 53118

7184 | 7 5822 | 00463 | 47562

7185	3*5819	9*00355
1*	10 0012	9900108
	7 5831	463
	9*	

The first of these two sums is the one I gave to illustrate Mr. Collingwood's Method of working with Divisors of the the form $(t^n - k)$.

It may interest the reader to see the three methods of working the above example—ordinary Division, Mr. Collingwood's Method, and my version of it—compared as to the amount of labour which each entails in the working :—

	Ordinary Division.	Mr. C.'s Method.	My version of it.
Digits written	202	82	44
Additions, or Subtractions	204	97	25
Multiplications	0	70	22

I am assuming that any one, working this example by ordinary Division, would begin by making a table of Multiples of 9993 for reference : so that he would have *no* Multiplications to do. Still, the great number of digits he would have to write, and of Additions and Subtractions he would have to do, involving a far greater risk of error than either of the other Methods, would quite outweigh this advantage.

By whatever process a Question in Long Division has been worked, it is very desirable to be able to test, easily and quickly, the correctness of the Answer. The ordinary test is to multiply together the Divisor and Quotient, add the Remainder, and observe whether these together make up the given Number, as they ought to do.

Thus, if N be the given Number, D the given Divisor, Q the Quotient, and R the Remainder, we ought to have

$$N = D . Q + R.$$

This test is specially easy to apply, when $D = (h . t'' \pm k)$, for then we ought to have

$$N = (h . t'' \pm k) . Q + R ;$$
$$= (h . Q . t'' + R) \pm k Q.$$

Now $hQ . t''$ may be found by multiplying Q by h, and tacking on n ciphers. Hence $(h Q . t'' + R)$ may be found by making R occupy the place of the n ciphers. If R contains less than n digits it must have ciphers prefixed ; if more, the overplus must be carried on into the next period, and added to $h Q$.

Having found our "Test," viz. ($hQ.\ t'' + R$), we can write it on a separate slip of paper, and place it below the working of the example, so as to come vertically below N, which is at the top. When the sign in D is " $-$ ", we must add $k\ Q$ to N, and see if the result $= T$; when it is "$+$" we must add $k\ Q$ to T, and see if the result $= N$.

Now it has been already pointed out that when, in the new Method, the 1st and 2nd Columns have been worked, the 1st period of the Quotient and the number at the foot of the 2nd Column are the Quotient and Remainder that would result if the Dividend ended with its 2nd period. Hence the Test can be at once applied, before dealing with the 3rd Column. This constitutes a very important new feature in my version of Mr. Collingwood's Method. Every two adjacent Columns contain a separate Division-sum, which can be tested *by itself*. Hence, in working my Method, as soon as I have entered the 1st period of the Quotient, I can test it, and, if I have made any mistake, I can correct it. But the hapless computator, who has spent, say, an hour in working out some gigantic sum in Long Division—whether by the ordinary process or by Mr. Collingwood's Method—and who has chanced to get a figure wrong at the very outset, which makes every subsequent figure wrong, has no warning of the fatal error till he has worked out the whole thing "to the bitter end," and has begun to test his Answer. Whereas, if working by *my* Method, he would have been warned of his mistake almost as soon as he made it, and would have been able to set it right before going any further.

As an aid to the reader, I will give the Mental Process in full, for the 2nd and 3rd Columns of the first of the examples worked above.

The Divisor is 6997 (where $h = 7$, $k = 3$). Here you are supposed to have just entered the 281 in the Quotient. The Dividend, for these two columns, is 1972 | 103 ; the Quotient is

281, and the Remainder 5946. The Test is $hQ.\ t^n + R$ (*i.e.*, $7 \times 281000 + 5946$), the Mental Process being as follows : Write down, on a separate slip of paper, the last three digits of R, viz., 946, and carry the 5 into the next period, adding it to the 7×281, thus, "5 and 7, 12." Enter the 2, and carry the 1. "1 and 56, 57." Enter the 7, and carry the 5. "5 and 14, 19." Enter it. Having got your Test, try whether $(N + kQ)$ is equal to it. This you compute, comparing it with your

6	5
407	103
281	
8968	5946
3	
1972	
281	

Test 1972	946

Test, digit by digit, as you go on, thus, "3 and 3, 6." Observe it in the Test. "o and 24, 24." Observe the 4, and carry the 2. "3 and 6, 9." Observe it. "1972 and o, 1972." Observe it. The Test is satisfied.

For Divisors of the form $(t^n \pm k)$ there is no need to write out the Test : the numbers, which compose it, already occur in the working, and may be used as they stand.

CHAPTER III.

LONG DIVISION, WHERE REMAINDER IS REQUIRED, BUT NOT QUOTIENT.

§ 1.

Divisors of the form $(t^n \pm 1)$.

THE Methods here required were described in the last Chapter, § 1, as processes preliminary to that of finding the Quotient.

For Divisors of the other forms there discussed, the methods, for finding Quotient and Remainder, can of course be used for finding Remainder only : the only cases which we need consider here are those in which, owing to the Quotient *not* being required, these Methods are capable of abridgment.

§ 2.

Divisors of the form $(ht \pm 1)$.

Here the Methods, described in the last Chapter, § 2, may be abridged by leaving out all the written work below the double line.

As examples of this abridged Method, let us take 27910385642558361 as our Dividend, and find its 29-Remainder, and its 71-Remainder.

The first, when worked, stands thus :—

29‖27910385642558361 Rem. 2,

the Mental Process being as follows : Begin by dividing 27 by 3, and adding its quotient, 9, to the number made up by prefixing its remainder, o, to the next digit, 9 : *i.e.*, you say "9 and 9, 18." Then divide this 18 by 3, and add its quotient, 6, to the number made up by prefixing its remainder, o, to the next digit, 1 : *i.e.*, say, "6 and 1, 7." Then say, "2 and 10, 12 ; 4 and 3, 7 ; 2 and 18, 20 ; 6 and 25, 31." Here you "cast out" a 29, and say "which gives 2." To this you tack on the next digit, 6, and proceed thus : "8 and 24, 32 ; which gives 3 ; 1 and 2, 3 ; 1 and 5, 6 ; 2 and 5, 7 ; 2 and 18, 20 ; 6 and 23, 29 : which gives o ; 2 and 1, 3 ; 1 and 1, 2."

The second, when worked, stands thus :—

71‖27910385642558361 Rem. 68,

the Mental Process being as follows : Begin by dividing 27 by

7, and subtracting its quotient, 3, from the number made up by prefixing its remainder, 6, to the next digit, 9 : *i.e.*, you say " 3 from 69, 66." Then divide this 66 by 7, and subtract its quotient, 9, from the number made up by prefixing its remainder, 3, to the next digit, 1 ; *i.e.*, say " 9 from 31, 22." Then say " 3 from 10, 7 ; 1 from 3, 2 ; 0 from 28, 28 ; 4 from 5, 1 ; 0 from 16, 16 ; 2 from 24, 22 ; 3 from 15, 12 ; 1 from 55, 54 ; 7 from 58, 51 ; 7 from 23, 16 ; 2 from 26, 24 ; 3 from 31, 28 ; 4 from 1, I can't, but " (here you throw in an extra Divisor) " 4 from 72, 68."

§ 3.

Powers of 10.

The 10-Remainder is the last digit : the 10^2-Remainder is the number composed of the last 2 digits ; and so on.

These Remainders will serve as trial-dividends for all numbers whose factors are powers of the factors of 10, viz., 2 and 5. Thus the 32-Remainder may be found by taking the number composed of the last 5 digits, and dividing by 32. Similarly, 80 is $2^4 \times 5$: hence the 10^4-Remainder will serve for it.

§ 4.

Factors of Divisors of the form $(ht \pm 1)$.

The 21-Remainder will serve as a trial-dividend for 7 (the factor, 3, is also a factor of 9). But this Remainder is (owing to the small value of h, which constantly gives a subtrahend greater than the minuend) so troublesome to find, that I should prefer to find the 7-Remainder by ordinary Division.

The 39-Remainder will serve for 13 ; the 51 for 17 ; the 69 for 23.

Of the three propositions which follow, the two theorems are very curious, and as the elucidation of them requires only a moderate acquaintance with geometry, I expect that many of my readers will be inclined to try their hands at discovering wherein lie their fallacies.

THEOREM I.

EVERY TRIANGLE IS ISOSCELES.

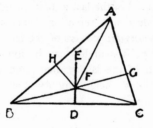

Let A B C be any Triangle. Bisect B C at D, and from D draw D E at right angles to B C. Bisect the angle B A C.

(1) If the bisector does not meet D E, they are parallel. Therefore the bisector is at right angles to B C. Therefore A B = A C, *i.e.*, A B C is isosceles.

(2) If the bisector meets D E, let them meet at F. Join F B, F C, and from F draw F G, F H, at right angles to A C, A B.

Then the Triangles A F C, A F H are equal, because they have the side A F common, and the angles F A G, A G F equal to the angles F A H, A H F.   Therefore A H = A G, and F H = F G.

Again, the Triangles B D F, C D F are equal, because B D = D C, D F is common, and the angles at D are equal. Therefore F B = F C.

Again, the Triangles F H B, F G C are right-angled. Therefore the square on F B = the squares on F H, H B ; and the square on F C = the squares on F G, G C.   But F B = F C, and F H = F G   Therefore the square on H B = the square on G C.   Therefore H B = G C.   Also, A H has been proved = to A G.   Therefore A B = A C ; *i.e.,* A B C is isosceles.

Therefore the Triangle A B C is always isosceles.

Q. E. D.

PROBLEM

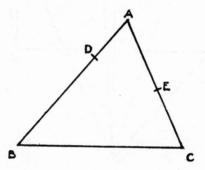

A B C is a given Triangle, and D and E are given points in A B and A C.

It is required to describe on the 3 sides, or those sides produced, 3 semi-circles, facing inwards, and touching each other ; two of them having their centres at D and E, and the third having its centre in B C.

THEOREM II.

AN OBTUSE ANGLE IS SOMETIMES EQUAL TO A RIGHT ANGLE

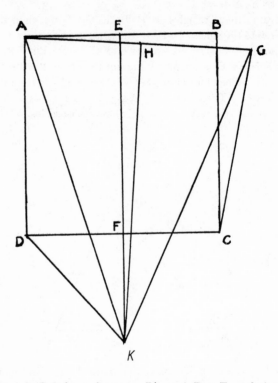

Let A B C D be a Square.   Bisect A B at E, and through E draw E F at right angles to A B, and cutting D C at F. Then D F = F C.

From C draw C G = C B.   Join A G, and bisect it at H. and from H draw H K at right angles to A G.

Since A B, A G are not parallel, E F, H K are not parallel. Therefore they will meet, if produced. Produce E F, and let them meet at K. Join K D, K A, K G, and K C.

The Triangles K A H, K G H are equal, because A H = H G, H K is common, and the angles at H are right. Therefore K A = K G.

The Triangles K D F, K C F are equal, because D F = F C, F K is common, and the angles at F are right. Therefore K D = K C, and angle K D C = angle K C D.

Also D A = C B = C G.

Hence the Triangles K D A, K C G have all their sides equal. Therefore the angles K D A, K C G are equal. From these equals take the equal angles K D C, K C D. Therefore the remainders are equal: *i.e.*, the angle G C D = the angle A D C. But G C D is an obtuse angle, and A D C is a right angle.

Therefore an obtuse angle is sometimes = a right angle.

Q. E. D.

In the " Life of Lewis Carroll " (pp. 317, 318) there is an allusion to a problem invented by him, and called there the " Monkey and Weight Problem." I have recently received from the Rev. Arthur Brook, of Chertsey, a solution which differs entirely from any of those which Mr. Dodgson received from his friends, and which seems worth reproducing here. For the benefit of those of my readers who do not possess a copy of my earlier volume, I will repeat the statement of the problem as given in it :—

A rope is supposed to be hung over a wheel fixed to the roof of a building; at one end of the rope a weight is fixed, which exactly counterbalances a monkey which is hanging on to the other end. Suppose that the monkey begins to climb the rope, what will be the result?

Mr. Brook writes as follows :—-

" I see you state that Lewis Carroll's diary illustrates the several possible answers. I venture to suggest another and (I believe) the correct answer—namely, that *the weight remains stationary.*

" It is clear that the weight can only move up by the pressure on the monkey's side being increased, or down by that pressure being lessened. Now the monkey by climbing cannot increase or lessen his own weight nor the weight of the rope on his side, nor can he alter the line of pressure; therefore the pressure on his side will remain unaltered, and the weight will neither move up nor down.

" The putting of his weight higher up the rope does not increase the pressure—whatever pressure he puts on the rope by lifting himself he at the same time takes a like pressure off the rope."

There seems to me to be one very obvious criticism on this solution. Mr. Brook says that " the monkey by climbing cannot increase or lessen his own weight," but surely as he climbs he increases the distance between him and the centre of gravity, and thus *does* lessen his weight. This would lead one to think that the monkey's end of the rope would go up, while the weight at the other end would descend, a conclusion reached also by Mr. Sampson, one of the tutors at Christ Church, who attempted to solve the problem.

In conclusion, I give two numerical curiosities, which I believe to have been discovered by Mr. Dodgson.

(1)

Put down any number of pounds not more than twelve, any number of shillings under twenty, and any number of pence under twelve. Under the pounds put the number of pence, under the shillings the number of shillings, and under the pence the number of pounds, thus reversing the line.

Subtract.

Reverse the line again.

Add.

Answer, £12 18s. 11d., *whatever* numbers may have been selected.

(2)

A MAGIC NUMBER.

142857.

285714 twice that number.

428571 thrice that number.

571428 four times that number.

714285 five times that number.

857142 six times that number.

Begin at the " 1 " in each line and it will be the same order of figures as the magic number up to six times that number, while seven times the magic number results in a row of 9's.

CHAPTER VI

GAMES AND PUZZLES

IN a MS. of Lewis Carroll's entitled "Analysis of Journals," I came upon an entry under the head of " Inventions " to the following effect :—

"8/1/75 idea of 'Alice's Puzzle-Book.'"

This idea of his grew into the conception of a volume to be called "Original Games and Puzzles," for which Miss E. Gertrude Thomson, the artist who illustrated his "Three Sunsets," had promised to provide a series of pictures. Although he left behind him no trace of any *literary* preparations for this volume, it has been an easy task for me to collect the rules of the games which he invented, for they were few in number ; as to the puzzles, I fear I have not been so successful. Many of them, I suspect, were never committed to writing, but simply stored up in his memory, to be retailed from time to time for the benefit of his "child friends."

"Castle Croquet" was invented by Mr. Dodgson, who elaborated the rules by means of playing a series of games with the Misses Liddell, daughters of the late Dean of Christ Church. These rules were printed in 1863, together with the diagram here reproduced.

CASTLE CROQUET.

For Four Players.

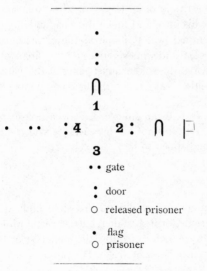

• • gate

⋮ door

O released prisoner

• flag
O prisoner

I.

This game requires 8 balls, 8 arches, and 4 flags ; 4 of the balls are called " soldiers," the others " sentinels." The arches and flags are set up as in the figure, making 4 "castles," and each player has a castle, a soldier, and a sentinel. To begin the game, the soldier is placed just within the gate, and the sentinel half-way between the gate and the door.

(N.B.—The distance from one gate to the next should be 6 or 8 yards, and the distance from the gate to the door, or from the door to the flag, 2 or 3 yards.)

II.

The soldiers are played first, in the order given in the figure, then the sentinels in the same order, and so on. Each player has to bring his soldier out of its castle, and with it " invade " the other castles in order (*e.g.*, No. 3 has to invade castles 4, 1, 2), re-enter his own, and touch the flag, and then to touch it with his sentinel (which, if out of the castle, must re-enter for this purpose) ; and whoever does all this first, wins. To "invade " a castle, the soldier must enter at the gate, go through the door (either way), touch the flag, and come out at the gate again.

(N.B.—No ball can enter or leave a castle except at the gate. A sentinel, that has not left his castle, is said to be " on duty," wherever he happen to be.)

III.

If a sentinel and soldier touch, while both are within the sentinel's castle, or if a soldier enter a castle while its sentinel and his own are both " on duty," the soldier becomes "prisoner" and is placed behind the flag. He cannot move till released which is done either by his own sentinel (on duty) coming and touching the flag, or by the sentinel leaving the castle. In the former case, his own sentinel is put back where he was at the beginning of the game; and in either case the released soldier is placed behind the door, and cannot be again taken prisoner until after his next turn.

IV.

When a soldier goes through an arch, or touches a flag, in his proper course, or plays after being released, or when a sentinel enters or leaves his castle, or takes a prisoner, he may be played again; but a sentinel may not enter or leave his castle twice in one turn.

(N.B.—A sentinel can only enter or leave *his own* castle : no account is taken of his going through any arch other than his own gate.)

V.

If a ball touch another (except a sentinel on duty, a prisoner, or a released prisoner who has not played since his release), the player may use it to croquêt his own with ; but may not move it in doing so, unless it be his own sentinel (not on duty). He may not croquêt himself twice in one turn with the same ball, unless he has done one of the things mentioned in Rule IV. meanwhile. In this game, croquêting does not give (as in he ordinary game) the right of playing again.

N.B.—The following arrangement of the 8 balls as soldiers and sentinels will be found convenient :—

Soldiers.	*Sentinels.*
Blue	Green
Black	Brown
Orange	Yellow
Red	Pink

The flags should match the soldiers in colour.

This game may be adapted for five players, by the addition of a light-blue and a light-green ball, and the 10 balls may be arranged thus :—

Soldiers.	*Sentinels.*
Blue	Light Blue
Black	Brown
Orange	Yellow
Green	Light Green
Red	Pink

The game of " Word-Links " or " Doublets," the most popular of all Lewis Carroll's games, was invented about the year 1878. Several editions of the rules have been published ; the following is a reprint of the 1880 edition, with the omission of the Glossary which accompanied it, and the greater part of the examples.

DOUBLETS

A WORD-PUZZLE

BY

LEWIS CARROLL

" Double, double,
Toil and trouble."

SECOND EDITION

LONDON
MACMILLAN AND CO.
1880

INSCRIBED

TO

JULIA AND ETHEL.

PREFACE.

On the 29th of March, 1879, the following article appeared in *Vanity Fair :—*

A NEW PUZZLE.

The readers of *Vanity Fair* have during the last ten years shown so much interest in the Acrostics and Hard Cases which were first made the object of sustained competition for prizes in this journal, that it has been sought to invent for them an entirely new kind of Puzzle, such as would interest them equally with those that have already been so successful. The subjoined letter from Mr. Lewis Carroll will explain itself, and will introduce a Puzzle so entirely novel and withal so interesting, that the transmutation of the original into the final word of the Doublets may be expected to become an occupation to the full as amusing as the. guessing of the Double Acrostics has already proved.

In order to enable readers to become acquainted with the new Puzzle, preliminary Doublets will be given during the next three weeks—that is to say, in the present number of *Vanity Fair* and in those of the 5th and 12th April. A competition will then be opened—beginning with the Doublets published on the 19th April, and including all those published subsequently, up to and including the number of the 26th July—for three prizes, consisting respectively of a Proof Album for the first and of ordinary Albums for the second and third prizes.

The rule of scoring will be as follows :—

A number of marks will be apportioned to each Doublet equal to the number of letters in the two words given. For

example, in the instance given below of " Head " and " Tail,"
the number of possible marks to be gained would be eight ; and
this maximum will be gained by each one of those who make
the chain with the least possible number of changes.   If it be
assumed that in this instance the chain cannot be completed
with less than the four links given, then those who complete it
with four links only will receive eight marks, while a mark will
be deducted for every extra link used beyond four.   Any competitor, therefore, using five links would score seven marks, any
competitor using eight links would score four, and any using
twelve links or more would score nothing.   The marks gained
by each competitor will be published each week.

" DEAR VANITY,—Just a year ago last Christmas, two young
ladies — smarting under that sorest scourge of feminine
humanity, the having 'nothing to do '—besought me to send
them 'some riddles.'   But riddles I had none at hand, and
therefore set myself to devise some other form of verbal torture
which should serve the same purpose.   The result of my medi-
tations was a new kind of Puzzle—new at least to me—which,
now that it has been fairly tested by a year's experience, and
commended by many friends, I offer to you, as a newly-gathered
nut, to be cracked by the omnivorous teeth which have already
masticated so many of your Double Acrostics.

" The rules of the Puzzle are simple enough.   Two words
are proposed, of the same length ; and the Puzzle consists in
linking these together by interposing other words, each of
which shall differ from the next word *in one letter only*.   That
is to say, one letter may be changed in one of the given words,
then one letter in the word so obtained, and so on, till we
arrive at the other given word.   The letters must not be interchanged among themselves, but each must keep to its own
place.   As an example, the word " head " may be changed
into 'tail' by interposing the words 'heal, teal, tell, tall.'   I
call the two given words 'a Doublet,' the interposed words

'Links,' and the entire series 'a Chain,' of which I here append an example :—

                    H E A D
                    h e a l
                    t e a l
                    t e l l
                    t a l l
                    T A I L

" It is, perhaps, needless to state that it is *de rigueur* that the links should be English words, such as might be used in good society.

" The easiest ' Doublets' are those in which the consonants in one word answer to consonants in the other, and the vowels to vowels ; 'head' and 'tail' constitute a Doublet of this kind. Where this is not the case, as in 'head' and 'hare,' the first thing to be done is to transform one member of the Doublet into a word whose consonants and vowels shall answer to those in the other member (*e.g.*, 'head, herd, here,') after which there is seldom much difficulty in completing the ' Chain.'

" I am told that there is an American game involving a similar principle. I have never seen it, and can only say of its inventors, '*pereant qui ante nos nostra dixerunt !*'

" LEWIS CARROLL."

RULES.

1. The words given to be linked together constitute a "Doublet," the interposed words are the "Links," and the entire series a "Chain." The object is to complete the Chain with the least possible number of Links.

2. Each word in the Chain must be formed from the pre-

ceding word by changing one letter in it, and one only. The substituted letter must occupy the same place, in the word so formed, which the discarded letter occupied in the preceding word, and all the other letters must retain their places.

3. When three or more words are given to be made into a Chain, the first and last constitute a "Doublet." The others are called "Set Links," and must be introduced into the Chain in the order in which they are given. A Chain of this kind must not contain any word twice over.

4. No word is admissible as a Link unless it (or, if it be an inflection, a word from which it comes) is to be found in the following Glossary. Comparatives and superlatives of adjectives and adverbs, when regularly formed, are regarded as "inflections" of the positive form, and are not given separately, *e.g.*, the word "new" being given, it is to be understood that "newer" and "newest" are also admissible. But nouns formed from verbs (as "reader" from "read") are *not* so regarded, and may not be used as Links unless they are to be found in the Glossary.

METHOD OF SCORING, Etc.

Adopted in "Vanity Fair."

1. The marks assigned to each Doublet are as follows :— If it be given without any Set Links, so many marks are assigned to it as there are letters in the two words together (*e.g.*, a four-letter Doublet would have eight marks assigned to it). If it be given with Set Links, so that the Chain is made up of two or more portions, so many marks are assigned to it as would have been assigned if each portion had been a separate Chain (*e.g.*, a four-letter Doublet which has two Set Links, so that the Chain is made up of three portions, would have twenty-four marks assigned to it).

2. Each competitor, who completes the Chain with the least possible number of Links, will receive the full number of marks assigned ; and each who uses more than the least possible number of Links will lose a mark for every additional Link.

3. Each competitor is required to send his three Chains, with his signature attached, written on *one* piece of paper.

4. The Editor of " Vanity Fair " will be glad to receive any suggestions, both as to words which it seems desirable to omit, and as to omitted words which it seems desirable to insert ; but any word proposed for insertion or for omission *should be exhibited as a Link between two other words.*

5. Alterations will not be made in this Glossary during any competition, but will be duly announced before the commencement of a new competition, so that those who already possess copies will be able to correct them, and will not be obliged to buy a new edition.

Vanity Fair OFFICE,

13, TAVISTOCK STREET, COVENT GARDEN, LONDON.

DOUBLETS ALREADY SET

In "Vanity Fair."

PRELIMINARY DOUBLETS.

1879.	Links Needed.
March 29.—Drive PIG into STY	4
Raise FOUR to FIVE	6
Make WHEAT into BREAD	6
April 5.—Dip PEN into INK...	5
Touch CHIN with NOSE	5
Change TEARS into SMILE	5

				Links Needed.
1879.				
April 12.—Change WET to DRY	...	...	...	3
Make HARE into SOUP	...	...	...	6
PITCH TENTS	...	...	...	5

FIRST COMPETITION.

April 19.—Cover EYE with LID	...	...	...	3
Prove PITY to be GOOD	...	...	...	6
STEAL COINS	...	...	...	7
26.—Make EEL into PIE	...	...	...	3
Turn POOR into RICH	...	...	...	5
Prove RAVEN to be MISER	...	...	3
May 3.—Change OAT to RYE	...	...	...	3
Get WOOD from TREE	...	...	...	7
Prove GRASS to be GREEN	...	...	7
10.—Evolve MAN from APE	...	...	...	5
Change CAIN into ABEL	...	...	...	8
Make FLOUR into BREAD	...	...	...	5
17.—Make TEA HOT	...	...	...	3
Run COMB into HAIR	...	...	...	6
Prove a ROGUE to be a BEAST	...	...	10
24.—Change ELM into OAK	...	...	...	7
Combine ARMY and NAVY	...	...	7
Place BEANS on SHELF	...	...	...	7
31.—HOOK FISH	...	...	...	6
QUELL a BRAVO	...	...	...	10
Stow FURIES in BARREL	...	...	...	5

	Links Needed.
1879.	
June 7.—Buy an Ass	7
Get Coal from Mine	5
Pay Costs in Pence	9
14.—Raise One to Two	7
Change Blue to Pink	8
Change Black to White...	6
21.—Change Fish to Bird	4
Sell Shoes for Crust	6
Make Kettle Holder	9
28.—Rest on Sofa	4
Trace River to Shore	10
Caress Parent	2
July 5.—Change Grub to Moth	9
Turn Witch into Fairy	12
Make Winter Summer	13
12.—Save Lamb from Lion	2
Crown Tiger with Roses...	5
Lay Quilt on Sheet	13
19.—Put Loaf into Oven	9
Make Bread into Toast	6
Put Rouge on Cheek	16
26.—Why Not ?...	3
Many will Fail	7
to get	
Prizes from Choker	9

SOLUTIONS OF DOUBLETS.

March 29.

```
P I G        T E A R S
w i g        s e a r s
w a g        s t a r s
w a y        s t a r e
s a y        s t a l e
S T Y        s t i l e
             S M I L E
```

```
F O U R
f o u l      April 12.
f o o l
f o o t      W E T
f o r t      b e t
f o r e      b e y
f i r e      d e y
F I V E      D R Y
```

```
W H E A T    H A R E
c h e a t    h a r k
c h e a p    h a c k
c h e e p    s a c k
c r e e p    s o a k
c r e e d    s o a p
b r e e d    S O U P
B R E A D
```

```
April 5.      P I T C H
P E N         p i n c h
e' e n        w i n c h
e e l         w e n c h
e l l         t e n c h
i l l         t e n t h
i l k         T E N T S
I N K
```

```
N O S E
n o t e
c o t e
c o r e
c o r n
c o i n
C H I N
```

April 19.

```
             R A V E N
E Y E        r i v e n
d y e        r i s e n
d i e        r i s e r
d i d        M I S E R
L I D
```

```
             May 3.
P I T Y      O A T
p i t s      r a t
p i n s      r o t
f i n s      r o e
f i n d      R Y E
f o n d
f o o d
G O O D
```

```
             T R E E
             f r e e
S T E A L    f l e e
s t e e l    f l e d
s t e e r    f e e d
s h e e r    w e e d
s h i e r    w e l d
s h i e s    w o l d
s h i n s    W O O D
c h i n s
C O I N S
```

```
             G R A S S
             c r a s s
April 26.     c r e s s
             t r e s s
E E L        t r e e s
e' e n       f r e e s
p e n        f r e e d
p i n        g r e e d
P I E        G R E E N
```

```
P O O R
b o o r
b o o k
r o o k
r o c k
r i c k
R I C H
```

FIRST COMPETITION (*continued*).

May 10.

```
A P E
a r e
e r e
e r r
e a r
m a r
M A N
```

```
C A I N
c h i n
s h i n
s p i n
s p u n
s p u d
s p e d
a p e d
a b e d
A B E L
```

```
F L O U R
f l o o r
f l o o d
b l o o d
b r o o d
b r o a d
B R E A D
```

May 17.

```
T E A
s e a
s e t
s o t
H O T
```

```
C O M B
c o m e
h o m e
h o l e
h a l e
h a l l
h a i l
H A I R
```

```
R O G U E
v o g u e
v a g u e
v a l u e
v a l v e
h a l v e
h e l v e
h e a v e
l e a v e
l e a s e
l e a s t
B E A S T
```

May 24.

```
E L M
e l l
a l l
a i l
a i r
f i r
f a r
o a r
O A K
```

```
A R M Y
a r m s
a i m s
d i m s
d a m s
d a m e
n a m e
n a v e
N A V Y
```

```
B E A N S
b e a m s
s e a m s
s h a m s
s h a m e
s h a l e
s h a l e
s h e l l
S H E L F
```

May 31.

```
H O O K
h o o t
h o s t
h i s t
f i s t
F I S H
```

```
Q U E L L
q u i l l
q u i l t
g u i l t
g u i l e
g u i d e
g l i d e
g l a d e
g r a d e
g r a v e
b r a v e
B R A V O
```

```
F U R I E S
b u r i e s
b u r i e d
b u r k e d
b a r k e d
b a r r e d
B A R R E L
```

June 7.

```
B U Y
b u d
b i d
a i d
a i m
a r m
a r k
a s k
A S S
```

```
M I N E
m i n t
m i s t
m o s t
m o a t
c o a t
C O A L
```

```
C O S T S
p o s t s
p e s t s
t e s t s
t e n t s
t e n t h
t e n c h
t e a c h
p e a c h
p e a c e
P E N C E
```

June 14.

```
O N E
o w e
e w e
e y e
d y e
d o e
t o e
t o o
T W O
```

```
B L U E
g l u e
g l u t
g o u t
p o u t
p o r t
p a r t
p a n t
p i n t
P I N K
```

```
B L A C K
b l a n k
b l i n k
c l i n k
c h i n k
c h i n e
w h i n e
W H I T E
```

FIRST COMPETITION (*continued*).

June 21.

```
FISH
fist
gist
girt
gird
BIRD

SHOES
shops
chops
crops
cross
cress
crest
CRUST

KETTLE
settle
settee
setter
better
betted
belted
bolted
bolter
bolder
HOLDER
```

June 28.

```
REST
lest
lost
loft
soft
SOFA

RIVER
rover
cover
coves
cores
corns
coins
chins
shins
shine
shone
SHORE
```

```
CARESS
carest
parest
PARENT
```

July 5.

```
GRUB
grab
gray
bray
brat
boat
bolt
bole
mole
mote
MOTH

WITCH
winch
wench
tench
tenth
tents
tints
tilts
tills
fills
falls
fails
fairs
FAIRY

WINTER
winner
wanner
wander
warder
harder
harper
hamper
damper
damped
dammed
dimmed
dimmer
simmer
SUMMER
```

July 12.

```
LION
limn
limb
LAMB

TIGER
tiler
tiles
tides
rides
rises
ROSES

QUILT
guilt
guile
guide
glide
slide
slice
spice
spine
spins
shins
shies
shier
sheer
SHEET
```

July 19.

```
LOAF
leaf
deaf
dear
deer
dyer
dyes
eyes
eves
even
OVEN

BREAD
break
bleak
bleat
blest
blast
boast
TOAST
```

```
ROUGE
rough
sough
south
sooth
booth
boots
boats
brats
brass
crass
cress
crest
chest
cheat
cheap
cheep
CHEEK
```

July 26.

```
WHY
who
woo
wot
NOT

MANY
mane
wane
wale
wile
will
wall
wail
FAIL

CHOKER
choked
cooked
looked
loosed
noosed
noised
poised
prised
prized
PRIZES
```

PREFACE TO GLOSSARY.[1]

The following Glossary is intended to contain all well-known English words (or, if they are inflections, words from which they come) of 3, 4, 5, or 6 letters each, which may be used in good society, and which can serve as Links. It is not intended to be used as a source from which words may be obtained, but only as a test of their being admissible.

That such a Glossary is needed may best be proved by quoting the following passage from *Vanity Fair* of May 17, 1879, premising that all the strange words, here used, had actually occurred in Chains sent in by competitors :—

"Choker humbly presents his compliments to the four thousand three hundred and seventeen (or thereabouts) indignant Doubleteers who have so strongly shent him, and pre to being soaked in the spate of their wrath, asks for a fiver of minutes for reflection. Choker is in a state of complete pye. He feels that there must be a stent to the admission of spick words. He is quite unable to sweal the chaffy spelt, to sile the pory cole, or to swill a spate from a piny ait to the song of the spink. Frils and the mystic Gole are strangers in his sheal : the chanceful Gord hath never brought him gold, nor ever did a cate become his ain. The Doubleteers will no doubt spank him sore, with slick quotations and wild words of yore, will pour upon his head whole steres of steens and poods of spiles points downwards. But he trusts that those alone who habitually use such words as these in good society, and whose discourse is universally there understood, will be the first to cast a stean at him."

---

[1] I have not thought it necessary to reproduce here the glossary of words which may be used to form links. The preface will give a sufficiently clear idea of the classes of words which are not admissible.

As the chief object aimed at has been to furnish a puzzle which shall be an amusing mental occupation at *all* times, whether a dictionary is at hand or not, it has been sought to include in this Glossary only such words as most educated people carry in their memories. If any doubt should arise as to whether any word that suggests itself is an admissible one, it may be settled by referring to the Glossary.

When there are two words spelt alike, one a noun and one a verb, or any other such combination, it has not been thought necessary to include *both*, so long as all the inflections can be obtained from *one:* *e.g.*, " aim " is given only as a verb, since " aims," the plural of the noun, is also the third person of the verb ; but " hale, *v, a,*" and " hale, *a,*" are both given, the one being needed to supply " hales " and " haled," and the other to supply " haler."

Two abbreviations, " e'en " and " e'er," have been included.

As to the many words which, though used and understood in good society, are yet not available as Links, owing to there being no other words into which they can be changed, it has been regarded as a matter of indifference whether they are included or not.

The games of " Syzygies " and " Lanrick," invented about the same time as " Doublets," are nevertheless a good deal more complicated, and have never been so popular. The rules which follow are taken from an edition printed in 1893 for private circulation.

CHAPTER I.

SYZYGIES.

A WORD-PUZZLE.

" Phœbus, what a name ! "

§ 1. DEFINITIONS.

Def. 1.

WHEN two words contain the same set of one or more consecutive letters, a copy of it, placed in a parenthesis between the two words, is called a "Syzygy," and is said to "yoke" one set to the other, and also to "yoke" each letter of one set to the corresponding letter of the other set.

Examples to Def. 1.

(1)	(2)	(3)	(4)
walrus	walrus	walrus	mine
(a)	(l)	(wal)	(mi)
swallow	swallow	swallow	mimic

N.B.—In Ex. (2), the Syzygy may be regarded as yoking the " l " in " walrus " to whichever " l " in " swallow " the writer may prefer. And in Ex. (4) the Syzygy may be regarded as yoking the " mi " in " mine " to whichever " mi " in " mimic " the writer may prefer.

Def. 2.

A set of four or more words, with a Syzygy between every two, is called a "Chain," of which all but the end-words are called "Links."

Def. 3.

In a "Syzygy-Problem," two words are given, which are to form the end-words of a Chain.

Example to Dej. 3.

If the given words are "walrus" and "carpenter" (the Problem might be stated in the form "*Introduce* Walrus *to* Carpenter"), the following Chain would be a solution of the Problem :—

> WALRUS
> (rus)
> peruse
> (per)
> harper
> (arpe)
> CARPENTER.

Def. 4.

Every letter in a Chain, which is not yoked to some other, is called " waste " ; but, if either of the end-words contains more than 7 letters, the extra ones are not counted as waste.

Thus, in the above Chain, the " wal " in " walrus," the " e " in " peruse," the " h " in " harper," and the " c " and the " nter " in " carpenter " are " waste " : so that this Chain has 10 waste letters ; but since 2 of the 5 waste letters in " carpenter " are not counted as waste, the Chain is reckoned as having only 8 waste letters.

Dej. 5.

When two words contain the same letter, but these two letters are forbidden to be yoked together, these two letters are said to be " barred" with regard to each other.

§ 2. RULES FOR MAKING CHAINS.

Rule 1.

A Chain should be written as in the Example to Def. 3. It does not matter which given word is placed at the top. Any number of alternative Chains may be sent in.

Rule 2.

Any word, used as a Link, must satisfy all the following tests :—

(*a*) It may not be foreign, unless it is in such common use that it may fairly be regarded as naturalised. (The words "ennui," "minimum," "nous," may be taken as specimens of words thus naturalised.)

(*b*) It must be in common use in conversation, letters, and books, in ordinary society. (Thus, slang words used only in particular localities, and words used only by specialists, are unlawful.)

(*c*) It may not be a proper name, when usually spelt with a capital letter. (Thus "Chinese" is unlawful ; but "china," used as the name of a substance, is lawful.)

(*d*) It may not be an abbreviated or a compound word, when usually written with an apostrophe, or hyphen. (Thus, "silver'd," "don't," "man's," "coach-house," are unlawful.)

N.B.—If the Scorer accepts the infinitive of a verb as "ordinary," he is bound to accept all its grammatical inflexions. Thus, if he accepts "to strop (a razor)" as an ordinary word, he is bound to accept "stroppest," "stroppeth," "stropping," and "stropped," even though the first two have probably never been used by any human being.

But, if he accepts the singular of a noun as "ordinary," he is not thereby bound to accept its plural ; and *vice versâ.*

Thus, he may accept "remorse" and "tidings" as "ordinary," and yet reject "remorses" and "tiding" as "non-ordinary."

Rule 3.

When two words begin with the same set of one or more consecutive letters, or would do so if certain prefixes were removed, each letter in the one set is " barred " with regard to the corresponding letter in the other set.

Examples to Rule 3.

Certain prefixes are here marked off by perpendicular lines, and the " barred " letters are printed in italics.

(1)	(2)	(3)	(4)
*do*g	*car*riage	un | *do*ne	un | *do*ne
*do*or	*car*case	*do*or	in *do*ors

N.B.—The letters are only " barred " as here marked. They may often be yoked in other ways: *e.g.*, in Ex. (2), the " ca " above may be yoked to the second " ca " below.

Rule 4.

When two words end with the same set of one or more consecutive letters, or would do so if certain suffixes were removed, each letter in the one set is " barred " with regard to the corresponding letter in the other set.

Examples to Rule 4

Certain suffixes are here marked off by perpendicular lines, and the " barred " letters are printed in italics.

(1)	(2)	(3)	(4)
me*at*	oni*on*	s*ink* | ing	s*ink* | ing
c*at*	mo*on*	l*ink*	l*ink*:s

(5)	(6)
infl*at* | ed	plu*ng* | es
sati*at* | ing	cha*ng* | ing

N.B.—The letters are only " barred " as here marked. They may often be yoked in other ways : *e.g.*, in Ex. (2), the first " on " above may be yoked to the " on " below ; in Ex. (3), (4), the second " in " above may be yoked to the " in " below ; in Ex. (5), the " at " above may be yoked to the first " at " below ; and, in Ex. (6), the " ng " above may be yoked to the second "ng " below.

Observe that, in Ex. (5), the reason why " at " is barred, is that the words become, when the suffixes are removed, "inflate " and " satiate," which end with the same 3 letters. Similarly, in Ex. (6), " plunge " and " change " end with the same 3 letters. But in the words " plunges " and " singer," the " ng " is *not* barred, since the words " plunge " and " sing " do not end with the same letters.

Rule 5.

Nouns and verbs are not to be regarded as prefixes or suffixes.

Thus " landlord (and) handmade " would be a lawful Syzygy.

Rule 6.

The letters " i " and " y " may be treated as if identical. Thus " busy(usy) using " would be a lawful Syzygy.

Rule 7.

The Score for a Chain may be calculated by writing down 7 numbers, as follows :—

(1) The greatest No. of letters in an end-Syzygy, *plus* twice the least.

(2) The least No. of letters in a Syzygy.

(3) The sum of (1) *plus* the product of the two numbers next above (2).

(4) The No. of Links.

(5) The No. of waste letters.

(6) The sum of twice (4) *plus* (5).

(7) The remainder left after deducting (6) from (3). If (6) be greater than (3), the remainder is written as " o."

No (7) is entered as the Score of the Chain.

Example to Rule 7.

The figures on the right indicate the Nos. of waste letters.

WALRUS	...	...	...	...	...	3
(rus)						
peruse	...	...	...	...	...	1
(per)						
harper	...	...	...	...	...	1
(arpe)						
CARPENTER ...	...	...	...	...	3

As the greatest No. of letters in an end-Syzygy is " 4," and the least is " 3," No. (1) is " 10." Also (No. 2) is " 3." Hence No. (3) is the sum of " 10" *plus* " 4 times 5," *i.e.*, it is " 30." Also there are 2 Links and 8 waste letters. Hence No. (4) is " 2," No. (5) is " 8 "; and No. (6) is the sum of "twice 2 " *plus* " 8 "; *i.e.*, it is " 12." Hence No. (7) is the remainder after deducting " 12 " from " 30 "; *i.e.*, it is " 18 "; which is the Score for the Chain.

The result may be conveniently recorded thus :—

10, 3, 30 ; 2, 8, 12 ; 18.

The formula for the Score may, for the benefit of Algebraists, be stated thus :—

Let a = greatest No. of letters in an end-Syzygy.
  b = least do.
  m = least No. in a Syzygy ;
  l = No. of Links ;
  w = No. of waste letters :
then the Score =
    (a + 2b) (m + 1). (m + 2) −(2l + w).

§ 3. RULES FOR SCORING CHAINS.

Rule 1.

If the writer of a Chain has omitted a Syzygy, the Scorer inserts a one-letter Syzygy, if he can find a lawful one.

Rule 2.

If the writer has omitted a Link, the Scorer erases the two adjacent Syzygies, and proceeds as in Rule 1.

Rule 3.

If a Link be mis-spelt, the Scorer corrects it

Rule 4.

If a Syzygy contains unlawful letters, the Scorer erases them, and deducts twice that number of marks from the Score.

Rule 5.

If one of two consecutive Syzygies contains the other, the Scorer erases the intermediate Link, and one Syzygy containing the other.

Examples to Rule 5.

(1)	(2)
meeting	meeting
(ting)	(ting)
tinge	tinge
(ing)	(ting)
loving	loving

N.B. In Ex. (1) the Scorer erases "tinge" and the first Syzygy : in Ex. (2), he erases "tinge" and either Syzygy. The results are :—

(1)	(2)
meeting	meeting
(ing)	(ting)
loving	loving

both of which are, by Rule 4, unlawful Syzygies.

Rule 6.

The penalty, awarded by the preceding Rule, cannot be evaded by writing shorter Syzygies than might be claimed, so as to avoid the result of one containing the other. In such a case, the Scorer would treat them as if written in full.

Examples to Rule 6.

meeting
(tin)
tinge
(ng)
parting

This would be treated as if it had been written, in full,

meeting
(ting)
tinge
(ting)
parting

Rule 7.

If the Chain now contains less than two Links, or an unlawful Link or Syzygy, the Scorer rejects it. Otherwise he calculates its Score.

Rule 8.

In reckoning "the least number of letters in a Syzygy," the Scorer takes no notice of any Syzygies inserted by himself, unless there are no others.

Rule 9.

If a writer sends in alternative Chains, the Scorer takes the best of them.

Rule 10.

If all be rejected, the Scorer puts "O" against the writer's name, assigning a reason for rejecting each Chain.

Rule 11.

In announcing a Problem, the Scorer may bar any word, that he likes to name, from being used as a Link. After receiving the "First-Chains," he must publish a list of the Links which he regards as violating Rule 2, and of the Syzygies which he regards as violating, owing to the occurrence of prefixes or suffixes, Rule 3 or Rule 4, and he must then allow time for sending in "Second-Chains." He may not, when scoring, reject any "First-Chain" for a defect which ought to have been, but was not, published in the above-named list.

§ 4. Hints on Making Chains.

I have tried to embody some useful hints on this subject in the form of a soliloquy, supposed to be indulged in by the possessor of what Tennyson would call "a second-rate sensitive mind," while solving the problem "*Turn* Camel *into* Dromedary."

"No use trying the whole Camel. Let's try four letters. 'Came.' That must be something ending in 'cament,' I fancy. That gives 'predicament,' and 'medicament': I can't think of any others: and either of these would lead to 'mental' or 'mention.' Then 'amel.' That gives 'tamely' and 'lamely.' 'Samely' is hardly an 'ordinary' word: and I'm afraid 'gamely' is slang! Well, we've got *four* Links, at any rate. Let's put them down : —

$$\text{Camel} \begin{cases} \text{(came)} & \begin{cases} \text{predicament (ment)} \\ \text{medicament} \end{cases} \begin{cases} \text{mental} \\ \text{mention} \end{cases} \\ \text{(amel)} & \begin{cases} \text{-tamely} \\ \text{lamely} \end{cases} \end{cases}$$

"Now for Dromedary. No. 5-letter Syzygy, that *I* can see. Let's try the 4's. 'Drom.' There's 'loxodrome,' but that's quite a *specialist's* word. And there's 'palindrome'—no, *that* won't do : 'palin' is a prefix. 'Rome.' That gives 'chrome,' which is *not* very hopeful to go on with. 'Omed.' That'll give us all the participles ending in 'omed': 'domed,' 'doomed,' 'groomed'; not very suggestive : however, there's 'comedy': *that* sounds hopeful. 'Meda.' Well,

there's ' medal,' and ' medalist,' and—and—that's all, I think :
but ' medalist' leads to ' listen,' or ' listless.' ' Edar.' That
leads to ' cedar,' and words beginning with ' re,' such as ' re-
darn this stocking'—no, I'm afraid that would have a hyphen !
However, ' cedar,' leads to ' dared,' or any participle ending in
'-ced. ' Dary.' There's ' daring ' : that might lead to
something, such as ' fringe,' or ' syringe.' Well, let's tabulate
again :—

DROMEDARY
- (omed) { domed, &c. / comedy
- (meda) { medal / medalist (list) { listen / listless
- (edar) cedar { (dar) dared / (ced) . . . ced
- (dary) daring (ring) { fringe / syringe

"Now, can we link any of these ragged ends together?
' Predicament.' That'll link on to ' dared,' though it's only a
3-letter Syzygy. That gives the Chain ' Camel (came) predicament (red) dared (dar) cedar (edar) dromedary.' But
there's something wrong there ! ' Edar ' contains ' dar.' We
must write it ' Camel (came) predicament (red) dared (dar)
dromedary.' That'll score 17. Let's try another Chain.
' Predicament' and ' cedar' can be linked by putting in ' enticed.' How will *that* work ? ' Camel (came) predicament
(ent) enticed (ced) cedar (edar) dromedary.' *That* scores only
16 ! Try again. ' Medicament.' Why that links straight on
to ' comedy,' with a 4-letter Syzygy ! That's the best chance
we've had yet. ' Camel (came) medicament (medi) comedy
(omed) dromedary.' And what does *that* score, I wonder ?
Why it actually scores 31 ! Bravo ! "

If any of my readers should fail, in attempting a similar

soliloquy, let her say to herself, " It is not that my mind is not *sensitive :* it is that it is not *second-rate !*" *Then* she will feel consoled !

§ 5. SOME *SYZYGY*-PROBLEMS.

The gentle reader (N.B. *All* readers are " gentle " : an *un*-gentle reader is a *lusus naturæ* never yet met with) may like to amuse herself by attempting (without referring to § 6) some of the following Problems, solutions of which have been published in the *Lady*. The appended scores are the highest hitherto attained.

(1) OH DO !	... ...	...	... 11
(2) INDULGE *an* IDIOSYNCRASY	...	...	15
(3) *Make* BULLETS *of* LEAD	...	...	17
(4) *Reconcile* DOG *to* CAT	...	...	19
(5) COOK *the* DINNER	...	...	20
(6) *Lay* KNIFE *by* FORK ...	...	...	21
(7) CONVERSE CHEERFULLY	...	...	25
(8) SPREAD *the* BANQUET	...	...	27
(9) WEDNESDAY AFTERNOON	...	...	28
(10) DEMAND *a* CORMORANT	...	...	29

§ 6. SOLUTIONS OF THE PROBLEMS.

The appended dates refer to the numbers of the *Lady* in which these solutions appeared.

(1) March 24, 1892.

OH	...	...	...	...	... 0
(oh)					
cohere	...	...	...	...	... 1
(ere)					
reredos	...	...	...	...	... 2
(do)					
DO	...	...	...	...	... 0

Score :—6, 2, 18 ; 2, 3, 7 : 11.

(2) March 3, 1892.

INDULGE 4
  (ndu)
unduly 1
  (duly)
incredulity 3
  (incr)
IDIOSYNCRASY 3

Score :—10, 3, 30 ; 2, 11, 15 : 15.

(3) March 17, 1892.

LEAD 1
  (lea)
plea 0
  (ple)
sample 0
  (sam)
jetsam 1
  (ets)
BULLETS 4

Score :—9, 3, 29 ; 3, 6, 12 : 17.

(4) October 1, 1891.

DOG 0
  (dog)
endogen 2
  (gen)
gentry 0
  (ntry)
intricate 2
  (cat)
CAT 0

Score :—9, 3, 29 ; 3, 4, 10 : 19.

(5) May 5, 1892.

COOK ...	...	...	...	...	1
(coo)					
scooping	...	...	...	...	2
(pin)					
pinned ...	...	...	...	...	1
(inne)					
DINNER ...	...	...	...	...	2

Score :— 10, 3, 30 ; 2, 6, 10 : 20.

(6) March 10, 1892.

KNIFE ...	...	...	...	...	1
(nife)					
manifest ...	...	...	...	...	2
(man)					
workman	...	...	...	...	1
(ork)					
FORK ...	...	...	...	...	1

Score :— 10, 3, 30 ; 2, 5, 9 : 21.

(7) May 26, 1892.

CONVERSE	...	...	...	...	3
(erse)					
persevering	...	...	...	...	3
(erin)					
merino ...	...	...	...	...	1
(meri)					
perfumery	...	...	...	...	1
(erfu)					
CHEERFULLY	...	...	...	...	3

Score :— 12, 4, 42 ; 3, 11, 17 : 25.

(8) May 12, 1892.

SPREAD 2
(read)

readiness   1
(ines)

shines 0
(shin)

vanquishing   3
(anqu)

BANQUET   3
Score :—12, 4, 42 ; 3, 9, 15 : 27.

(9) April 14, 1892.

WEDNESDAY   2
(ednes)

blessedness   3
(esse)

finesse 1
(iness)

craftiness   1
(raft)

rafter 0
(after)

AFTERNOON   2
Score :—15, 4, 45 ; 4, 9, 17 : 28.

(10) March 31, 1892.

DEMAND   2
(eman)

gentleman   1
(gent)

tangent 1
(ange)

orange 0
(oran)

CORMORANT   3
Score :—12, 4, 42 ; 3, 7, 13 : 29.

CHAPTER II.

LANRICK.

A GAME FOR TWO PLAYERS.

"The muster-place be Lanrick-mead."

§ 1. REQUISITES FOR THE GAME.

THIS Game requires a chess or draughts board, 8 men of one colour and 8 of another (chess-pawns, draughts, or counters), and 9 pieces of card, cut to the size of a square, to serve as markers.

§ 2. DEFINITIONS.

Def. 1.

A "Rendezvous" is a set of squares, into which each Player tries to get his men. The position of its central square is determined by that of the Mark, and the number of its square is always one less than that of the men which are on the Board when the Mark is set. There are two kinds of Rendezvous, "close" and "open."

Def. 2.

A Rendezvous must be "close," when the number of its squares is odd. It consists of the marked square and certain adjacent squares, as shown in the following diagrams, in which the Players are supposed to be at the upper and lower edges. The numerals indicate the number of Rendezvous-squares, the letter "m" the Mark, and the asterisks the Rendezvous-squares.

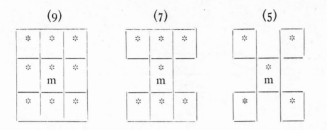

A 3-square Rendezvous consists of a line of 3 square having the marked square in the middle, in any position, straight or slanting, chosen by the Player who sets the Mark.

Def. 3.

A Rendezvous must be " open," when the number of its squares is even. It consists of certain border-squares, which would be in " check " if the Mark were a chess-queen, as shown in the following diagrams, which are to be interpreted as in Def. 2.

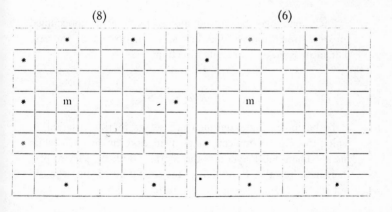

(4)

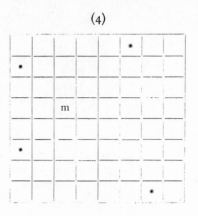

For any but a 9-square Rendezvous, it will be found convenient to mark the Rendezvous-squares with pieces of card.

§ 3. RULES.

Rule 1.

Each man may be moved along any line of unoccupied squares, straight or slanting, but may not (except in the case named in Rule 6) change its direction.

Rule 2.

To begin the game, ten men are set as in this diagram, in which the five B's indicate black men, and the five W's white men. Then one Player sets the Mark. Both then try to play their men into the Rendezvous thus determined, he, who did not set the Mark, having the first turn.

BLACK.

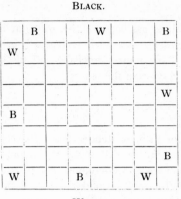

WHITE.

Rule 3.

In playing the first turn for a Rendezvous, a Player may move 2 squares only. In any other turn he may move 5, 4, or 3 squares, according as he has on the Board more than 4, 4, or less than 4 men. He may divide these squares among his men as he likes, but may not move more than 3 of them with any one man, unless it be his only man outside the Rendezvous. He need not move more than one square in one turn. While playing, he should count aloud the squares through or into which he moves a man. After once playing a man and letting go of it, he may not move it again in that turn.

Rule 4.

The Mark, for any Rendezvous, may be set on any but a border-square; for a 3-square Rendezvous it may be set on any but a corner-square, provided that he, who sets it, has no man in the Rendezvous thus determined.

Rule 5.

When the Mark has been set, he, who did not set it, may, before playing, demand an " interchange "; in which case he, who set the Mark, must interchange all his own men with whichever he chooses of the others.

Rule 6.

In playing for an open Rendezvous, a Player may move any man, that is on the border, along it, without regarding the corners, as if it were one continuous line of squares ; and any such man, if not moved beyond the first Rendezvous-square, reckons as having been moved *one* square only ; but, if it be moved beyond, each square so moved must be counted as in Rule 3.

Rule 7.

When a Player has got all his men into the Rendezvous, it being not yet full, he removes one of the outlying men from the Board, replacing it with a fresh man of his own colour ; and this ends his turn.

Rule 8.

When a Player has got all his men into the Rendezvous, it being now full, he removes the outlying man from the Board. Then he who has fewest men on the Board, or in case of equality he who has just lost a man, sets the Mark for the next Rendezvous, as in Rule 4.

Rule 9.

When a Player has only one man left, he has lost the Game.

§ 4. Hints to Players.

In playing for a "close" Rendezvous, remember that you have *two* objects in view—one to get your own men *in*, the other to keep the enemy's men *out*. A mere race for the Rendezvous is not always your best course ; much may be done by getting into the way of the enemy's men, and checking *their* advance. Do not try to block *all* his men ; *one* is generally as much as you can hope ultimately to exclude : hence it is often good play to select that man of the enemy's who is furthest from the Rendezvous and to devote to his especial benefit the services of (say) *three* of your own men, whose duty it will be to march, in close rank, in front of him, as a kind of "guard of honour," taking care to march *in* in front of him, so as to be able to announce his approach, and secure his being received with all proper respect !

It is an advantage to get *hold* of the *central* square of a "close" Rendezvous, and also of a square at that corner (or side) of it where you wish to bring in another man. As soon as the outsider has reached a square adjacent to this corner-man, he can be played in, in the following turn, by first moving the central man into some vacant Rendezvous-square, then the corner-man into the central square, and then the outsider into the corner-square.

For instance, supposing it to be a nine-square Rendezvous, and that your 5 men are A, B, C, D, E (A being in the centre), and that the enemy's 5 men

B	C	D	E
a	A	d	e
b	c		

are *a*, *b*, *c*, *d*, *e*, and that it is your turn to play ; you may win the Rendezvous by moving A into the vacant square, D

a	C	D	E
B	c	d	e
b	A		

into A's place, and E into D's. Or, if the men be arranged

thus (*c* being in the centre), you may win it by moving A into the vacant square, B into A's place, C into B's, D into C's, and E into D's.

Similarly, in playing for an " open " Rendezvous, supposing it to consist of 8 squares (here marked by asterisks), and that your 4 men are A, B, C, D, and the enemy's 5 men *a, b, c, d, e*

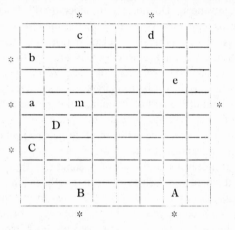

and that it is your turn to play ; you may win the Rendezvous by moving A into the vacant Rendezvous-square, B into A's place, C into B's, and D into C's.

You should also arrange your men, that are already *in* the Rendezvous, so as to make things comfortable for those of the enemy's men who are on their way towards it. For instance, if it be a 9-square Rendez- vous, and if there are four such men approaching from the East : by placing three of your men in the squares marked with asterisks, you may form an impene- trable wall across the Rendezvous, and thus provide a set of

three vacant squares to accommodate the *four* weary travellers
—a polite attention which they will not soon forget. Similarly,
if there are *two* of the enemy's men approach-
ing from the North-East : by placing three of
your men, as here indicated, you will provide
one vacant square for the two guests, who will
probably indulge in the pathetic strain, "Now
one of us must stop outside, But that one
won't be *me!* So, Tommy, make room for your Uncle !"

Should you find that the enemy is likely to get all his men
into the Rendezvous, while you still have two or three men
outside, remember that, as soon as all his men are in, he will
replace one of your outlying men with a fresh man of his own
colour ; and that he will most certainly choose for this purpose
whichever of the outlying men is nearest to the Rendezvous.
Consequently, *your* best course is to have no one of them
nearer than the others. Keep them all together, at the same
distance from the Rendezvous, so that, whichever of them he
transforms into an enemy, you can at once bar its progress
with your other outlying men.

The advice I have given, as to barring the progress of the
enemy's men rather than merely hurrying on with your own,
is also worth remembering when playing for an "open"
Rendezvous.

In carrying out the operation described in Rule 5—the
interchanging of the two sets of men—difficulties may arise,
when men have been taken off their squares, in settling *which*
squares they came from. These difficulties may lead to angry
disputes ; thence to mutual accusations of unveracity ; thence
to estrangement of friends ; and thence to family feuds, lasting
through several generations. These deplorable results may all
be avoided by observing the following simple Rule :—

Move every one of the men, which are to be interchanged,
into a corner of its square. Place a card-marker on a square

occupied by a white man (I am supposing the two colours to be " white " and " black "), and take the white man off its square.   Place this white man in the centre of a square occupied by a *black* man, and take the *black* man off its square.   Place this *black* man in the centre of a square occupied by another *white* man.   Proceed thus till all the men on the Board are in the centres of squares, and you have one black man in hand, which of course you place on the square indicated by the card-marker.

Rule 5 serves to prevent the Mark from being so set that he who sets it is quite certain to get his men in first—which certainly would rob the Game of much of its interest.   In playing for a final 3-square Rendezvous, the mere setting of the Mark would, but for this Rule, decide the Game.

Among the puzzles which I have collected for this chapter, the place of honour must be given to the following " Logical Paradox," with which Lewis Carroll was very fond of bewildering his friends during the last few years of his life.

A LOGICAL PARADOX.

" What, *nothing* to do ? " said Uncle Jim.   " Then come along with me down to Allen's.   And you can just take a turn while I get myself shaved."

" All right," said Uncle Joe.   " And the Cub had better come too, I suppose ? "

The " Cub " was *me*, as the reader will perhaps have guessed for himself.   I'm turned *fifteen*—more than three months ago ; but there's no sort of use in mentioning *that* to Uncle Joe ; he'd only say, " Go to your cubbicle, little boy ! " or, " Then I

suppose you can do cubbic equations ? " or some equally vile
pun. He asked me yesterday to give him an instance of a
Proposition in A.   And I said, " All uncles make vile puns."
And I don't think he liked it.   However, that's neither here
nor there.   I was glad enough to go.   I *do* love hearing those
uncles of mine " chop logic," as they call it ; and they're
desperate hands at it, *I* can tell you !

"That is not a logical inference from my remark," said
Uncle Jim.

" Never said it was," said Uncle Joe ; " it's a *Reductio ad
Absurdum.*"

" An *Illicit Process of the Minor !* " chuckled Uncle Jim.

That's the sort of way they always go on, whenever *I'm*
with them.   As if there was any fun in calling me a Minor !

After a bit, Uncle Jim began again, just as we came in
sight of the barber's.   " I only hope *Carr* will be at home,"
he said.   " Brown's so clumsy.   And Allen's hand has been
shaky ever since he had that fever."

" Carr's *certain* to be in," said Uncle Joe.

" I'll bet you sixpence he *isn't !* " said I.

" Keep your bets for your betters," said Uncle Joe.   " I
mean "—he hurried on, seeing by the grin on my face what a
slip he'd made—" I mean that I can *prove* it, logically.   It
isn't a matter of *chance.*"

" Prove it *logically !* " sneered Uncle Jim.   " Fire away,
then !   I defy you to do it ! "

" For the sake of argument," Uncle Joe began, " let us
assume Carr to be *out.*   And let us see what that assumption
would lead to.   I'm going to do this by *Reductio ad Absurdum.*'

" Of course you are ! " growled Uncle Jim.   " Never knew
any argument of *yours* that didn't end in some absurdity or
other ! "

" Unprovoked by your unmanly taunts," said Uncle Joe in

a lofty tone, " I proceed.   Carr being out, you will grant that, if Allen is *also* out, *Brown* must be at home ? "

" What's the good of *his* being at home ? " said Uncle Jim. " I don't want *Brown* to shave me !   He's too clumsy."

" Patience is one of those inestimable qualities——" Uncle Joe was beginning; but Uncle Jim cut him off short.

" *Argue !* " he said.   " Don't *moralise !* "

" Well, but *do* you grant it ? " Uncle Joe persisted.   " Do you grant me that, if Carr is out, it follows that if Allen is out Brown *must* be in ? "

" Of course he must," said Uncle Jim ;   " or there'd be nobody to mind the shop."

" We see, then, that the absence of Carr brings into play a certain Hypothetical, whose *protasis* is ' Allen is out,' and whose *apodosis* is Brown is in.'   And we see that, so long as Carr remains out, this Hypothetical remains in force ? "

" Well, suppose it does.   What then ? " said Uncle Jim.

" You will also grant me that the truth of a Hypothetical — I mean its *validity* as a logical *sequence*—does not in the least depend on its *protasis* being actually *true*, nor even on its being *possible*.   The Hypothetical ' If you were to run from here to London in five minutes you would surprise people,' remains true as a sequence, whether you can do it or not."

" I can't do *it*," said Uncle Jim.

" We have now to consider *another* Hypothetical.   What was that you told me yesterday about Allen ? "

" I told you," said Uncle Jim, " that ever since he had that fever he's been so nervous about going out alone, he always takes Brown with him."

" Just so," said Uncle Joe.   " Then the Hypothetical ' If Allen is out Brown is out ' is *always* in force, isn't it ? "

" I suppose so," said Uncle Jim.   (He seemed to be getting a little nervous himself now.)

" Then, if Carr is out, we have *two* Hypotheticals, ' if Allen is out Brown is *in*,' and ' if Allen is out Brown is *out*,' in force at once. And two *incompatible* Hypotheticals, mark you ! They can't *possibly* be true together ! "

" *Can't* they ? " said Uncle Jim.

" How *can* they ? " said Uncle Joe. " How *can* one and the same *protasis* prove two contradictory *apodoses*? You grant that the two *apodoses*, ' Brown is *in* ' and ' Brown is *out*,' *are* contradictory, I suppose ? "

" Yes, I grant *that*," said Uncle Jim.

" Then I may sum up," said Uncle Jim. " If Carr is out, these two Hypotheticals are true together. And we know that they *cannot* be true together. Which is absurd. Therefore Carr *cannot* be out. There's a nice *Reductio ad Absurdum* for you ! "

Uncle Jim looked thoroughly puzzled ; but after a bit he plucked up courage, and began again. " I don't feel at all clear about that *incompatibility*. Why shouldn't those two Hypotheticals be true together ? It seems to me that would simply prove ' *Allen* is in.' Of course it's clear that the *apodoses* of those two Hypotheticals are incompatible—' Brown is in ' and ' Brown is out.' But why shouldn't we put it like this ? If Allen is out Brown is *out*. If Carr and Allen are *both* out, Brown is *in*. Which is absurd. Therefore Carr and Allen can't be *both* of them out. But, so long as Allen is *in*, I don't see what's to hinder Carr from going out."

" My dear, but most illogical brother ! " said Uncle Joe. (Whenever Uncle Joe begins to " dear " you, you may make pretty sure he's got you in a cleft stick !) " Don't you see that you are wrongly dividing the *protasis* and the *apodosis* of that Hypothetical ? Its *protasis* is simply ' Carr is out '; and its *apodosis* is a sort of sub-Hypothetical, ' If Allen is out, Brown is *in*." And a most absurd apodosis it is, being hope-lessly incompatible with that other Hypothetical, that we know *is always* true, ' If Allen is out, Brown is *out*.' And it's simply the assumption 'Carr is out' that has caused this absurdity.   So there's only *one* possible conclusion—*Carr is in !* "

How long this argument *might* have lasted I haven't the least idea.   I believe *either* of them could argue for six hours at a stretch.   But just at this moment we arrived at the barber's shop ; and, on going inside, we found—

The following diagram, which should be copied

.64·65

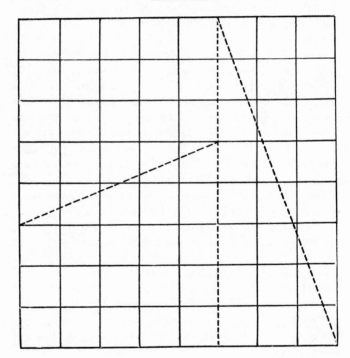

upon a square piece of paper, and then cut out along the dotted lines, represents another favourite puzzle of Mr. Dodgson's. When the square has been divided into its four sections it will be found that they may not only be arranged as a square, but also as an oblong. In the first case the figure appears to be made up of sixty-four small squares, in the second of sixty-five, and the puzzle is to account for this discrepancy.

The first of the three puzzles which conclude this chapter bears a strong resemblance to the well-known old difficulty about the safe conveying of " the fox, and the goose, and the bag of corn," which was also a great favourite of Lewis Carroll's when he had to amuse some of his smaller " child-friends."

1.

Four gentlemen and their wives wanted to cross the river in a boat that would not hold more than two at a time.

The conditions were, that no gentleman must leave his wife on the bank unless with only women or by herself, and also that some one must always bring the boat back.

How did they do it?

2.

A customer bought goods in a shop to the amount of 7/3. The only money he had was a half-sovereign, a florin, and a sixpence : so he wanted change. The shopman only had a

crown, a shilling, and a penny. But a friend happened to
come in, who had a double-florin, a half-crown, a fourpenny-
bit, and a threepenny-bit.

Could they manage it ?

3.

A captive Queen and her son and daughter were shut up in
the top room of a very high tower.   Outside their window
was a pulley with a rope round it, and a basket fastened at
each end of the rope of equal weight.   They managed to
escape with the help of this and a weight they found in the
room, quite safely.   It would have been dangerous for any
of them to come down if they weighed more than 15 lbs.
more than the contents of the lower basket, for they would do
so too quick, and they also managed not to weigh less either.

The one basket coming down would naturally of course
draw the other up.

How did they do it?

The Queen weighed 195 lbs., daughter 165, son 90, and
the weight 75.

This is an addition to the puzzle—

The Queen had with her in the room, besides her son and
daughter and the weight, a pig weighing 60 lbs., a dog 45 lbs.,
and a cat 30.   These have to be brought down safely, too,
with the same restriction.   The weight can come down any
way, of course.

The additional puzzle consists in this—there must be
some one at each end to put the animals into and out of
the baskets.

DEAN LIDDELL'S HOUSE AND DAUGHTERS.
Morris L. Parrish Collection, Princeton University Library

MICHAEL HICKS-BEACH.
Morris L. Parrish Collection, Princeton University Library

CHAPTER VII

MISCELLANEA CARROLLIANA

UNDER the above head I have gathered together several papers of Lewis Carroll's, both grave and gay, and also some reminiscences of him from various sources. I take first a journal which he wrote for Miss Isa Bowman to commemorate a visit which she paid him at Oxford in 1888:

ISA'S VISIT TO OXFORD, 1888.

CHAPTER I.

ON Wednesday, the Eleventh of July, Isa happened to meet a friend at Paddington Station at half-past ten. She can't remember his name, but she says he was an old old old gentleman, and he had invited her, she thinks, to go with him somewhere or other, she can't remember where.

CHAPTER II.

THE first thing they did, after calling at a shop, was to go to the Panorama of the " Falls of Niagara." Isa thought it very wonderful. You seemed to be on the top of a tower, with miles and miles of country all round you. The things in front were real, and somehow they joined into the picture behind, so that you couldn't tell where the real things ended and the picture began. Near the foot of the Falls, there was a steampacket crossing the river, which showed what a tremendous height the Falls must be, it looked so tiny. In the road in front were two men and a dog, standing looking the other way. They may have been wooden figures, or part of the picture, there was no knowing which. The man, who stood next to Isa, said to another man, " That dog looked round just now. Now see, I'll whistle to him, and make him look round again !" and he began whistling : and Isa almost expected, it looked so exactly like a real dog, that it would turn its head to see who was calling it.

After that Isa and her friend (the Aged Aged man) went to the house of a Mr. Dymes—Mrs. Dymes gave them some dinner, and two of her children, called Helen and Maud, went with them to Terry's Theatre, to see the play of " Little Lord Fauntleroy." Little Vera Beringer was the little Lord Fauntleroy. Isa would have liked to play the part, but the Manager at the theatre did not allow her, as she did not know the words, which would have made it go off badly. Isa liked the whole play very much : the passionate old Earl, and the gentle Mother of the little boy, and the droll " Mr. Hobbs " and all of them.

Then they all went off by the Metropolitan Railway, and the Miss Dymeses got out at their station, and Isa and the A.A.M. went on to Oxford. A kind old lady, called Mrs. Symonds, had invited Isa to come and sleep at her house : and she was soon fast asleep, and dreaming that she and little Lord Fauntleroy were going in a steamer down the Falls of Niagara, and whistling to a dog, who was in such a hurry to go up the Falls that he wouldn't attend to them.

CHAPTER III.

THE next morning Isa set off, almost before she was awake, with the A.A.M. to pay a visit to a little college, called "Christ Church." You go under a magnificent tower, called "Tom Tower," nearly four feet high (so that Isa had hardly to stoop at all, to go under it) and into the Great Quadrangle (which very vulgar people call "Tom Quad"). You should always be polite, even when speaking to a Quadrangle : it might seem not to take any notice, but it doesn't like being called names. On their way to Christ Church they saw a tall monument, like the spire of a church, called the "Martyrs' Memorial," put up in memory of three Bishops, Cranmer, Ridley and Latimer, who were burned in the reign of Queen Mary, because they would not be Roman Catholics. Christ Church was built in 1546.

They had breakfast at Ch. Ch. in the rooms of the A.A.M., and then Isa learned how to print with the "Type-Writer," and printed several beautiful volumes of poetry, all of her own invention. By this time it was 1 o'clock, so Isa paid a visit to the Kitchen, to make sure that the chicken for her dinner was being properly roasted. The Kitchen is about the oldest part of the College, so was built about 1546. It has a fire-grate large enough to roast forty legs of mutton at once.

Then they saw the Dining Hall, in which the A.A.M. has dined several times (about 8,000 times, perhaps). After dinner, they went, through the quadrangle of the Bodleian Library, into Broad Street, and as a band was just going by, of course they followed it.   (Isa likes Bands better than anything in the world, except Lands, and walking on Sands, and wringing her Hands.)   The Band led them into the gardens of Wadham College (built in 1613), where there was a school-treat going on.   The treat was, first marching twice round the garden— then having a photograph done of them, all in a row—then a *promise* of "Punch and Judy," which wouldn't be ready for 20 minutes, so Isa and Co. wouldn't wait, but went back to Ch. Ch., and saw the "Broad Walk."   In the evening they played at "Reversi," till Isa had lost the small remainder of her temper.   Then she went to bed, and dreamed she was Judy, and was beating Punch with a stick of barley-sugar.

CHAPTER IV

ON Friday morning (after taking her medicine very amiably), went with the A.A.M. (who *would* go with her, though she told him over and over she would rather be alone) to the gardens of Worcester College (built in 1714), where they didn't see the swans (who ought to have been on the lake), nor the hippopotamus, who ought not to have been walking about among the flowers, gathering honey like a busy bee.

After breakfast Isa helped the A.A.M. to pack his luggage, because he thought he would go away, he didn't know where, some day, he didn't know when—so she put a lot of things, she didn't know what, into boxes, she didn't know which.

After dinner they went to St. John's College (built in 1555), and admired the large lawn, where more than 150 ladies, dressed in robes of gold and silver, were not walking about.

Then they saw the Chapel of Keble College (built in 1870) and then the New Museum, where Isa quite lost her heart to a charming stuffed Gorilla, that smiled on her from a glass case. The Museum was finished in 1860. The most curious thing they saw there was a "Walking Leaf," a kind of insect that looks exactly like a withered leaf.

Then they went to New College (built in 1386), and saw, close to the entrance, a " skew " arch (going slantwise through the wall), one of the first ever built in England. After seeing the gardens, they returned to Ch. Ch. (Parts of the old City walls run round the gardens of New College: and you may still see some of the old narrow slits, through which the defenders could shoot arrows at the attacking army, who could hardly succeed in shooting through them from the outside.)

They had tea with Mrs. Paget, wife of Dr. Paget, one of the Canons of Ch. Ch. Then after a sorrowful evening, Isa went to bed, and dreamed she was buzzing about among the flowers, with the dear Gorilla : but there wasn't any honey in them— only slices of bread-and-butter, and multiplication-tables.

CHAPTER V.

ON Saturday Isa had a Music Lesson, and learned to play on an American Orguinette. It is not a *very* difficult instrument to play, as you have only to turn a handle round and round : so she did it nicely. You put a long piece of paper in, and it goes through the machine, and the holes in the paper make different notes play. They put one in wrong end first, and had a tune backwards, and soon found themselves in the day before yesterday. So they dared not go on, for fear of making Isa so young she would not be able to talk. The A.A.M. does not like visitors who only howl, and get red in the face, from morning to night.

In the afternoon they went round Ch. Ch. meadow, and saw

the Barges belonging to the Colleges, and some pretty views of Magdalen Tower through the trees.

Then they went through the "Botanical Gardens," built in the year—no, by the bye, they never were built at all. And then to Magdalen College. At the top of the wall in one corner they saw a very large jolly face, carved in stone, with a broad grin, and a little man at the side, helping him to laugh by pulling up the corner of his mouth for him. Isa thought that, the next time she wants to laugh, she will get Nellie and Maggie to help her. With two people to pull up the corners of your mouth for you, it is as easy to laugh as can be!

They went into Magdalen Meadow, which has a pretty walk all round it, arched over with trees ; and there they met a lady "from Amurrica," as she told them, who wanted to know the way to "Addison's Walk," and particularly wanted to know if there would be "any danger" in going there. They told her the way, and that *most* of the lions and tigers and buffaloes, round the meadow, were quite gentle and hardly ever killed people : so she set off, pale and trembling, and they saw her no more : only they heard her screams in the distance, so they guessed what had happened to her.

Then they rode in a tram-car to another part of Oxford, and called on a lady called Mrs. Jeune, and her little grand-daughter, called "Noel," because she was born on Christmas Day ("Noel" is the French name for "Christmas"). And there they had so much Tea that at last Isa nearly turned into "Teaser."

Then they went home, down a little narrow street, where there was a little dog standing fixed in the middle of the street, as if its feet were glued to the ground : they asked it how long it meant to stand there, and it said (as well as it could) "till the week after next."

Then Isa went to bed, and dreamed she was going round Magdalen Meadow, with the "Amurrican" lady, and there

"ALICE IN BUMBLELAND."

(*From a drawing by Sir John Tenniel. Reproduced here by kind permission of the Proprietors of "Punch."*)

was a buffalo sitting at the top of every tree, handing her cups
of tea as she went underneath: but they all held the cups
upside down, so that the tea poured all over her head and
ran down her face.

CHAPTER VI.

ON Sunday morning they went to St. Mary's Church, in
High Street.   In coming home, down the street next to the
one where they had found a fixed dog, they found a fixed cat
—a poor little kitten, that had put out its head through the
bars of the cellar window, and couldn't get back again.   They
rang the bell at the next door, but the maid said the cellar
wasn't in that house, and before they could get to the right
door the cat had unfixed its head—either from its neck or
from the bars—and had gone inside.   Isa thought the animals
in this city have a curious way of fixing themselves up and
down the place, as if they were hat pegs.

They then went back to Ch. Ch., and looked at a lot of
dresses, which the A.A.M. kept in a cupboard, to dress up
children in, when they came to be photographed.   Some of
the dresses had been used in Pantomimes at Drury Lane:
some were rags, to dress up beggar-children in: some had
been very magnificent once, but were getting quite old and
shabby.   Talking of old dresses, there is one College in Oxford so old that it is not known for certain when it was built.
The people, who live there, say it was built more than 1,000
years ago: and, when they say this, the people who live in the
other Colleges never contradict them, but listen most respectfully—only they wink a little with one eye, as if they didn't
quite believe it.

The same day, Isa saw a curious book of pictures of
ghosts.   If you look hard at one for a minute, and then look

at the ceiling, you see another ghost there—only, when you have a black one in the book, it is a *white* one on the ceiling —when it is green in the book, it is *pink* on the ceiling.

In the middle of the day, as usual, Isa had her dinner, but this time it was grander than usual. There was a dish of " Meringues " (this is pronounced " Marangs "), which Isa thought so good that she would have liked to live on them all the rest of her life.

They took a little walk in the afternoon, and in the middle of Broad Street they saw a cross buried in the ground, very near the place where the Martyrs were buried. Then they went into the gardens of Trinity College (built in 1554) to see the " Lime Walk," a pretty little avenue of lime-trees. The great iron " gates " at the end of the garden are not real gates, but all done in one piece, and they couldn't open them, even if you knocked all day. Isa thought them a miserable sham.

Then they went into the " Parks " (this word doesn't mean " parks of grass, with trees and deer," but " parks " of guns ; that is, great rows of cannons, which stood there when King Charles the First was in Oxford, and Oliver Cromwell was fighting against him.

They saw " Mansfield College," a new College just begun to be built, with such tremendously narrow windows that Isa was afraid the young gentlemen who come there will not be able to see to learn their lessons, and will go away from Oxford just as wise as they came.

They then went to the evening service at New College, and heard some beautiful singing and organ-playing. Then back to Ch. Ch., in pouring rain. Isa tried to count the drops ; but, when she had counted four millions, three hundred and seventy-eight thousand, two hundred and forty-seven, she got tired of counting, and left off.

After dinner, Isa got somebody or other (she is not sure

We lived beneath the mat
Warm and snug and fat
But one woe, & that
Was the cat!
To our joys
a clog, In
our eyes a
fog, On our
hearts a log
Was the dog!
When the
cat's away,
Then
the mice
will
play,
But, alas!
one day, (So they say)
Came the dog and
cat, Hunting
for a
rat,
Crushed
the mice
all flat,
Each
one
as
he
sat
Underneath the mat, Warm & snug & fat—Think of that!

"THE MOUSE'S TAIL."

(*From " Alice's Adventures Underground."*)

who it was) to finish this story for her. Then she went to bed, and dreamed she was fixed in the middle of Oxford, with her feet fast to the ground, and her head between the bars of a cellar window, in a sort of final tableau. Then she dreamed the curtain came down, and the people all called out "encore!" But she cried out, "Oh, not again! It would bee *too* dreadful to have my visit all over again!" But, on second thoughts, she smiled in her sleep, and said, "Well, do you know, after all I think I wouldn't mind so very *much* if I *did* have it all over again!"

LEWIS CARROLL.

The Legend of "Scotland" was written by Lewis Carroll for the daughters of Archbishop Longley, while he was, as Bishop of Durham, living at Auckland Castle, and between the years 1856–1860. The legend was suggested by some markings upon the walls of a cellar in a part of the Castle which, from its remoteness and chilliness, was, and perhaps still is, called "Scotland."

***

THE LEGEND OF "SCOTLAND."

BEING a true and terrible report touching the rooms of Auckland Castell, called Scotland, and of the things there endured by Matthew Dixon, Chaffer, and of a certain Ladye, called Gaunless of some, there apparent, and how that none durst in these days sleep therein, (belike through fear,) all which things fell out in ye days of Bishop Bec, of chearfull memorie, and were writ down by mee in the Yeere One

Thousand Three Hundred and Twenty Five, in the Month February, on a certayn Tuesday and other days.

EDGAR CUTHWELLÎS.

Now the said Matthew Dixon, having fetched wares unto that place, my Loords commended the same, and bade that hee should be entertained for that night, (which in sooth hee was, supping with a grete Appetite,) and sleep in a certayn roome of that apartment now called Scotland—From whence at Midnight hee rushed forth with so grete a Screem, as awaked all men, and hastily running into those Passages, and meeting him so screeming, hee presentlie faynted away.

Whereon they hadde hym into my Loorde's parlour, and with much ado set hym on a Chaire, wherefrom hee three several times slipt even to the grounde, to the grete admiration of all men.

But being stayed with divers Strong Liquors, (and, chiefest, wyth Gin,) hee after a whyle gave foorth in a lamentable tone these following particulars, all which were presentlie sworn to by nine painful and stout farmers, who lived hard by, which witness I will heare orderlie set downe.

Witness of Matthew Dixon, Chaffer, being in my right minde, and more than Fortie Yeeres of Age, though sore affrighted by reason of Sightes and Sounds in This Castell endured by mee, as touching the Vision of Scotland, and the Ghosts, all two of them, therein contayned, and of A certayn straunge Ladye, and of the lamentable thyngs by her uttered, with other sad tunes and songs, by her and by other Ghosts devised, and of the coldness and shakyng of my Bones, (through soe grete feer,) and of other things very pleasant to knowe, cheefly of a Picture hereafter suddenlie to bee taken, and of what shall befall thereon, (as trulie foreshowne by

Ghosts,) and of Darkness, with other things more terrible than Woordes, and of that which Men call Chimera.

Matthew Dixon, Chaffer, deposeth : " that hee, having supped well over Night on a Green Goose, a Pasty, and other Condiments of the Bishop's grete bountie provided, (looking, as hee spake, at my Loorde, and essaying toe pull offe hys hatte untoe hym, but missed soe doing, for that hee hadde yt not on hys hedde,) soe went untoe hys bedde, where of a long tyme hee was exercysed with sharp and horrible Dreems. That hee saw yn hys Dreem a yong Ladye, habited, (not as yt seemed) yn a Gaun, but yn a certayn sorte of Wrapper, per-chance a Wrap-Rascal." (Hereon a Mayde of the House affirmed that noe Ladye woold weare such a thing, and hee answered, " I stand corrected," and indeed rose from hys chaire, yet fayled to stand.)

Witness continued : " that ye sayde Ladye waved toe and froe a Grete Torche, whereat a thin Voyce shreeked ' Gaun-less ! Gaunless ! ' and Shee standyng yn the midst of the floor, a grete Chaunge befell her, her Countenance waxing ever more and more Aged, and her Hayr grayer, shee all that tyme saying yn a most sad Voyce, ' Gaunless, now, as Ladyes bee : yet yn yeeres toe come they shall not lacke for Gauns.' At whych her Wrapper seemed slowlie toe melte, chaunging into a gaun of sylk, which puckered up and down, yea, and flounced itself out not a lyttle : " (at thys mye Loorde, waxing impatient, smote hym roundlie onne the hedde, bydding hym finish hys tale anon.)

Witness continued : " that the sayd Gaun thenne chaunged ytself into divers fashyons whych shall hereafter bee, loopyng ytself uppe yn thys place and yn that, soe gyving toe View ane pettycote of a most fiery hue, even Crimson toe looke upon, at whych dismal and blode-thirstie sight hee both groned and wepte. That at the laste the shyrt swelled unto a Vastness beyond Man's power toe tell ayded, (as hee judged,) bye Hoops, Cartwheels, Balloons, and the lyke, bearing yt uppe within. That yt fylled alle that Chamber, crushing hym flat untoe hys bedde, tylle such tyme as she appeered toe depart, fryzzling hys Hayre with her Torche as she went.

"That hee, awakyng from such Dreems, herd thereon a Rush, and saw a Light." (Hereon a Mayde interrupted hym, crying out that there was yndeed a Rush-Light burning yn that same room, and woulde have sayde more, but that my Loorde checkt her, and sharplie bade her stow that, meening thereby, that she shoulde holde her peece.)

Witness continued : " that being muche affrited thereat, whereby hys Bones were, (as hee sayde,) all of a dramble, hee essayed to leep from hys bedde, and soe quit. Yet tarried hee some whyle, not, as might bee thought from being stout of Harte, but rather of Bodye ; whych tyme she chaunted snatches of old lays, as Maister Wil Shakespeare hath yt."

Hereon my Loorde questioned what lays, byddyng hym syng the same, and saying hee knew but of two lays : " 'Twas yn Trafalgar's bay wee saw the Frenchmen lay," and " There wee lay all that day yn the Bay of Biscay—O," whych hee forthwyth hummed aloud, yet out of tune, at whych some smyled.

Witness continued : " that hee perchaunce coulde chaunt the sayde lays wyth Music, but unaccompanied hee durst not." On thys they hadde hym to the Schoolroom, where was a Musical Instrument, called a Paean-o-Forty, (meening that yt hadde forty Notes, and was a Paean or Triumph of Art,) whereon two yong Ladyes, Nieces of my Loorde, that abode there, (lerning, as they deemed, Lessons ; but, I wot, idlynge not a lyttle,) did wyth much thumpyng playe certyn Music wyth hys synging, as best they mighte, seeing that the Tunes were such as noe Man had herde before.

> " Lorenzo dwelt at Heighington,
>   (Hys cote was made of Dimity,)

> Least-ways yf not exactly there,
>> Yet yn yt's close proximity.
> Hee called on mee—hee stayed to tee—
>> Yet not a word hee ut-tered,
> Untyl I sayd, ' D'ye lyke your bread
> Dry ?' and hee answered ' But-tered.' "

(Chorus whereyn all present joyned with fervor).
> " Noodle dumb
>> Has a noodle-head,
> I hate such noodles, *I* do."

Witness continued : "that shee then appeered unto hym habited yn the same loose Wrapper, whereyn hee first saw her yn hys Dreem, and yn a stayd and piercing tone gave forth her History as followeth."

THE LADYE'S HISTORY.

"On a dewie autum evening, mighte have been seen, pacing yn the grounds harde by Aucklande Castell, a yong Ladye of a stiff and perky manner, yet not ill to look on, nay, one mighte saye, faire to a degree, save that haply that hadde been un-true.

"That yong Ladye, O miserable Man, was I " (whereon I demanded on what score shee held mee miserable, and shee replied, yt mattered not). " I plumed myself yn those tymes on my exceeding not soe much beauty as loftinesse of Figure, and gretely desired that some Painter might paint my picture : but they ever were too high, not yn skyll I trow, byt yn charges." (At thys I most humbly enquired at what charge the then Painters wrought, but shee loftily affirmed that money-matters were vulgar and that shee knew not, no, nor cared.)

"Now yt chaunced that a certyn Artist, hight Lorenzo, came toe that Quarter, having wyth hym a merveillous machine called by men a Chimera (that ys, a fabulous and wholly incredible thing ;) where wyth hee took manie pictures, each yn a single stroke of Tyme, whiles that a Man might name 'John, the son of Robin' (I asked her, what might a stroke of Tyme bee, but shee, frowning, answered not).

"He yt was that undertook my Picture : yn which I mainly required one thyng, that yt shoulde bee at full-length, for yn none other way mighte my Loftiness bee trulie set forth. Nevertheless, though hee took manie Pictures, yet all fayled yn thys : for some, beginning at the Hedde, reeched not toe the Feet ; others, takyng yn the Feet, yet left out the Hedde ; whereof the former were a grief unto myself, and the latter a Laughing-Stocke unto others.

"At these thyngs I justly fumed, having at the first been frendly unto hym (though yn sooth hee was dull), and oft smote hym gretely on the Eares, rending from hys Hedde certyn Locks, whereat crying out hee was wont toe saye that I made hys lyfe a burden untoe hym, whych thyng I not so much doubted as highlie rejoyced yn.

"At the last hee counselled thys, that a Picture shoulde bee made, showing so much skyrt as mighte reesonably bee gotte yn, and a Notice set below toe thys effect : 'Item, two yards and a Half Ditto, and then the Feet.' But thys no Whit contented mee, and thereon I shut hym ynto the Cellar, where hee remaned three Weeks, growing dayly thinner and thinner, till at the last hee floted up and downe like a Feather.

"Now yt fell at thys tyme, as I questioned hym on a certyn Day, yf hee woulde nowe take mee at full-length, and hee replying untoe mee, yn a little moning Voyce, lyke a Gnat, one chaunced to open the Door : whereat the Draft bore hym uppe ynto a Cracke of the Cieling, and I remaned awaytyng hym, holding uppe my Torche, until such tyme as I also faded ynto a Ghost, yet stickyng untoe the Wall."

Then did my Loorde and the Companie haste down ynto the Cellar, for to see thys straunge sight, to whych place when

they came, my Loorde bravely drew hys sword, loudly crying
" Death ! " (though to whom or what he explained not) ; then
some went yn, but the more part hung back, urging on those
yn front, not soe largely bye example, as Words of cheer : yet
at last all entered, my Loorde last.

Then they removed from the wall the Casks and other stuff,
and founde the sayd Ghost, dredful toe relate, yet extant on
the Wall, at which horrid sight such screems were raysed as yn
these days are seldom or never herde : some faynted, others
bye large drafts of Beer saved themselves from that Extremity,
yet were they scarcely alive for Feer.

Then dyd the Ladye speak unto them yn suchwise :—

> " Here I bee, and here I byde,
> Till such tyme as yt betyde
> That a Ladye of thys place,
> Lyke to mee yn name and face,
> (Though my name bee never known,
> My initials shall bee shown,)
> Shall be fotograffed aright—
> Hedde and Feet bee both yn sight—
> Then my face shall disappeer,
> Nor agayn affrite you heer."

Then sayd Matthew Dixon unto her, "Wherefore holdest
thou uppe that Torche ? " to whych shee answered, " Candles
Gyve Light " : but none understood her.

After thys a thyn Voyce sang from overhedde :—

> " Yn the Auckland Castell cellar,
> Long, long ago,
> I was shut—a brisk yong feller—
> Woe, woe, ah woe !
> To take her at full-lengthe
> I never hadde the strengthe
> Tempore (and soe I tell her,)
> Praeterito !

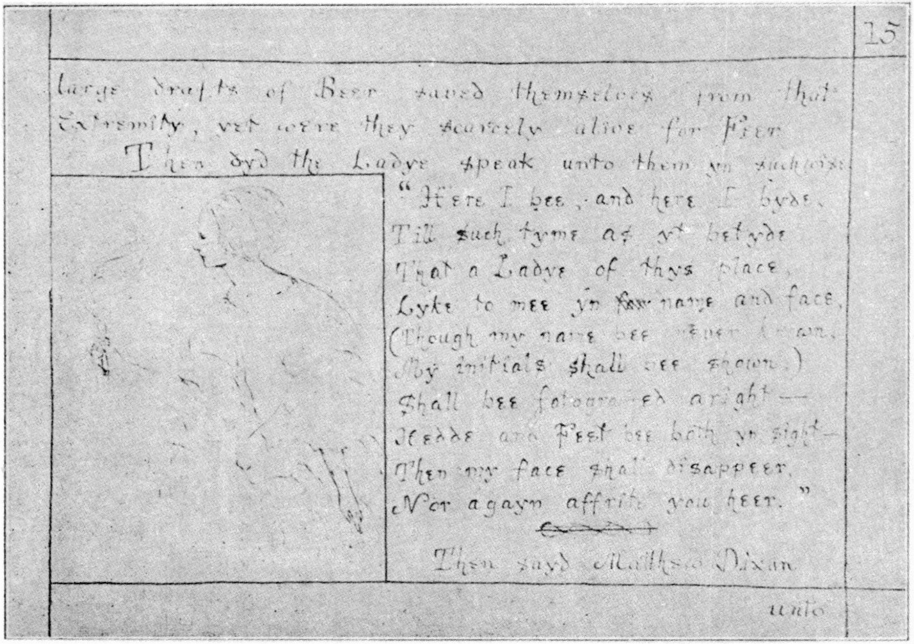

A PAGE FROM THE ORIGINAL MS. OF "SCOTLAND."

(Yn thys Chorus they durst none joyn, seeing that Latyn was untoe them a Tongue unknown.)

> "She was hard—oh, she was cruel—
> Long, long ago,
> Starved mee here—not even gruel—
> No, believe mee, no !—
> Frae Scotland could I flee,
> I'd gie my last bawbee,—
> Arrah, bhoys, fair play's a jhewel,
> Lave me, darlints, goe !"

Then my Loorde, putting bye hys Sworde, (whych was layd up thereafter, yn memory of soe grete Bravery,) bade hys Butler fetch hym presentlie a Vessel of Beer, whych when yt was broughte at hys nod, (nor, as hee merrily sayd, hys "nod, and Bec, and wreathed symle,") hee drank hugelie thereof: "for why?" quoth hee, "surely a Bec ys no longer a Bec, when yt ys Dry."

The serious aspect of Lewis Carroll's character has not received sufficient attention at the hands of most of those who have written about him since his death. Even for the children, perhaps *especially* for the children, he wrote and spoke much on the deeper side of life. I have been privileged to read many letters of his which partook of this character, but have found in them nothing more touching and beautiful than the little sermon which follows, and which he delivered to a congregation of children. The report, an excellent one to all appearance, is extracted from the November, 1897, number of the *Parish Magazine* of the Church of St. Mary Magdalen, St. Leonard's-on-Sea.

A little girl named Margaret went to a Harvest Festival Service one Sunday. The Church was beautiful with flowers and fruit and sweet music of thanksgiving. And the preacher spoke of God's great love and goodness in giving us everything that we possess, and that we must try to show our thankfulness to Him by offering of our best to Him in return. Some of us — and especially the children — perhaps thought they had nothing to give, or worthy to offer, to God, but the preacher said that God would accept even a little deed of love, or a simple act of kindness to one of His creatures, and that children, especially, could do these if they would try.

When the service was over and the people had gone away, little Margaret lingered in the churchyard thinking about what the preacher had said, and a lark started up from her feet and sang soaring into the blue sky with such gladness that Margaret said to herself, " Ah, he is trying to thank God as well as he can—how much I wish there were something that such a little girl as I could do too ! "

She sat down on the grass in the sunshine to think, and presently she noticed a rose-bush growing near, and that the roses were hanging their heads, quite withered in the sun for want of water. So she ran to the brook, and making a cup of her hands dipped them into the water and ran and threw the water on the roses. She did so again and again, and the roses revived.

Little Margaret then walked on till she passed a cottage, where a baby was sitting on the doorstep and crying sadly because his toy was broken. It was a paper windmill, and the sails had become all crumpled up and would not go round any more.   Margaret took the toy from the baby and straightened out the sails, and a wind came by and turned them round merrily, so that the baby stretched out his hands and laughed for joy.

Then little Margaret thought she must go home, but as she passed the brook again she saw a little brown bird struggling in the water.   He had fallen in and was being drowned, and growing weaker in his struggles.   So Margaret caught hold of a bough, and stretching as far as she could, with her other hand she lifted the little bird out of the water and laid him safely on the bank.

And now she began to feel very tired, and at last reached her home.   She climbed up to her room, and lay down on her little bed, very white and still, and closed her eyes.   And then she said to herself, " I think this must be dying—yes, I am dying—and soon I shall be dead."   And her friends came in and said, " Ah, she is dying, poor little Margaret ! "

But a rose that was growing outside by the garden path heard it, and began to grow, and climbed and grew till it reached the window, and crept in through the window into the room, and crept all round the walls and little bed till there were wreaths of lovely roses filling the room with their sweetness.   And the roses bent over Margaret's little pale face till her cheeks began to take a faint colour too.   And just then a soft wind came blowing in at the window and fanned her face, and a little brown bird outside began to sing so prettily, that Margaret smiled, and opened her eyes and . . . well, she was still sitting on the grass outside the Church, in the soft sunshine—for it was a dream !

I read this story in a book, and put it by to tell you, dear children, this afternoon ; but now I will tell you three stories of love and kindness.   For—

> " He prayeth well, who loveth well
> Both man and bird and beast."

Some forty years ago there was a great singer, named Jenny Lind, and her voice and her singing were so beautiful that people who heard her felt as if they were listening to an angel. And they would go in crowds, and pay any money, to hear her sing.

On one occasion when she was singing at Manchester, she was caught by the rain during her morning walk and she took shelter in a poor little cottage, where a poor old woman lived alone. Jenny Lind talked kindly to her at once, and the poor old woman (of course not knowing who she was) told her about the wonderful Singer, who, "she was told was going to sing that afternoon," and how everybody was " mad " to hear her, and how very very much she wished that she could hear her too. But that of course was impossible "for a poor old body like me!" Then Jenny Lind told the old woman that she was the Singer, and said she, "and I will sing to you." So then and there, in that poor little cottage, the great Singer sang three or four of her sweetest songs, and gave the poor old woman the desire of her heart.

Again—a man walking along a country lane heard such a fluttering and chirping in the hedge that he stopped to look what it could be; and he saw that a young bird had fallen out of its nest, and its wings having caught on a thorn, it was hanging helpless. The mother bird was close to it fluttering and crying with all her might, but powerless to release her little one. She did not move as the man gently lifted the young bird and replaced it in the nest, but then instantly hopped on to the nest herself, and spread her wings over her little ones without a trace of fear, but in perfect confidence in the person who had come to her aid.

And now one more true tale, and this of a child's kindness to one of God's creatures. You will, I think, all have heard of Florence Nightingale. Hers is a name to make all English hearts beat warm as long as they exist;—one of England's noblest women, for she was the first who thought of going to nurse our poor wounded soldiers on the battle-field.

From her childhood Florence Nightingale was always wanting to help and heal those in pain, and her first patient was a dog ! She was but a child when one day she met a shepherd whom she knew, and he was in great distress because his faithful old dog, that had served him for so many years, was near his end. Some cruel boys—or I would rather say, thoughtless boys—had stoned the poor old dog, and he was so much hurt that he had only just been able to drag himself home to die ! He was well-nigh worn out, but " Now he's done for, and I must do away with him," said the shepherd, as he led the child to the cottage to show her the dog, and then he went sadly away to get the means of putting him out of his misery.

Florence Nightingale sat down beside the poor suffering creature, her kind heart full of pity. Presently she saw some one pass the door who she knew understood all about animals, and calling him in, she showed him the dog. After examining him, her friend said, " Well, he's very bad, but there are no bones broken ; all you can do is to wring out some cloths in hot water and lay them on the wounds, and keep on doing that for a long time." And the child set to work at once, lighted a fire, boiled the water, and persevered in her work for many hours, and to her joy the old dog began to get better and better. When the shepherd came home, Florence Nightingale said to him, " Call him, oh ! do call him ; " and so he called the old dog, who got up and greeted his master.

> " He prayeth best, who loveth best
>   All things both great and small ;
>   For the dear God who loveth us,
>   He made and loveth all."

And now, dear children, I want you to promise me that

you will each one try, every day, to do some loving act of kindness for others. Perhaps you have never really tried before; will you begin to-day—the beginning of a new week? Last week is gone for ever; this week will be quite different. As you rub out the sums on your slate that have not come right, and begin all over again, so leave behind the disobedience, or selfishness, or ill-temper of last week, and begin quite fresh to try your very best, every day, to do what you can towards fulfilling God's law of love.

Among the books which death prevented Lewis Carroll from completing, the one on which his heart was most set was a collection of essays on religious difficulties, for he felt that, as a clergyman, to associate his name with such a work would be more fitting than that he should only be known as a writer of humorous and scientific books. However, it was not to be so; he only lived long enough to finish one of the several papers of which the volume was to consist; the subject—Eternal Punishment—was one on which he felt very deeply, and his method of treating it is entirely his own. In a few pages he puts the whole matter before one, clearly, concisely and logically, pointing out the fallacies which underlie some of the common ways of evading the difficulty, but leaving the necessary conclusion for the reader to arrive at by himself.

"ETERNAL PUNISHMENT."

The most common form of the difficulty, felt in regard to this doctrine, may be thus expressed :—

" I believe that God is perfectly good. Yet I seem compelled to believe that He will inflict Eternal Punishment on certain human beings, in circumstances which would make it, according to the voice of my conscience, unjust, and therefore wrong."

This difficulty, when stated in logical form, will be found to arise from the existence of *three* incompatible Propositions, each of which has, apparently, a strong claim for our assent. They are as follows :—

I. God is perfectly good.

II. To inflict Eternal Punishment on certain human beings, and in certain circumstances, would be wrong.

III. God is capable of acting thus.

One mode of escape from this difficulty is, no doubt, to let the whole subject alone. But to many such a position is a cause of distress ; they feel that one of these three Propositions *must* be false ; and yet to regard any one of them as false plunges them into difficulties and bewilderment.

The first thing to be done is to settle, as clearly as possible, what we *mean* by each of these Propositions, and then to settle, if possible, *which* two of the three rest, in our minds, on the deepest and firmest foundations, and thus to discover *which* one, of the three, must perforce be abandoned.

First, then, let us settle, as clearly as possible, what we *mean* by each of these Propositions.

I.

God is perfectly good.

As to the meaning of this word " good," I assume that the Reader accepts, as an Axiom antecedent to any of these three Propositions, the Proposition that the ideas of Right and Wrong rest on eternal and self-existent principles, and not on the arbitrary will of any being whatever. I assume that he accepts the Proposition that God wills a thing because it is *right*, and *not* that a thing is right because God wills it. Any Reader, of whom these assumptions are not true, can feel no difficulty in abandoning Proposition II., and saying, "If God inflicts it, it will be *right*." He, therefore, is *not* one of those for whom I am now writing.

I assume, then, that this Proposition means that God always acts in accordance with the eternal principle of Right, and that He is, therefore, perfectly good.

II.

To inflict " Eternal Punishment," on certain human beings and in certain circumstances, would be wrong.

The word "Punishment" I assume to mean, here, "suffering inflicted on a human being who has sinned, and *because* he has sinned." I use the word "suffering," rather than "pain," because the latter word is so often understood as implying *physical* pain only, whereas *mental* pain might *also* serve as punishment.

Hence we may at once simplify this inquiry by excluding from our consideration, the case of suffering inflicted where the sin of the creature is *not* a necessary cause. Taking "sin" to mean (as already defined) a "conscious and *voluntary*" act, so that, if the act be *involuntary*, it ceases to be sin, we may set aside the Calvinistic theory, which contemplates the infliction of suffering on creatures unable to abstain from sin, and whose sins are therefore *involuntary*: This theory will be considered elsewhere.

The word "Eternal" I assume to mean "without end."

As to the human beings who are here contemplated as the

subjects of Eternal Punishment, there are three conceivable cases, viz. :—

(A) The case of one who has ceased to possess Free-Will, and who therefore has no further power either to sin or to repent. In such a case, Eternal Punishment would be suffering inflicted through infinite time, and therefore itself infinite in amount as punishment for sins committed during a finite time.

(B) The case of one who retains Free-Will, and who has ceased to sin, has repented of all past sins, and is choosing good *as good*. In this case also Eternal Punishment would be infinite suffering, inflicted as punishment for sins committed during a finite time.

(C) The case of one who does not come under either of these descriptions, that is, one who retains Free-Will and continues for ever to choose *evil*. In such a case Eternal Punishment would be infinite suffering, inflicted as punishment for infinite sin.

I assume that the reader would *not* feel any difficulty in recognising the justice of inflicting continuous suffering as punishment for continuous sin.

Hence we may set aside case (C) altogether.

Also we may combine cases (A) and (B) into one, and interpret Proposition II. as asserting that it would be wrong to inflict infinite suffering, on human beings who have ceased to sin, as punishment for sins committed during a finite time.

Proposition III. does not seem to need any explanation.

It will be well before going further to re-state the three incompatible Propositions, in order to give to Proposition II. the form it has now assumed.

I. *God is perfectly good.*

II. *To inflict infinite suffering on human beings who have ceased to sin, as punishment for sins committed during a finite time, would be wrong.*

III. *God is capable of acting thus.*

We know with *absolute* certainty that *one* at least of these three Propositions is *untrue*. Hence, however overwhelming may be the weight of evidence with which each seems to claim our assent, we know that *one* at least may reasonably be abandoned.

Let us now take them, one by one, and consider, for each in turn, what are the grounds on which it claims our assent, and what would be the logical consequences of abandoning it. It may be that the Reader will then be able to see for himself *which* two of the three have the *strongest* claims on his assent, and *which* he must, therefore, abandon.

First, then, let us consider the Proposition.

I. " *God is perfectly good.*"

The grounds on which this claims our assent, seem to be, first, certain *intuitions* (for which, of course, no *proofs* can be offered), such as " I believe that I have Free-Will, and am capable of choosing right or wrong ; that I am responsible for my conduct ; that I am not the outcome of blind material forces, but the creature of a being who has given me Free-Will and the sense of right and wrong, and to whom I am responsible, and who is therefore perfectly good. And this being I call ' God.' "

And these *intuitions* are confirmed for us in a thousand ways by all the facts of revelation, by the facts of our own spiritual history, by the answers we have had to our prayers, by the irresistible conviction that this being whom we call " God " *loves* us, with a love so wonderful, so beautiful, so immeasurable, so wholly undeserved, so unaccountable on any ground save His own perfect goodness, that we can but abase ourselves to the dust before Him, and dimly hope that we may be able some day to love Him with a love more like His great love for us.

The abandonment of this Proposition would mean practically, for most of us, the abandonment of the belief in a God, and the acceptance of Atheism.

Secondly, let us consider the Proposition.

II. *To inflict infinite suffering, on human beings who have ceased to sin, as punishment for sins committed during a finite time, would be wrong.*

Here it will greatly simplify our inquiry to begin by considering what are the various *purposes* for which punishment may be supposed to be, first, *enacted*, and secondly, *inflicted ;* and what are the *principles* which, in view of those purposes, would make us regard its enactment and infliction as right or wrong.

Punishment, when enacted or inflicted, by human beings upon each other is necessarily limited in its purposes. We cannot read the *minds* of others, and therefore can never know whether any human being is or is not really *guilty* in anything he does. Consequently, human punishment can never reach beyond the outward *act :* we dare not attempt to punish *thoughts*, however sinful, that have not resulted in *action*. And, even here, our principal purpose must necessarily be to save *Society* from the injury that such acts would cause to it. Hence there is little in the principles affecting punishment, when inflicted by *Man*, that we can safely appeal to in considering punishment as inflicted by *God*. There is, however, *one* principle which clearly applies equally to both : we recognise that some *proportion* should be observed, between the amount of crime and the amount of punishment inflicted : for instance, we should have no hesitation in condemning as unjust the conduct of a judge who, in sentencing two criminals, had awarded the *greater* punishment to the one whose crime was clearly the *lesser* of the two.

But, in the sight of *God*, our guilt consists in the sinful *choice*, and we rightly hold that two men, who had resolved, in similar circumstances, on committing the same crime, would be equally guilty in His sight, even though only *one* had actually committed the crime, while the *other* had been accidentally prevented from carrying out his intention.

Hence we may assume that God's purpose, in the enactment of punishment, is the prevention of the sinful *choice*, with all the evils consequent upon it.   When once the punishment has been *enacted*, it must necessarily, unless some change takes place in the circumstances contemplated in the enactment, be *inflicted*.   We may easily imagine a *man*, who has enacted some punishment, finding good reasons for not inflicting it ; for instance, he might find that he had made a mistake in enacting it, or that he had failed to take account of some unforeseen circumstance.   We might even imagine a *man* to have threatened a punishment without any intention of ever inflicting it.   But none of these suppositions can be made as to punishment enacted by *God*.   We cannot believe *Him* to be ignorant of any of the circumstances, or capable of announcing that He will do what He does not really intend to do.

We must trust His perfect knowledge of the thoughts of men, for judging who is guilty and who is not, and the only principle of right and wrong that seems reasonably applicable, is the sense that some *proportion* should be observed between the amount of sin and the amount of the punishment awarded to it.

And here comes in the one consideration which, as I believe, causes all the difficulty and distress felt on this subject.   We feel intuitively that sins committed by a human being during a finite period must necessarily be *finite* in amount ; while punishment continued during an infinite period must necessarily be *infinite* in amount.   And we feel that such a proportion is unjust.

Once suppose the punishment to be *finite* for finite sin, so that if at any period of time the sinful *choice* ceased to exist,

the punishment would *not* be infinite, and I believe this difficulty would no longer be felt, and that we should be ready
to recognise punishment as *deserved*, and therefore as justly
inflicted ; and also to recognise the many good purposes, such
as the reformation of the sinner, or the warning given to others,
which the punishment might serve.

There is another intuition, felt, I believe, by most of us, of
which no account has yet been taken. It is that there is some
eternal *necessity*, wholly beyond our comprehension, that *sin*
must result in suffering. This principle is, I believe, en-
shrouded in, and may to some extent make more credible to
us, the unfathomable mystery of the Atonement. And this
principle must be allowed for, I think, in considering the
present subject.

There is also a difficulty, that will probably occur to some
readers, which ought to be noticed here. It is the doubt
whether the man who checks and puts out of his mind a
sinful wish merely from fear of *punishment*, can really be less
guilty in the sight of God. "Granted," it may be urged,
"that Divine punishment is incurred by the evil wish, whether
or no it result in evil *act*, so that its enactment may serve to
prevent that wish, yet surely what God requires is that we
should love good *as good*, and hate evil *as evil*. If a man
checks the evil wish merely from fear of punishment, and not
because it *is* an evil wish, does he thereby cease to sin?"
Here it must be admitted, I think, that the enactment of
punishment for evil wishes does not, of *itself*, produce the love
of good *as good*, and the hatred of evil *as evil*. Yet surely it
may help in that direction? God uses, I believe, such motives
as best suit the present need ; at one time, perhaps, *fear* may
be the only one that will influence the sinner ; later on, when,
through fear, some *habit* of self-restraint has been formed, the
evil wish may be checked by the consideration that indulgence
of it might lead to acts which the man is beginning dimly to

recognise as evil ; later still, when this recognition has grown clearer, a higher motive (such as human love) may be appealed to ; and later still, the love of good *as good*, and the love of God as the Being whose essence is *goodness*.

When all this has been considered, its outcome seems to me to be the irresistible intuition that infinite punishment for finite sin would be unjust, and therefore wrong. We feel that even weak and erring Man would shrink from such an act. And we cannot conceive of God as acting on a lower standard of right and wrong. In the words of Dean Church, " Can *we* be so compassionate and so just, and cannot we trust *Him* to be so?"

To set aside this intuition, and to accept, as a just and righteous act, the infliction on human beings of infinite punishment for finite sin, is virtually the abandonment of *Conscience* as a guide in questions of Right and Wrong, and the embarking, without compass or rudder, on a boundless ocean of perplexity.

In taking this position, we have to face such questions as these : " Why do I accept whatever God does as being right, though my conscience declares it to be wrong ? Is it that He is my *Maker* ? What ground have I for holding that the power of *creating* is a guarantee for *goodness* ? Or is it that He loves me ? But I know already that wicked beings can love. No. The only reasonable ground for accepting what He does as being right seems to be the assurance that He is perfectly *good*. And how can I be assured of this, if I put aside as useless the *only* guide that I profess for distinguishing between right and wrong, the voice of *Conscience* ? "

Such are the difficulties that meet us, if we propose to take the *second* possible course, and to reject Proposition II.

The *third* possible course is to accept Propositions I. and II., and to reject III. We should thus take the following position. " I believe that God will *not* act thus. Yet I also believe that, whatever He has declared He will do, He *will* do. Hence I believe that He has *not* declared that He will act thus."

The difficulties, entailed by choosing this *third* course, may be well exhibited in another set of incompatible Propositions, as follows :—

1. *God has not declared that He will act thus.*

2. *All that the Bible tells us, as to the relations between God and man, are true.*

3. *The Bible tells us that God has declared that He will act thus.*

As these three Propositions cannot possibly be *all* of them true, the acceptance of (1) necessarily entails the rejection of either (2) or (3).

If we reject (2), we are at once involved in all the perplexities that surround the question of Biblical Inspiration. The theory of *Plenary* Inspiration—which asserts that *every* statement in the Bible is absolute and infallibly true—has been largely modified in these days, and most Christians are now, I think, content to admit the existence of a *human* element in the Bible, and the possibility of *human* error in such of its statements as do not involve the relations between God and Man. But, as to *those* statements, there appears to be a general belief that the Bible has been providentially protected from error : in fact, on any other theory, it would be hard to say what value there would be in the Bible or for what purpose it could have been written.

The more likely course would seem to be to reject (3). Let us consider what difficulties *this* would entail.

We are now supposed to have taken up the following position : " I do not believe that the Bible tells us that God has declared He will inflict Eternal Punishment on human beings, who are either incapable of sinning, or who, being capable of sinning, have ceased to sin."

It is well to remind the Reader that, in taking up this position, he entirely escapes from the original difficulty on account of which we entered on this discussion. And how widely different this is from what we considered as the *first* of the courses possible to us ! *That* would have involved us in the abandonment of Christianity itself ; this entails many difficulties, no doubt : but they all belong to the infinitely less important field of Biblical Criticism.

The Reader who is unable, whether from want of time or from want of the necessary learning, to investigate this question for himself, must perforce accept the judgment of others : and all he needs here to be told is that the interpretation of the passages, which are believed to teach the doctrine of " Eternal Punishment," depends largely, if not entirely, on the meaning given to one single word (αἰών). This is rendered, in our English Bibles, by the word " eternal " or " everlasting " : but there are many critics who believe that it does not necessarily mean "endless." If this be so, then the punishment, which we are considering, is finite punishment for finite sin, and the original difficulty no longer exists.

In conclusion, I will put together in one view the various modes of escape, from the original difficulty, which may be adopted without violating the inexorable laws of logical reasoning. They are as follows :—

(1) " I believe that the infliction, on human beings, of endless punishment, for sins committed during a finite time, would be unjust, and therefore wrong. Yet I cannot resist the evidence that God has declared His intention of acting thus. Consequently I hold Him to be capable of sinning."

This would practically mean the abandonment of Christianity.

(2) " I believe that God is perfectly good, and therefore that such infliction of punishment would be right, though my conscience declares it to be wrong."

This would practically mean the abandonment of conscience as a guide to distinguish right from wrong, and would leave the phrase " I believe that God is perfectly *good* " without any intelligible meaning.

(3) " I believe that God is perfectly good. Also I believe that such infliction of punishment would be wrong. Consequently I believe that God is not capable of acting thus. I find that the Bible tells us that He *is* capable of acting thus. Consequently I believe that what the Bible tells us of the relations between God and Man cannot be relied on as true."

This would practically mean the abandonment of the Bible as a trustworthy book.

(4) " I believe that God is perfectly good. Also I believe that such infliction of punishment would be wrong. Consequently I believe that God is not capable of acting thus. I find that the Bible, in the English Version, seems to tell us that He *is* capable of acting thus. Yet I believe that it is a book inspired by God, and protected by Him from error in what it tells us of the relations between God and Man, and therefore that what it says, according to the real meaning of the words, may be relied on as true. Consequently I hold that the word, rendered in English as 'eternal' or 'everlasting,' has been mistranslated, and that the Bible does not really assert more than that God will inflict suffering, of unknown duration but *not* necessarily eternal, punishment for sin."

Any one of these four views may be held, without violating the laws of logical reasoning.

Here ends my present task; since my object has been, throughout, *not* to indicate one course rather than another, but to help the Reader to see clearly *what* the possible courses are, and *what* he is virtually accepting, or denying, in choosing any *one* of them.

I now come to the reminiscences to which I alluded at the beginning of this Chapter, and first I will give a few extracts out of letters from

Mr. York Powell, Regius Professor of Modern History at Oxford :—

" Mr. Dodgson was an excellent after-dinner speaker, though he did not like to have to speak. He made a wonderfully humorous speech at the Censor's dinner, but I can only recall the very delightful impression. It was a *souffle* of a speech, light, pleasant, digestible, and nourishing also.

.   .   .   .

" I can't remember anything of his stories.   He did not often make stories.   He told old stories very well with a (Charles) Lamb-like stutter.

" He made me laugh once till I nearly cried in Hall over a story that was true, of a child, too small to talk much, being put to bed and calling to its nurse, ' Nursey, my feet, my feet !'   So nurse took it out of its cot, and brought it into the nursery, and got some hot water and vinegar and bathed its legs and feet, and got it some warm milk and gave it to drink, and put it to bed again.   But again the child cried out, ' Nursey, my feet, my feet !   I feel so untumfy.'   So she had it out again, and couldn't find anything amiss with its feet and legs.   However, she thought it wouldn't do it any harm to bathe them again, so she put a little more vinegar in the water and bathed them, and then rubbed and dried them very carefully, and put the child, who was now very sleepy, back again.   But again came the cry, ' Nursey, my feet, my feet ! I'm so untumfy.'   So she took a light and bethought her of examining the cot, when she found that the elder brothers had made it an ' apple-pie ' bed, so that its feet could not get down to the comfortable length.

" The comic idea of the child wondering how hot water and vinegar were to make its feet comfortable under the circumstances roused me in the sense of incongruity that lies at the root of much laughter. But I have met many people who wouldn't admit that this was a funny story. It certainly amused Dodgson, and I still laugh when I think of it."

With respect to Mr. Dodgson's humanity towards animals, and detestation of cruelty, I have received the following recollections from one of his sisters :—

"Mention has been made of Lewis Carroll's consideration for animals. I send some instances of this I heard of from himself. When away from home he saw a kitten in the street with a fish-hook in its mouth. Knowing what suffering this would cause, he carrried the kitten to the house of a medical man for relief. 'Your own cat, I suppose?' said the doctor, but any knowledge of it was disclaimed. Happily the removal of the hook was no difficult matter. Lewis Carroll held the kitten, and I think the doctor was able to snip off the barbed end, so that the hook came easily out. Payment having been declined, Lewis Carroll took the kitten back to where he had found it.

"On another occasion, compassionating some horses which were being worked with bearing-reins on, he spoke to the man with them, and put the case against bearing-reins so convincingly that they were then and there taken off, and the man had the satisfaction of seeing his animals work all the better for being allowed the natural use of their necks.

"With regard to some papers he enclosed he wrote to me : 'It is greatly to be hoped that the suggestions for a painless death for the animals used as food may do good. I quite believe that the time will come when, in England at any rate, such death will be painless.'

" To get rid of mice in his rooms a square live trap was used, and he had a wood and wire compartment made which fitted on to the trap whose door could then be opened for the mice to run into the compartment, a sliding door shut them in, and the compartment could then be taken from the trap and put under water; thus all chance of the mice having an agonised struggle on the surface of the water was removed."

After the death of a pet dog he wrote :—

" I am very sorry to hear of your sad loss.   Well, you have certainly given to *one* of God's creatures a *very* happy life through a good many years—a pleasant thing to remember.

" H. H. D.

" Brighton."

The following letter from Canon Duckworth, with which I conclude, is very interesting because of the share which he had in the beginnings of " Alice " :—

" Five-and-thirty years ago, when I was an Oxford tutor, I received frequent notes from the Rev. C. L. Dodgson, but I am afraid that these have all been destroyed, and since I left Oxford in 1866 I have seldom had communication with him.

" I was very closely associated with him in the production and publication of ' Alice in Wonderland.'   I rowed *stroke* and he rowed *bow* in the famous Long Vacation voyage to Godstow, when the three Miss Liddells were our passengers, and the story was actually composed and spoken *over my shoulder* for the benefit of Alice Liddell, who was acting as ' cox ' of our gig.   I remember turning round and saying, Dodgson, is this an extempore romance of yours?'   And he

"THE QUEEN'S CROQUÊT PARTY."

(*From "Alice's Adventures Underground."*)

replied, 'Yes, I'm inventing as we go along.'   I also well remember how, when we had conducted the three children back to the Deanery, Alice said, as she bade us good-night, 'Oh, Mr. Dodgson, I wish you would write out Alice's adventures for me.'   He said he should try, and he afterwards told me that he sat up nearly the whole night, committing to a MS. book his recollections of the drolleries with which he had enlivened the afternoon.   He added illustrations of his own, and presented the volume, which used often to be seen on the drawing-room table at the Deanery.

"One day Henry Kingsley, when on a visit to the Dean, took up the MS., and read it through with the greatest delight, urging Mrs. Liddell to persuade the author to publish it.   On hearing this, Dodgson wrote and asked me if I would come and read 'Alice's Adventures,' and give him my candid opinion whether it was worthy of publication or not, as he himself felt very doubtful, and could not afford to lose money over it.   I assured him that, if only he could induce John Tenniel to illustrate it, the book would be perfectly certain of success, and at my instance he sent the MS. to Tenniel, who soon replied in terms of warm admiration, and said that he should feel it a pleasure to provide the illustrations for so delightful a story.   Every time that a batch of Tenniel's drawings arrived, Dodgson sent me word inviting me to dine, and to feast after dinner on the pictures which the world now knows so well.

"I figure as the 'duck' in the 'Adventures,' Lorina Liddell (now Mrs. Skene) is the 'lory' or parrot, Edith Liddell (now no more) is the 'eagle.'

"I wish I had preserved some of the interesting notes which Dodgson had occasion to write to me before and after the publication of the book which has made him famous ; but in those days one did not foresee the interest which was destined to attach to his name."

APPENDIX

THE VULTURE AND THE HUSBANDMAN.[1]

("THE LIGHT GREEN," NO. I., 1872.)

By LOUISA CAROLINE.

N.B.—A Vulture is a rapacious and obscene bird, which destroys its prey by *plucking* it limb from limb with its powerful beak and talons. A *Husbandman* is a man in a low position of life, who supports himself by the use of the *plough*. (Johnson's Dictionary.)

> The rain was raining cheerfully,
>   As if it had been May;
> The Senate-House appeared inside
>   Unusually gay;
> And this was strange, because it was
>   A Viva-Voce day.
>
> The men were sitting sulkily,
>   Their paper work was done;
> They wanted much to go away
>   To ride or row or run;
> "It's very rude," they said, "to keep
>   Us here, and spoil our fun."

[1] This poem is inserted here by the kind permission of the proprietors of *The Light Green*, which has recently been reprinted.

361

The papers they had finished lay
   In piles of blue and white,
They answered everything they could,
   And wrote with all their might,
But, though they wrote it all by rote,
   They did not write it right.

The Vulture and the Husbandman
   Beside these piles did stand,
They wept like anything to see
   The work they had in hand,
" If this were only finished up,"
   Said they, "it would be grand."

" If seven D's or seven C's
   We give to all the crowd,
Do you suppose," the Vulture said,
   "That we could get them ploughed ? "
" I think so," said the Husbandman,
   " But pray don't talk so loud."

" O Undergraduates, come up,"
   The Vulture did beseech,
" And let us see if you can learn
   As well as we can teach ;
We cannot do with more than two
   To have a word with each."

Two Undergraduates came up,
   And slowly took a seat,
They knit their brows, and bit their thumbs,
   As if they found them sweet,
And this was odd, because you know
   Thumbs are not good to eat.

"The time has come," the Vulture said,
  "To talk of many things,
Of Accidence and Adjectives,
  And names of Jewish kings,
How many notes a sackbut has
  And whether shawms have strings."

"Please, Sir," the Undergraduates said,
  Turning a little blue,
"We did not know that was the sort
  Of thing we had to do"
"We thank you much," the Vulture said,
  "Send up another two."

Two more came up, and then two more;
  And more, and more, and more;
And some looked upward at the roof,
  Some down upon the floor,
But none were any wiser than
  The pair that went before.

"I weep for you," the Vulture said,
  "I deeply sympathise!"
With sobs and tears he gave them all
  D's of the largest size,
While at the Husbandman he winked
  One of his streaming eyes.

"I think," observed the Husbandman,
  "We're getting on too quick.
Are we not putting down the D's
  A little bit too thick?"
The Vulture said with much disgust,
  "Their answers make me sick."

" Now, Undergraduates," he cried,
  " Our fun is nearly done ;
Will anybody else come up ? "
  But answer came there none ;
And this was scarcely odd, because,
  They'd ploughed them every one !

" JABBERWOCKY " RENDERED INTO LATIN ELEGIACS.

BY THE LATE MR. HASSARD DODGSON, a Master in the Court
of Common Pleas.

Hora aderat briligi.   Nunc et Slythæia Tova
  Plurima gyrabant gymbolitare vabo ;
Et Borogovorum mimzebant undique formae,
  Momiferique omnes exgrabuêre Rathi.

" Cave, Gaberbocchum moneo tibi, nate cavendum
  (Unguibus ille rapit.   Dentibus ille necat.)
Et fuge Jubbubbum, quo non infestior ales,
  Et Bandersnatcham, quae fremit usque, cave."

Ille autem gladium vorpalem cepit, et hostem
  Manxonium longâ sedulitate petit ;
Tum sub tumtummi requiescens arboris umbrâ
  Stabat tranquillus, multa animo meditans.

Dum requiescebat meditans uffishia, monstrum
  Praesens ecce ! oculis cui fera flamma micat,
Ipse Gaberbocchus dumeta per horrida sifflans
  Ibat, et horrendum burbuliabat iens !

Ter, quater, atque iterum cito vorpalissimus ensis
Snicsnaccans penitus viscera dissecuit.
Exanimum corpus linquens caput abstulit heros
Quocum galumphat multa, domumque redit.

"Tune Gaberbocchum potuisti, nate, necare?
Bemiscens puer! ad brachia nostra veni.
Oh! frabiusce dies! iterumque caloque calâque
Laetus eo" ut chortlet chortla superba senex.

Hora aderat briligi.   Nunc et Slythæia Tova
Plurima gyrabant gymbolitare vabo;
Et Borogovorum mimzebant undique formae,
Momiferique omnes exgrabuêre Rathi.

THE JABBERWOCK TRACED TO ITS TRUE SOURCE.[1]

("Macmillan's Magazine," Feb., 1872.)

BY THOMAS CHATTERTON.

To the Editor of MACMILLAN'S MAGAZINE.

SIR,—I was invited by a friend, one evening last week, to a *séance* of Spiritualists; and having been reading "Through the Looking-Glass" before I left home, I was much astonished to find that the first "communication" made to the party was on the subject of that work.   How it had reached the Spirits, was not clearly made out.

[1] Reproduced here by kind permission of the proprietors of *Macmillan's Magazine.*

Among many indistinct rappings, only the words *Post-Obit* and *Dead Letters* were distinguishable.

The Spirit announced himself as Hermann von Schwindel—a name doubtless known to many of your readers ; and he complained that the celebrated *Jabberwock* was taken from a German ballad by the well - known author of the *Lyre* (he spelt it *Lyar ;* but this is not surprising in a German ghost using the English language) *and Sword.* And he proceeded, with great fluency, to tap out the following verses :—

> Der Jammerwoch
> Es brillig war.　Die schlichte Toven
> 　Wirrten und wimmelten in Waben ;
> Und aller-mümsige Burggoven
> 　Die mohmen Räth' ausgraben.
>
> Bewahre doch vor Jammerwoch !
> 　Die Zähne knirschen, Krallen kratzen !
> Bewahr' vor Jubjub—Vogel, vor
> 　Frumiösen Banderschnätzchen !
>
> Er griff sein vorpals Schwertchen zu,
> 　Er suchte lang das manchsam' Ding ;
> Dann, stehend unten Tumtum Baum,
> 　Er an-zu-denken-fing.
>
> Als stand er tief in Andacht auf,
> 　Des Jammerwochen's Augen-feuer
> Durch tulgen Wald mit wiffek kam
> 　Ein burbelnd ungeheuer !

Eins, Zwei! Eins, Zwei! Und durch und durch
  Sein vorpals Schwert zerschnifer-schnück,
Da blieb es todt! Er, Kopf in Hand,
  Geläumfig zog zurück.

Und schlugst Du ja den Jammerwoch?
  Umarme mich, mien Böhm' sches Kind!
O Freuden-Tag! O Halloo-Schlag!
  Er chortelt froh-gesinnt.

Es brillig war, &c.

On my return home I thought the matter over,
and am inclined to agree with the lamented Von
Schwindel, for various reasons, which may be
summed up as follows :—

The *Jabberwock* is only a *Jammerwoch* with a
cold in its head, like "the young Babood" for
"the young May moon." And this name, "the
week of woe," is a mythical expression for the
Seven Years' War, and hence for other devasta-
tions of the Fatherland. Humpty Dumpty's interpretation I of course utterly repudiate. He is
a mere rationalising Euhemerist. My theory is
that the ballad is the product of the war against
Napoleon I., and the Jammerwoch, of course, is
"the Corsican Fiend" himself. Now, apply this
to the first stanza, which indicates the patriotic
combination against him of the "Burggoven"

(*Burggrafen*, the nobility in general); the "Räthe" (whether "Hof" or "Geheim"), the Bureaucracy, and the "schlichte Toven," the simple coves of the lower class, neither noble nor official. And note the touch of irony with which in the end the aristos leave these in the lurch, "wirrend und wimmelnd," and only "dig out" (*aus-graben*) the bureaucracy for their own purposes, keeping them "mum" (*mohme*) and voiceless.

There is something strikingly Teutonic in the attitude of the hero under the tree, where, after seeking for the Jammerwoch, he "took to thinking!" "Auf" also must be original, for "uffish thought" is manifestly intended as a translation of it! But who is the hero? I think that the sixth stanza will reveal this to any one possessed of a historico‑critical sense. If it had been a North German who wrote the ballad, no doubt the hero would have been Scharnhörst, or Blücher, or some of the other Prussian heroes. But the language is rather Austrian (speaking of the Austrian Empire as it was at that date, without reference to nationalities); and no North German would have celebrated the "Böhm'sches kind," which is, not as the English copy so

strangely translates it, "beamish," nor even
(which would have been happier) "my bump-
tious boy," but "my young Bohemian." And,
therefore, I think that Von Schwindel's memory
must have failed him. Doubtless he was acquainted with other *Lyres* and other *Swords*, as
well as Körner's, and he may have confused them.
We may safely identify the hero with the Arch-
duke Charles; who (it is true) did *not* slay the
Jammerwoch, but did his best to do it, and was
a genuine hero of the Austrian Empire.

THE FIREPLACE IN LEWIS CARROLL'S STUDY AT

CH. CH.

(See Illustration on page 234.)

No doubt the photograph of a fireplace as an
illustration is something of a curiosity, but this
particular fireplace and the tiles which surround
it will, I hope, recall many pleasant scenes and
conversations to the minds of those of Mr. Dodgson's younger friends who used to visit him at
Oxford, and for whose benefit the picture and
the explanation which follows are principally
intended.

Lewis Carroll had two ways of explaining the designs on these tiles—one literal and the other allegorical.

From the literal standpoint the creature at the bottom right-hand corner is the Beaver, the only animal which the Butcher of " The Hunting of the Snark " knew how to kill—

> " Whenever the Butcher was by,
> The Beaver kept looking the opposite way,
> And appeared unaccountably shy."

At the top right-hand corner is the Eaglet, one of the competitors in the " Caucus-Race " in " Alice in Wonderland " ; below it is the Gryphon.

The ship in the centre is, of course, that famous vessel which the Bellman steered, not without difficulty, for " the bowsprit got mixed with the rudder sometimes," but—

> " The principal failing occurred in the sailing,
> And the Bellman, perplexed and distressed,
> Said he *had* hoped, at least, when the wind blew due East,
> That the ship would *not* travel due West ! "

On the left side the two uppermost tiles represent the Lory and the Dodo, also of " Caucus-Race " fame ; the lowest is the Fawn which couldn't remember its name. ("Through the Looking Glass," page 63.)

"As I sat on Mr. Dodgson's knee before the fire," writes Miss Enid Stevens, who has supplied me with the above particulars, "he used to make the creatures have long and very amusing conversations between themselves. The little creatures on the intervening tiles used to 'squirm' in at intervals. I think they suggested the 'Little birds are feeding,' &c., in 'Sylvie and Bruno.'"

Mr. Dodgson's allegorical explanation of several of the pictures—for instance, the bird which is running its beak through a fish, and the dragon which is hissing defiance over its left shoulder— was that they were representations of the various ways in which he was accustomed to receive his guests.

INDEX

CATALOGUE OF DOVER BOOKS

Books Explaining Science and Mathematics

WHAT IS SCIENCE?, N. Campbell. The role of experiment and measurement, the function of mathematics, the nature of scientific laws, the difference between laws and theories, the limitations of science, and many similarly provocative topics are treated clearly and without technicalities by an eminent scientist. "Still an excellent introduction to scientific philosophy," H. Margenau in PHYSICS TODAY. "A first-rate primer . . . deserves a wide audience," SCIENTIFIC AMERICAN. 192pp. 5⅜ x 8. S43 Paperbound **$1.25**

THE NATURE OF PHYSICAL THEORY, P. W. Bridgman. A Nobel Laureate's clear, non-technical lectures on difficulties and paradoxes connected with frontier research on the physical sciences. Concerned with such central concepts as thought, logic, mathematics, relativity, probability, wave mechanics, etc. he analyzes the contributions of such men as Newton, Einstein, Bohr, Heisenberg, and many others. "Lucid and entertaining . . . recommended to anyone who wants to get some insight into current philosophies of science," THE NEW PHILOSOPHY. Index. xi + 138pp. 5⅜ x 8. S33 Paperbound **$1.25**

EXPERIMENT AND THEORY IN PHYSICS, Max Born. A Nobel Laureate examines the nature of experiment and theory in theoretical physics and analyzes the advances made by the great physicists of our day: Heisenberg, Einstein, Bohr, Planck, Dirac, and others. The actual process of creation is detailed step-by-step by one who participated. A fine examination of the scientific method at work. 44pp. 5⅜ x 8. S308 Paperbound **75¢**

THE PSYCHOLOGY OF INVENTION IN THE MATHEMATICAL FIELD, J. Hadamard. The reports of such men as Descartes, Pascal, Einstein, Poincaré, and others are considered in this investigation of the method of idea-creation in mathematics and other sciences and the thinking process in general. How do ideas originate? What is the role of the unconscious? What is Poincaré's forgetting hypothesis? are some of the fascinating questions treated. A penetrating analysis of Einstein's thought processes concludes the book. xiii + 145pp. 5⅜ x 8. T107 Paperbound **$1.25**

THE NATURE OF LIGHT AND COLOUR IN THE OPEN AIR, M. Minnaert. Why are shadows sometimes blue, sometimes green, or other colors depending on the light and surroundings? What causes mirages? Why do multiple suns and moons appear in the sky? Professor Minnaert explains these unusual phenomena and hundreds of others in simple, easy-to-understand terms based on optical laws and the properties of light and color. No mathematics is required but artists, scientists, students, and everyone fascinated by these "tricks" of nature will find thousands of useful and amazing pieces of information. Hundreds of observational experiments are suggested which require no special equipment. 200 illustrations; 42 photos. xvi + 362pp. 5⅜ x 8. T196 Paperbound **$2.00**

*MATHEMATICS IN ACTION, O. G. Sutton. Everyone with a command of high school algebra will find this book one of the finest possible introductions to the application of mathematics to physical theory. Ballistics, numerical analysis, waves and wavelike phenomena, Fourier series, group concepts, fluid flow and aerodynamics, statistical measures, and meteorology are discussed with unusual clarity. Some calculus and differential equations theory is developed by the author for the reader's help in the more difficult sections. 88 figures. Index. viii + 236pp. 5⅜ x 8. T440 Clothbound **$3.50**

SOAP-BUBBLES: THEIR COLOURS AND THE FORCES THAT MOULD THEM, C. V. Boys. For continuing popularity and validity as scientific primer, few books can match this volume of easily-followed experiments, explanations. Lucid exposition of complexities of liquid films, surface tension and related phenomena, bubbles' reaction to heat, motion, music, magnetic fields. Experiments with capillary attraction, soap bubbles on frames, composite bubbles, liquid cylinders and jets, bubbles other than soap, etc. Wonderful introduction to scientific method, natural laws that have many ramifications in areas of modern physics. Only complete edition in print. New Introduction by S. Z. Lewin, New York University. 83 illustrations; 1 full-page color plate. xii + 190pp. 5⅜ x 8½. T542 Paperbound **95¢**

CATALOGUE OF DOVER BOOKS

THE STORY OF X-RAYS FROM RÖNTGEN TO ISOTOPES, A. R. Bleich, M.D. This book, by a member of the American College of Radiology, gives the scientific explanation of x-rays, their applications in medicine, industry and art, and their danger (and that of atmospheric radiation) to the individual and the species. You learn how radiation therapy is applied against cancer, how x-rays diagnose heart disease and other ailments, how they are used to examine mummies for information on diseases of early societies, and industrial materials for hidden weaknesses. 54 illustrations show x-rays of flowers, bones, stomach, gears with flaws, etc. 1st publication. Index. xix + 186pp. 5⅜ x 8.　　　　　　　　　T622 Paperbound **$1.35**

SPINNING TOPS AND GYROSCOPIC MOTION, John Perry. A classic elementary text of the dynamics of rotation — the behavior and use of rotating bodies such as gyroscopes and tops. In simple, everyday English you are shown how quasi-rigidity is induced in discs of paper, smoke rings, chains, etc., by rapid motions; why a gyrostat falls and why a top rises; precession; how the earth's motion affects climate; and many other phenomena. Appendix on practical use of gyroscopes. 62 figures. 128pp. 5⅜ x 8.　　　　　　　T416 Paperbound **$1.00**

SNOW CRYSTALS, W. A. Bentley, M. J. Humphreys. For almost 50 years W. A. Bentley photographed snow flakes in his laboratory in Jericho, Vermont; in 1931 the American Meteorological Society gathered together the best of his work, some 2400 photographs of snow flakes, plus a few ice flowers, windowpane frosts, dew, frozen rain, and other ice formations. Pictures were selected for beauty and scientific value. A very valuable work to anyone in meteorology, cryology; most interesting to layman; extremely useful for artist who wants beautiful, crystalline designs. All copyright free. Unabridged reprint of 1931 edition. 2453 illustrations. 227pp. 8 x 10½.　　　　　　　　　　　　　　　T287 Paperbound **$3.00**

A DOVER SCIENCE SAMPLER, edited by George Barkin. A collection of brief, non-technical passages from 44 Dover Books Explaining Science for the enjoyment of the science-minded browser. Includes work of Bertrand Russell, Poincaré, Laplace, Max Born, Galileo, Newton; material on physics, mathematics, metallurgy, anatomy, astronomy, chemistry, etc. You will be fascinated by Martin Gardner's analysis of the sincere pseudo-scientist, Moritz's account of Newton's absentmindedness, Bernard's examples of human vivisection, etc. Illustrations from the Diderot Pictorial Encyclopedia and De Re Metallica. 64 pages.　　**FREE**

THE STORY OF ATOMIC THEORY AND ATOMIC ENERGY, J. G. Feinberg. A broader approach to subject of nuclear energy and its cultural implications than any other similar source. Very readable, informal, completely non-technical text. Begins with first atomic theory, 600 B.C. and carries you through the work of Mendelejeff, Röntgen, Madame Curie, to Einstein's equation and the A-bomb. New chapter goes through thermonuclear fission, binding energy, other events up to 1959. Radioactive decay and radiation hazards, future benefits, work of Bohr, moderns, hundreds more topics. "Deserves special mention . . . not only authoritative but thoroughly popular in the best sense of the word," Saturday Review. Formerly, "The Atom Story." Expanded with new chapter. Three appendixes. Index. 34 illustrations. vii + 243pp. 5⅜ x 8.　　　　　　　　　　　　　　　　　　T625 Paperbound **$1.60**

THE STRANGE STORY OF THE QUANTUM, AN ACCOUNT FOR THE GENERAL READER OF THE GROWTH OF IDEAS UNDERLYING OUR PRESENT ATOMIC KNOWLEDGE, B. Hoffmann. Presents lucidly and expertly, with barest amount of mathematics, the problems and theories which led to modern quantum physics. Dr. Hoffmann begins with the closing years of the 19th century, when certain trifling discrepancies were noticed, and with illuminating analogies and examples takes you through the brilliant concepts of Planck, Einstein, Pauli, Broglie, Bohr, Schroedinger, Heisenberg, Dirac, Sommerfeld, Feynman, etc. This edition includes a new, long postscript carrying the story through 1958. "Of the books attempting an account of the history and contents of our modern atomic physics which have come to my attention, this is the best," H. Margenau, Yale University, in "American Journal of Physics." 32 tables and line illustrations. Index. 275pp. 5⅜ x 8.　　　　　　　　　　　T518 Paperbound **$1.50**

SPACE AND TIME, E. Borel. Written by a versatile mathematician of world renown with his customary lucidity and precision, this introduction to relativity for the layman presents scores of examples, analogies, and illustrations that open up new ways of thinking about space and time. It covers abstract geometry and geographical maps, continuity and topology, the propagation of light, the special theory of relativity, the general theory of relativity, theoretical researches, and much more. Mathematical notes. 2 Indexes. 4 Appendices. 15 figures. xvi + 243pp. 5⅜ x 8.　　　　　　　　　　　　　　　　　T592 Paperbound **$1.45**

FROM EUCLID TO EDDINGTON: A STUDY OF THE CONCEPTIONS OF THE EXTERNAL WORLD, Sir Edmund Whittaker. A foremost British scientist traces the development of theories of natural philosophy from the western rediscovery of Euclid to Eddington, Einstein, Dirac, etc. The inadequacy of classical physics is contrasted with present day attempts to understand the physical world through relativity, non-Euclidean geometry, space curvature, wave mechanics, etc. 5 major divisions of examination: Space; Time and Movement; the Concepts of Classical Physics; the Concepts of Quantum Mechanics; the Eddington Universe. 212pp. 5⅜ x 8. T491 Paperbound **$1.35**

Nature

AN INTRODUCTION TO BIRD LIFE FOR BIRD WATCHERS, Aretas A. Saunders. Fine, readable introduction to birdwatching. Includes a great deal of basic information on about 160 different varieties of wild birds—elementary facts not easily found elsewhere. Complete guide to identification procedures, methods of observation, important habits of birds, finding nests, food, etc. "Could make bird watchers of readers who never suspected they were vulnerable to that particular virus," CHICAGO SUNDAY TRIBUNE. Unabridged, corrected edition. Bibliography. Index. 22 line drawings by D. D'Ostilio. Formerly "The Lives of Wild Birds." 256pp. 5⅜ x 8½.
                                                                T1139 Paperbound **$1.00**

LIFE HISTORIES OF NORTH AMERICAN BIRDS, Arthur Cleveland Bent. Bent's historic, all-encompassing series on North American birds, originally produced under the auspices of the Smithsonian Institution, now being republished in its entirety by Dover Publications. The twenty-volume collection forms the most comprehensive, most complete, most-used source of information in existence. Each study describes in detail the characteristics, range, distribution, habits, migratory patterns, courtship procedures, plumage, eggs, voice, enemies, etc. of the different species and subspecies of the birds that inhabit our continent, utilizing reports of hundreds of contemporary observers as well as the writings of the great naturalists of the past. Invaluable to the ornithologist, conservationist, amateur naturalist, and birdwatcher. All books in the series contain numerous photographs to provide handy guides for identification and study.

LIFE HISTORIES OF NORTH AMERICAN BIRDS OF PREY. Including hawks, eagles, falcons, buzzards, condors, owls, etc. Index. Bibliographies of 923 items. 197 full-page plates containing close to 400 photographs. Total of 907pp. 5⅜ x 8½.   Vol. I: T931 Paperbound **$2.50**
                                                                Vol. II: T932 Paperbound **$2.50**
                                                                The set Paperbound **$5.00**

LIFE HISTORIES OF NORTH AMERICAN SHORE BIRDS. Including 81 varieties of such birds as sandpipers, woodcocks, snipes, phalaropes, oyster catchers, and many others. Index for each volume. Bibliographies of 449 entries. 121 full-page plates including over 200 photographs. Total of 860 pp. 5⅜ x 8½.   Vol. I: T933 Paperbound **$2.35**
                                                                Vol. II: T934 Paperbound **$2.35**
                                                                The set Paperbound **$4.70**

LIFE HISTORIES OF NORTH AMERICAN WILD FOWL. Including 73 varieties of ducks, geese, mergansers, swans, etc. Index for each volume. Bibliographies of 268 items. 106 full-page plates containing close to 200 photographs. Total of 685pp. 5⅜ x 8½.
                                                                Vol. I: T285 Paperbound **$2.50**
                                                                Vol. II: T286 Paperbound **$2.50**
                                                                The set Paperbound **$5.00**

LIFE HISTORIES OF NORTH AMERICAN GULLS AND TERNS. 50 different varieties of gulls and terns. Index. Bibliography. 93 plates including 149 photographs. xii + 337pp. 5⅜ x 8½.
                                                                T1029 Paperbound **$2.75**

LIFE HISTORIES OF NORTH AMERICAN GALLINACEOUS BIRDS. Including partridge, quail, grouse, pheasant, pigeons, doves, and others. Index. Bibliography. 93 full-page plates including 170 photographs. xiii + 490pp. 5⅜ x 8½.   T1028 Paperbound **$2.75**

THE MALAY ARCHIPELAGO, Alfred Russel Wallace. The record of the explorations (8 years, 14,000 miles) of the Malay Archipelago by a great scientific observer. A contemporary of Darwin, Wallace independently arrived at the concept of evolution by natural selection, applied the new theories of evolution to later genetic discoveries, and made significant contributions to biology, zoology, and botany. This work is still one of the classics of natural history and travel. It contains the author's reports of the different native peoples of the islands, descriptions of the island groupings, his accounts of the animals, birds, and insects that flourished in this area. The reader is carried through strange lands, alien cultures, and new theories, and will share in an exciting, unrivalled travel experience. Unabridged reprint of the 1922 edition, with 62 drawings and maps. 3 appendices, one on cranial measurements. xvii + 515pp. 5⅜ x 8.   T187 Paperbound **$2.00**

THE TRAVELS OF WILLIAM BARTRAM, edited by **Mark Van Doren.** This famous source-book of American anthropology, natural history, geography is the record kept by Bartram in the 1770's, on travels through the wilderness of Florida, Georgia, the Carolinas. Containing accurate and beautiful descriptions of Indians, settlers, fauna, flora, it is one of the finest pieces of Americana ever written. Introduction by Mark Van Doren. 13 original illustrations. Index. 448pp. 5⅜ x 8.   T13 Paperbound **$2.00**

COMMON SPIDERS OF THE UNITED STATES, J. H. Emerton. Only non-technical, but thorough, reliable guide to spiders for the layman. Over 200 spiders from all parts of the country, arranged by scientific classification, are identified by shape and color, number of eyes, habitat and range, habits, etc. Full text, 501 line drawings and photographs, and valuable introduction explain webs, poisons, threads, capturing and preserving spiders, etc. Index. New synoptic key by S. W. Frost. xxiv + 225pp. 5⅜ x 8.   T223 Paperbound **$1.45**

LIFE HISTORIES OF NORTH AMERICAN MARSH BIRDS. A wealth of data on 54 different kinds of marsh bird (flamingo, ibis, bittern, heron, egret, crane, crake, rail, coot, etc.). Index. Bibliography. 98 full-page plates containing 179 black-and-white photographs. xiv + 392pp. 5⅜ x 8½.
T1082 Paperbound **$2.75**

LIFE HISTORIES OF NORTH AMERICAN DIVING BIRDS. Thirty-six different diving birds including grebe, loon, auk, murre, puffin, and the like. Index. Bibliography. 55 full-page plates (92 photographs). xiv + 239pp. 5⅜ x 8½.
T1091 Paperbound **$2.75**

LIFE HISTORIES OF NORTH AMERICAN WOOD WARBLERS. Covers about 58 types. Index. Bibliography. 83 full-page plates containing 125 black-and-white photographs. xi + 734pp. of text. 5⅜ x 8½.
Vol. I: T1153 Paperbound **$2.50**
Vol. II: T1154 Paperbound **$2.50**
The set Paperbound **$5.00**

LIFE HISTORIES OF NORTH AMERICAN FLYCATCHERS, LARKS, SWALLOWS, AND THEIR ALLIES. Complete information on about 78 different varieties. Index. Bibliography. 70 full-page plates (117 photographs). xi + 555pp. of text. 5⅜ x 8½.
T1090 Paperbound **$2.75**

AMERICAN WILDLIFE, AND PLANTS: A GUIDE TO WILDLIFE FOOD HABITS, A. C. Martin, H. S. Zim, A. L. Nelson. Result of 75 years of research by U. S. Fish and Wildlife Service into food and feeding habits of more than 1,000 species of birds and mammals, their distribution in America, migratory habits, and the most important plant-animal relationships. Treats over 300 common species of birds, fur and game animals, small mammals, hoofed browsers, fish, amphibians, reptiles by group, giving data on their food, ranges, habits and economies. Also focuses on the different genera of plants that furnish food for our wildlife, animals that use them, and their value. Only thorough study of its kind in existence. "Of immense value to sportsmen, naturalists, bird students, foresters, landscape architects, botanists," NATURE. "Undoubtedly an essential handbook," SCIENTIFIC MONTHLY. Unabridged republication of 1951 edition. Over 600 illustrations, maps, etc. Classified bibliography. Index. x + 500pp. 5⅜ x 8.
T793 Paperbound **$2.50**

HOW TO KNOW THE WILD FLOWERS, Mrs. Wm. Starr Dana. A Guide to the names, haunts, and habits of wild flowers. Well-known classic of nature lore. Informative and delightful. Plants classified by color and season of their typical flowers for easy identification. Thorough coverage of more than 1,000 important flowering, berry-bearing and foliage plants of Eastern and Central United States and Canada. Complete botanical information about each important plant. Also history, uses, folklore, habitat, etc. Nomenclature modernized by C. J. Hylander. 174 full-page illustrations by Marion Satterlee. xii + 481pp. 5⅜ x 8½.
T332 Paperbound **$2.00**

HOW PLANTS GET THEIR NAMES, L. H. Bailey. Introduction to botanical nomenclature for the horticulturist and garden-lover. Discussions of Carl Linnaeus, "father of botany," and analysis of his definitions of genus and species, a brief history of the science before Linnaean systematization, a chapter on plant identification, a mine of information on the rules of nomenclature and Latin stems and word-endings used in botanical nomenclature, with pronunciation guides. An important section contains a full list of generic terms of horticultural literature and common Latin words and their English botanical applications and meanings. "Written with knowledge and authority, charm and eloquence and poetic imagination on the varied aspects of the author's specialty," New York Times. 11 illustrations. vi + 181pp. 5⅜ x 8½.
T796 Paperbound **$1.25**

THE CACTACEAE: DESCRIPTIONS AND ILLUSTRATIONS OF PLANTS OF THE CACTUS FAMILY, N. L. Britton and J. N. Rose. Definitive study of plants of the Cactus Family. The authors devoted more than 15 years of research to this monumental task and produced an exhaustive, rigorously scientific account never likely to be superseded. 3 major classifications, or tribes, are recognized, under which they arrange and describe in full detail 124 genera and 1,235 species of cactus from all over the world. Complete data on each species: leaves, flowers, seeds, fruit, distribution, growth, spines, stem structure, economic uses, etc. In addition, 125 keys facilitate identification of genera and species. For teachers and students of botany and forestry, naturalists, conservationists, and nature lovers, this is an indispensable work. Unabridged republication of second (1937) edition. First edition originally published under the auspices of the Carnegie Institution, Washington, D.C. 4 vols. bound as 2. 1279 illustrations, photographs, sketches, etc. 137 plates. Total of xxvii + 1039pp. 8 x 10¼.
T771 Clothbound, 2-volume set **$20.00**

GUIDE TO SOUTHERN TREES, Elwood S. and J. George Harrar. A handy, comprehensive 700-page manual with numerous illustrations and information on more than 350 different kinds of trees, covering the entire area south of the Mason-Dixon line from the Atlantic Ocean to the Florida Keys and western Texas. Descriptions range from the common pine, cypress, walnut, beech, and elm to such rare species as Franklinia, etc. A mine of information on leaves, flowers, twigs, bark, fruit, distribution etc. of each kind of tree. Eminently readable, written in non-technical language, it is an indispensable handbook for all lovers of the outdoors. Revised edition. Index. 81-item bibliography. Glossary. 200 full-page illustrations. ix + 709pp. 4⅝ x 6⅜.
T945 Paperbound **$2.35**

WESTERN FOREST TREES, James B. Berry. For years a standard guide to the trees of the Western United States. Covers over 70 different subspecies, ranging from the Pacific shores to western South Dakota, New Mexico, etc. Much information on range and distribution, growth habits, appearance, leaves, bark, fruit, twigs, etc. for each tree discussed, plus material on wood of the trees and its uses. Basic division (Trees with needle-like leaves, scale-like leaves, and compound, lobed or divided, and simple broadleaf trees), along with almost 100 illustrations (mostly full-size) of buds, leaves, etc., aids in easy identification of just about any tree of the area. Many subsidiary keys. Revised edition. Introduction. 12 photos. 85 illustrations by Mary E. Eaton. Index. xii + 212pp. 5⅜ x 8.

T1138 Paperbound **$1.35**

MANUAL OF THE TREES OF NORTH AMERICA (EXCLUSIVE OF MEXICO), Charles Sprague Sargent. The magnum opus of the greatest American dendrologist. Based on 44 years of original research, this monumental work is still the most comprehensive and reliable sourcebook on the subject. Includes 185 genera and 717 species of trees (and many shrubs) found in the U.S., Canada, and Alaska. 783 illustrative drawings by C. E. Faxon and Mary W. Gill. An all-encompassing lifetime reference book for students, teachers of botany and forestry, naturalists, conservationists, and all nature lovers. Includes an 11-page analytical key to genera to help the beginner locate any tree by its leaf characteristics. Within the text over 100 further keys aid in easy identification. Synopsis of families. Glossary. Index. 783 illustrations, 1 map. Total of 1 + 891pp. 5⅜ x 8.

T277 Vol. I Paperbound **$2.25**
T278 Vol. II Paperbound **$2.25**
The set **$4.50**

TREES OF THE EASTERN AND CENTRAL UNITED STATES AND CANADA, W. M. Harlow, Professor of Wood Technology, College of Forestry, State University of N. Y., Syracuse, N. Y. This middle-level text is a serious work covering more than 140 native trees and important escapes, with information on general appearance, growth habit, leaf forms, flowers, fruit, bark, and other features. Commercial uses, distribution, habitat, and woodlore are also given. Keys within the text enable you to locate various species with ease. With this book you can identify at sight almost any tree you are likely to encounter; you will know which trees have edible fruit, which are suitable for house planting, and much other useful and interesting information. More than 600 photographs and figures. xiii + 288pp. 4⅝ x 6½.

T395 Paperbound **$1.35**

FRUIT KEY AND TWIG KEY TO TREES AND SHRUBS (FRUIT KEY TO NORTHEASTERN TREES, TWIG TREE TO DECIDUOUS WOODY PLANTS OF EASTERN NORTH AMERICA), W. M. Harlow. The only guides with photographs of every twig and fruit described—especially valuable to the novice. The fruit key (both deciduous trees and evergreens) has an introduction explaining seeding, organs involved, fruit types and habits. The twig key introduction treats growth and morphology. In the keys proper, identification is easy and almost automatic. This exceptional work, widely used in university courses, is especially useful for identification in winter, or from the fruit or seed only. Over 350 photos, up to 3 times natural size. Bibliography, glossary, index of common and scientific names, in each key. xvii + 125pp. 5⅝ x 8⅜.

T511 Paperbound **$1.25**

HOW TO KNOW THE FERNS, F. T. Parsons. Ferns, among our most lovely native plants, are all too little known. This modern classic of nature lore will enable the layman to identify any American fern he is likely to come across. After an introduction on the structure and life of ferns, the 57 most important ferns are fully pictured and described (arranged upon a simple identification key). Index of Latin and English names. 61 illustrations and 42 full-page plates. xiv + 215pp. 5⅜ x 8.

T740 Paperbound **$1.35**

OUR SMALL NATIVE ANIMALS: THEIR HABITS AND CARE, R. Snedigar, Curator of Reptiles, Chicago Zoological Park. An unusual nature handbook containing all the vital facts of habitat, distribution, foods, and special habits in brief life histories of 114 different species of squirrels, chipmunks, rodents, larger mammals, birds, amphibians, lizards and snakes. Liberally sprinkled with first-hand anecdotes. A wealth of information on capturing and caring for these animals: proper pens and cages, correct diet, curing diseases, special equipment required, etc. Addressed to the teacher interested in classroom demonstrations, the camp director, and to anyone who ever wanted a small animal for a pet. Revised edition, New preface. Index. 62 halftones. 14 line drawings. xviii + 296pp. 5⅜ x 8⅛.

T1022 Paperbound **$1.75**

INSECT LIFE AND INSECT NATURAL HISTORY, S. W. Frost. Unusual for emphasizing habits, social life, and ecological relations of insects, rather than more academic aspects of classification and morphology. Prof. Frost's enthusiasm and knowledge are everywhere evident as he discusses insect associations, and specialized habits like leaf-mining, leaf-rolling, and casemaking, the gall insects, the boring insects, aquatic insects, etc. He examines all sorts of matters not usually covered in general works, such as: insects as human food; insect music and musicians; insect response to electric and radio waves; use of insects in art and literature. The admirably executed purpose of this book, which covers the middle ground between elementary treatment and scholarly monographs, is to excite the reader to observe for himself. Over 700 illustrations. Extensive bibliography. x + 524pp. 5⅜ x 8.

T517 Paperbound **$2.45**

Biological Sciences

AN INTRODUCTION TO GENETICS, A. H. Sturtevant and G. W. Beadle. A very thorough exposition of genetic analysis and the chromosome mechanics of higher organisms by two of the world's most renowned biologists, A. H. Sturtevant, one of the founders of modern genetics, and George Beadle, Nobel laureate in 1958. Does not concentrate on the biochemical approach, but rather more on observed data from experimental evidence and results . . . from Drosophila and other life forms. Some chapter titles: Sex chromosomes; Sex-Linkage; Autosomal Inheritance;; Chromosome Maps; Intra-Chromosomal Rearrangements; Inversions—and Incomplete Chromosomes; Translocations; Lethals; Mutations; Heterogeneous Populations; Genes and Phenotypes; The Determination and Differentiation of Sex; etc. Slightly corrected reprint of 1939 edition. New preface by Drs. Sturtevant and Beadle. 1 color plate. 126 figures. Bibliographies. Index. 391pp. 5⅜ x 8½. **S306 Paperbound $2.00**

THE GENETICAL THEORY OF NATURAL SELECTION, R. A. Fisher. 2nd revised edition of a vital reviewing of Darwin's Selection Theory in terms of particulate inheritance, by one of the great authorities on experimental and theoretical genetics. Theory is stated in mathematical form. Special features of particulate inheritance are examined: evolution of dominance, maintenance of specific variability, mimicry and sexual selection, etc. 5 chapters on man and his special circumstances as a social animal. 16 photographs. Bibliography. **Index.** x + 310pp. 5⅜ x 8. **S466 Paperbound $2.00**

THE ORIENTATION OF ANIMALS: KINESES, TAXES AND COMPASS REACTIONS, Gottfried S. Fraenkel and Donald L. Gunn. A basic work in the field of animal orientations. Complete, detailed survey of everything known in the subject up to 1940s, enlarged and revised to cover major developments to 1960. Analyses of simpler types of orientation are presented in Part I: kinesis, klinotaxis, tropotaxis, telotaxis, etc. Part II covers more complex reactions originating from temperature changes, gravity, chemical stimulation, etc. The twolight experiment and unilateral blinding are dealt with, as is the problem of determinism or volition in lower animals. The book has become the universally-accepted guide to all who deal with the subject—zoologists, biologists, psychologists, and the like. Second, enlarged edition, revised to 1960. Bibliography of over 500 items. 135 illustrations. Indices. xiii + 376pp. 5⅜ x 8½. **T786 Paperbound $2.25**

THE BEHAVIOUR AND SOCIAL LIFE OF HONEYBEES, C. R. Ribbands. Definitive survey of all aspects of honeybee life and behavior; completely scientific in approach, but written in interesting, everyday language that both professionals and laymen will appreciate. Basic coverage of physiology, anatomy, sensory equipment; thorough account of honeybee behavior in the field (foraging activities, nectar and pollen gathering, how individuals find their way home and back to food areas, mating habits, etc.); details of communication in various field and hive situations. An extensive treatment of activities within the hive community—food sharing, wax production, comb building, swarming, the queen, her life and relationship with the workers, etc. A must for the beekeeper, natural historian, biologist, entomologist, social scientist, et al. "An indispensable reference," J. Hambleton, BEES. "Recommended in the strongest of terms," AMERICAN SCIENTIST. 9 plates. 66 figures. Indices. 693-item bibliography. 252pp. 5⅜ x 8½. **T1137 Paperbound $2.00**

BIRD DISPLAY: AN INTRODUCTION TO THE STUDY OF BIRD PSYCHOLOGY, E. A. Armstrong. The standard work on bird display, based on extensive observation by the author and reports of other observers. This important contribution to comparative psychology covers the behavior and ceremonial rituals of hundreds of birds from gannet and heron to birds of paradise and king penguins. Chapters discuss such topics as the ceremonial of the gannet, ceremonial gaping, disablement reactions, the expression of emotions, the evolution and function of social ceremonies, social hierarchy in bird life, dances of birds and men, songs, etc. Free of technical terminology, this work will be equally interesting to psychologists and zoologists as well as bird lovers of all backgrounds. 32 photographic plates. New introduction by the author. List of scientific names of birds. Bibliography. 3-part index. 431pp. 5⅜ x 8½. **T1128 Paperbound $2.00**

THE SPECIFICITY OF SEROLOGICAL REACTIONS, Karl Landsteiner. With a Chapter on Molecular Structure and Intermolecular Forces by Linus Pauling. Dr. Landsteiner, winner of the Nobel Prize in 1930 for the discovery of the human blood groups, devoted his life to fundamental research and played a leading role in the development of immunology. This authoritative study is an account of the experiments he and his colleagues carried out on antigens and serological reactions with simple compounds. Comprehensive coverage of the basic concepts of immunolgy includes such topics as: The Serological Specificity of Proteins, Antigens, Antibodies, Artificially Conjugated Antigens, Non-Protein Cell Substances such as polysaccharides, etc., Antigen-Antibody Reactions (Toxin Neutralization, Precipitin Reactions, Agglutination, etc.). Discussions of toxins, bacterial proteins, viruses, hormones, enzymes, etc. in the context of immunological phenomena. New introduction by Dr. Merrill Chase of the Rockefeller Institute. Extensive bibliography and bibliography of author's writings. Index. xviii + 330pp. 5⅜ x 8½. **S299 Paperbound $2.00**

CULTURE METHODS FOR INVERTEBRATE ANIMALS, P. S. Galtsoff, F. E. Lutz, P. S. Welch, J. G. Needham, eds. A compendium of practical experience of hundreds of scientists and technicians, covering invertebrates from protozoa to chordata, in 313 articles on 17 phyla. Explains in great detail food, protection, environment, reproduction conditions, rearing methods, embryology, breeding seasons, schedule of development, much more. Includes at least one species of each considerable group. Half the articles are on class insecta. Introduction. 97 illustrations. Bibliography. Index. xxix + 590pp. 5⅜ x 8. S526 Paperbound **$3.00**

THE BIOLOGY OF THE LABORATORY MOUSE, edited by G. D. Snell. 1st prepared in 1941 by the staff of the Roscoe B. Jackson Memorial Laboratory, this is still the standard treatise on the mouse, assembling an enormous amount of material for which otherwise you spend hours of research. Embryology, reproduction, histology, spontaneous tumor formation, genetics of tumor transplantation, endocrine secretion & tumor formation, milk, influence & tumor formation, inbred, hybrid animals, parasites, infectious diseases, care & recording. Classified bibliography of 1122 items. 172 figures, including 128 photos. ix + 497pp. 6⅛ x 9¼. S248 Clothbound **$6.00**

MATHEMATICAL BIOPHYSICS: PHYSICO-MATHEMATICAL FOUNDATIONS OF BIOLOGY, N. Rashevsky. One of most important books in modern biology, now revised, expanded with new chapters, to include most significant recent contributions. Vol. 1: Diffusion phenomena, particularly diffusion drag forces, their effects. Old theory of cell division based on diffusion drag forces, other theoretical approaches, more exhaustively treated than ever. Theories of excitation, conduction in nerves, with formal theories plus physico-chemical theory. Vol. 2: Mathematical theories of various phenomena in central nervous system. New chapters on theory of color vision, of random nets. Principle of optimal design, extended from earlier edition. Principle of relational mapping of organisms, numerous applications. Introduces into mathematical biology such branches of math as topology, theory of sets. Index. 236 illustrations. Total of 988pp. 5⅜ x 8. S574 Vol. 1 (Books 1, 2) Paperbound **$2.50**
S575 Vol. 2 (Books 3, 4) Paperbound **$2.50**
2 vol. set **$5.00**

ELEMENTS OF MATHEMATICAL BIOLOGY, A. J. Lotka. A pioneer classic, the first major attempt to apply modern mathematical techniques on a large scale to phenomena of biology, biochemistry, psychology, ecology, similar life sciences. Partial Contents: Statistical meaning of irreversibility; Evolution as redistribution; Equations of kinetics of evolving systems; Chemical, inter-species equilibrium; parameters of state; Energy transformers of nature, etc. Can be read with profit even by those having no advanced math; unsurpassed as study-reference. Formerly titled ELEMENTS OF PHYSICAL BIOLOGY. 72 figures. xxx + 460pp. 5⅜ x 8. S346 Paperbound **$2.45**

THE BIOLOGY OF THE AMPHIBIA, G. K. Noble, Late Curator of Herpetology at the Am. Mus. of Nat. Hist. Probably the most used text on amphibia, unmatched in comprehensiveness, clarity, detail. 19 chapters plus 85-page supplement cover development; heredity; life history; speciation; adaptation; sex, integument, respiratory, circulatory, digestive, muscular, nervous systems; instinct, intelligence, habits, environment, economic value, relationships, classification, etc. "Nothing comparable to it," C. H. Pope, Curator of Amphibia, Chicago Mus. of Nat. Hist. 1047 bibliographic references. 174 illustrations. 600pp. 5⅜ x 8. S206 Paperbound **$2.98**

STUDIES ON THE STRUCTURE AND DEVELOPMENT OF VERTEBRATES, E. S. Goodrich. A definitive study by the greatest modern comparative anatomist. Exceptional in its accounts of the ossicles of the ear, the separate divisions of the coelom and mammalian diaphragm, and the 5 chapters devoted to the head region. Also exhaustive morphological and phylogenetic expositions of skeleton, fins and limbs, skeletal visceral arches and labial cartilages, visceral clefts and gills, vacular, respiratory, excretory, and peripheral nervous systems, etc., from fish to the higher mammals. 754 illustrations. 69 page biographical study by C. C. Hardy. Bibliography of 1186 references. "What an undertaking . . . to write a textbook which will summarize adequately and succinctly all that has been done in the realm of Vertebrate Morphology these recent years," Journal of Anatomy. Index. Two volumes. Total 906pp. 5⅜ x 8. Two vol. set S449-50 Paperbound **$5.00**

A TREATISE ON PHYSIOLOGICAL OPTICS, H. von Helmholtz, Ed. by J. P. C. Southall. Unmatched for thoroughness, soundness, and comprehensiveness, this is still the most important work ever produced in the field of physiological optics. Revised and annotated, it contains everything known about the subject up to 1925. Beginning with a careful anatomical description of the eye, the main body of the text is divided into three general categories: The Dioptrics of the Eye (covering optical imagery, blur circles on the retina, the mechanism of accommodation, chromatic aberration, etc.); The Sensations of Vision (including stimulation of the organ of vision, simple and compound colors, the intensity and duration of light, variations of sensitivity, contrast, etc.); and The Perceptions of Vision (containing movements of the eyes, the monocular field of vision, direction, perception of depth, binocular double vision, etc.). Appendices cover later findings on optical imagery, refraction, ophthalmoscopy, and many other matters. Unabridged, corrected republication of the original English translation of the third German edition. 3 volumes bound as 2. Complete bibliography, 1911-1925. Indices. 312 illustrations. 6 full-page plates, 3 in color. Total of 1,749pp. 5⅜ x 8. Two-volume set S15, 16 Clothbound **$15.00**

Psychology

YOGA: A SCIENTIFIC EVALUATION, Kovoor T. Behanan. A complete reprinting of the book that for the first time gave Western readers a sane, scientific explanation and analysis of yoga. The author draws on controlled laboratory experiments and personal records of a year as a disciple of a yoga, to investigate yoga psychology, concepts of knowledge, physiology, "supernatural" phenomena, and the ability to tap the deepest human powers. In this study under the auspices of Yale University Institute of Human Relations, the strictest principles of physiological and psychological inquiry are followed throughout. Foreword by W. A. Miles, Yale University. 17 photographs. Glossary. Index. xx + 270pp. 5⅜ x 8. T505 Paperbound **$2.00**

CONDITIONED REFLEXES: AN INVESTIGATION OF THE PHYSIOLOGICAL ACTIVITIES OF THE CEREBRAL CORTEX, I. P. Pavlov. Full, authorized translation of Pavlov's own survey of his work in experimental psychology reviews entire course of experiments, summarizes conclusions, outlines psychological system based on famous "conditioned reflex" concept. Details of technical means used in experiments, observations on formation of conditioned reflexes, function of cerebral hemispheres, results of damage, nature of sleep, typology of nervous system, significance of experiments for human psychology. Trans. by Dr. G. V. Anrep, Cambridge Univ. 235-item bibliography. 18 figures. 445pp. 5⅜ x 8.   S614 Paperbound **$2.35**

EXPLANATION OF HUMAN BEHAVIOUR, F. V. Smith. A major intermediate-level introduction to and criticism of 8 complete systems of the psychology of human behavior, with unusual emphasis on theory of investigation and methodology. Part I is an illuminating analysis of the problems involved in the explanation of observed phenomena, and the differing viewpoints on the nature of causality. Parts II and III are a closely detailed survey of the systems of McDougall, Gordon Allport, Lewin, the Gestalt group, Freud, Watson, Hull, and Tolman. Biographical notes. Bibliography of over 800 items. 2 Indexes. 38 figures. xii + 460pp. 5½ x 8¾.   T253 Clothbound **$6.00**

SEX IN PSYCHO-ANALYSIS (formerly CONTRIBUTIONS TO PSYCHO-ANALYSIS), S. Ferenczi. Written by an associate of Freud, this volume presents countless insights on such topics as impotence, transference, analysis and children, dreams, symbols, obscene words, masturbation and male homosexuality, paranoia and psycho-analysis, the sense of reality, hypnotism and therapy, and many others. Also includes full text of THE DEVELOPMENT OF PSYCHO-ANALYSIS by Ferenczi and Otto Rank. Two books bound as one. Total of 406pp. 5⅜ x 8.   T324 Paperbound **$1.85**

BEYOND PSYCHOLOGY, Otto Rank. One of Rank's most mature contributions, focussing on the irrational basis of human behavior as a basic fact of our lives. The psychoanalytic techniques of myth analysis trace to their source the ultimates of human existence: fear of death, personality, the social organization, the need for love and creativity, etc. Dr. Rank finds them stemming from a common irrational source, man's fear of final destruction. A seminal work in modern psychology, this work sheds light on areas ranging from the concept of immortal soul to the sources of state power. 291pp. 5⅜ x 8.   T485 Paperbound **$2.00**

ILLUSIONS AND DELUSIONS OF THE SUPERNATURAL AND THE OCCULT, D. H. Rawcliffe. Holds up to rational examination hundreds of persistent delusions including crystal gazing, automatic writing, table turning, mediumistic trances, mental healing, stigmata, lycanthropy, live burial, the Indian Rope Trick, spiritualism, dowsing, telepathy, clairvoyance, ghosts, ESP, etc. The author explains and exposes the mental and physical deceptions involved, making this not only an exposé of supernatural phenomena, but a valuable exposition of characteristic types of abnormal psychology. Originally titled "The Psychology of the Occult." 14 illustrations. Index. 551pp. 5⅜ x 8.   T503 Paperbound **$2.00**

THE PRINCIPLES OF PSYCHOLOGY, William James. The full long-course, unabridged, of one of the great classics of Western literature and science. Wonderfully lucid descriptions of human mental activity, the stream of thought, consciousness, time perception, memory, imagination, emotions, reason, abnormal phenomena, and similar topics. Original contributions are integrated with the work of such men as Berkeley, Binet, Mills, Darwin, Hume, Kant, Royce, Schopenhauer, Spinoza, Locke, Descartes, Galton, Wundt, Lotze, Herbart, Fechner, and scores of others. All contrasting interpretations of mental phenomena are examined in detail — introspective analysis, philosophical interpretation, and experimental research. "A classic," JOURNAL OF CONSULTING PSYCHOLOGY. "The main lines are as valid as ever," PSYCHO-ANALYTICAL QUARTERLY. "Standard reading . . . a classic of interpretation," PSYCHIATRIC QUARTERLY. 94 illustrations. 1408pp. 2 volumes. 5⅜ x 8.   Vol. 1, T381 Paperbound **$2.50**
Vol. 2, T382 Paperbound **$2.50**

THE DYNAMICS OF THERAPY IN A CONTROLLED RELATIONSHIP, Jessie Taft. One of the most important works in literature of child psychology, out of print for 25 years. Outstanding disciple of Rank describes all aspects of relationship or Rankian therapy through concise, simple elucidation of theory underlying her actual contacts with two seven-year olds. Therapists, social caseworkers, psychologists, counselors, and laymen who work with children will all find this important work an invaluable summation of method, theory of child psychology. xix + 296pp. 5⅜ x 8.   T325 Paperbound **$1.75**

Puzzles, Mathematical Recreations

SYMBOLIC LOGIC and THE GAME OF LOGIC, Lewis Carroll. "Symbolic Logic" is not concerned with modern symbolic logic, but is instead a collection of over 380 problems posed with charm and imagination, using the syllogism, and a fascinating diagrammatic method of drawing conclusions. In "The Game of Logic" Carroll's whimsical imagination devises a logical game played with 2 diagrams and counters (included) to manipulate hundreds of tricky syllogisms. The final section, "Hit or Miss" is a lagniappe of 101 additional puzzles in the delightful Carroll manner. Until this reprint edition, both of these books were rarities costing up to $15 each. Symbolic Logic: Index. xxxi + 199pp. The Game of Logic: 96pp. 2 vols. bound as one. 5⅜ x 8.　　　　　　　　　　　　　　　　　　　　T492 Paperbound **$1.50**

PILLOW PROBLEMS and A TANGLED TALE, Lewis Carroll. One of the rarest of all Carroll's works, "Pillow Problems" contains 72 original math puzzles, all typically ingenious. Particularly fascinating are Carroll's answers which remain exactly as he thought them out, reflecting his actual mental process. The problems in "A Tangled Tale" are in story form, originally appearing as a monthly magazine serial. Carroll not only gives the solutions, but uses answers sent in by readers to discuss wrong approaches and misleading paths, and grades them for insight. Both of these books were rarities until this edition, "Pillow Problems" costing up to $25, and "A Tangled Tale" $15. Pillow Problems: Preface and Introduction by Lewis Carroll. xx + 109pp. A Tangled Tale: 6 illustrations. 152pp. Two vols. bound as one. 5⅜ x 8.　　　　　　　　　　　　　　　　　　T493 Paperbound **$1.50**

AMUSEMENTS IN MATHEMATICS, Henry Ernest Dudeney. The foremost British originator of mathematical puzzles is always intriguing, witty, and paradoxical in this classic, one of the largest collections of mathematical amusements. More than 430 puzzles, problems, and paradoxes. Mazes and games, problems on number manipulation, unicursal and other route problems, puzzles on measuring, weighing, packing, age, kinship, chessboards, joiners', crossing river, plane figure dissection, and many others. Solutions. More than 450 illustrations. vii + 258pp. 5⅜ x 8.　　　　　　　　　　　　　　　　　　　　T473 Paperbound **$1.25**

THE CANTERBURY PUZZLES, Henry Dudeney. Chaucer's pilgrims set one another problems in story form. Also Adventures of the Puzzle Club, the Strange Escape of the King's Jester, the Monks of Riddlewell, the Squire's Christmas Puzzle Party, and others. All puzzles are original, based on dissecting plane figures, arithmetic, algebra, elementary calculus and other branches of mathematics, and purely logical ingenuity. "The limit of ingenuity and intricacy," The Observer. Over 110 puzzles. Full Solutions. 150 illustrations. vii + 225pp. 5⅜ x 8.　　　　　　　　　　　　　　　　　　　　T474 Paperbound **$1.25**

MATHEMATICAL EXCURSIONS, H. A. Merrill. Even if you hardly remember your high school math, you'll enjoy the 90 stimulating problems contained in this book and you will come to understand a great many mathematical principles with surprisingly little effort. Many useful shortcuts and diversions not generally known are included: division by inspection, Russian peasant multiplication, memory systems for pi, building odd and even magic squares, square roots by geometry, dyadic systems, and many more. Solutions to difficult problems. 50 illustrations. 145pp. 5⅜ x 8.　　　　　　　　　　　　　　　　　　T350 Paperbound **$1.00**

MAGIC SQUARES AND CUBES, W. S. Andrews. Only book-length treatment in English, a thorough non-technical description and analysis. Here are nasik, overlapping, pandiagonal, serrated squares; magic circles, cubes, spheres, rhombuses. Try your hand at 4-dimensional magical figures! Much unusual folklore and tradition included. High school algebra is sufficient. 754 diagrams and illustrations. viii + 419pp. 5⅜ x 8.　　　　　　　　　　　　T658 Paperbound **$1.85**

CALIBAN'S PROBLEM BOOK: MATHEMATICAL, INFERENTIAL AND CRYPTOGRAPHIC PUZZLES, H. Phillips (Caliban), S. T. Shovelton, G. S. Marshall. 105 ingenious problems by the greatest living creator of puzzles based on logic and inference. Rigorous, modern, piquant; reflecting their author's unusual personality, these intermediate and advanced puzzles all involve the ability to reason clearly through complex situations; some call for mathematical knowledge, ranging from algebra to number theory. Solutions. xi + 180pp. 5⅜ x 8.　　　　　　　　　　　　　　　　　　　　T736 Paperbound **$1.25**

MATHEMATICAL PUZZLES FOR BEGINNERS AND ENTHUSIASTS, G. Mott-Smith. 188 mathematical puzzles based on algebra, dissection of plane figures, permutations, and probability, that will test and improve your powers of inference and interpretation. The Odic Force, The Spider's Cousin, Ellipse Drawing, theory and strategy of card and board games like tit-tat-toe, go moku, salvo, and many others. 100 pages of detailed mathematical explanations. Appendix of primes, square roots, etc. 135 illustrations. 2nd revised edition. 248pp. 5⅜ x 8.　　　　　　　　　　　　　　　　　　T198 Paperbound **$1.00**

MATHEMAGIC, MAGIC PUZZLES, AND GAMES WITH NUMBERS, R. V. Heath. More than 60 new puzzles and stunts based on the properties of numbers. Easy techniques for multiplying large numbers mentally, revealing hidden numbers magically, finding the date of any day in any year, and dozens more. Over 30 pages devoted to magic squares, triangles, cubes, circles, etc. Edited by J. S. Meyer. 76 illustrations. 128pp. 5⅜ x 8.　　　　　　　　　　T110 Paperbound **$1.00**

MATHEMATICAL RECREATIONS, M. Kraitchik. One of the most thorough compilations of unusual mathematical problems for beginners and advanced mathematicians. Historical problems from Greek, Medieval, Arabic, Hindu sources. 50 pages devoted to pastimes derived from figurate numbers, Mersenne numbers, Fermat numbers, primes and probability. 40 pages of magic, Euler, Latin, panmagic squares. 25 new positional and permutational games of permanent value: fairy chess, latruncles, reversi, jinx, ruma, lasca, tricolor, tetrachrome, etc. Complete rigorous solutions. Revised second edition. 181 illustrations. 333pp. 5⅜ x 8.
T163 Paperbound **$1.75**

MATHEMATICAL PUZZLES OF SAM LOYD, selected and edited by M. Gardner. Choice puzzles by the greatest American puzzle creator and innovator. Selected from his famous collection, "Cyclopedia of Puzzles," they retain the unique style and historical flavor of the originals. There are posers based on arithmetic, algebra, probability, game theory, route tracing, topology, counter, sliding block, operations research, geometrical dissection. Includes the famous "14-15" puzzle which was a national craze, and his "Horse of a Different Color" which sold millions of copies. 117 of his most ingenious puzzles in all, 120 line drawings and diagrams. Solutions. Selected references. xx + 167pp. 5⅜ x 8. T498 Paperbound **$1.00**

MATHEMATICAL PUZZLES OF SAM LOYD, Vol. II, selected and edited by Martin Gardner. The outstanding 2nd selection from the great American innovator's "Cyclopedia of Puzzles": speed and distance problems, clock problems, plane and solid geometry, calculus problems, etc. Analytical table of contents that groups the puzzles according to the type of mathematics necessary to solve them. 166 puzzles, 150 original line drawings and diagrams. Selected references. xiv + 177pp. 5⅜ x 8. T709 Paperbound **$1.00**

ARITHMETICAL EXCURSIONS: AN ENRICHMENT OF ELEMENTARY MATHEMATICS, H. Bowers and J. Bowers. A lively and lighthearted collection of facts and entertainments for anyone who enjoys manipulating numbers or solving arithmetical puzzles: methods of arithmetic never taught in school, little-known facts about the most simple numbers, and clear explanations of more sophisticated topics; mysteries and folklore of numbers, the "Hin-dog-abic" number system, etc. First publication. Index. 529 numbered problems and diversions, all with answers. Bibliography. 60 figures. xiv + 320pp. 5⅜ x 8. T770 Paperbound **$1.65**

CRYPTANALYSIS, H. F. Gaines. Formerly entitled ELEMENTARY CRYPTANALYSIS, this introductory-intermediate level text is the best book in print on cryptograms and their solution. It covers all major techniques of the past, and contains much that is not generally known except to experts. Full details about concealment, substitution, and transposition ciphers; periodic mixed alphabets, multafid, Kasiski and Vigenere methods, Ohaver patterns, Playfair, and scores of other topics. 6 language letter and word frequency appendix. 167 problems, now furnished with solutions. Index. 173 figures. vi + 230pp. 5⅜ x 8.
T97 Paperbound **$2.00**

CRYPTOGRAPHY, L. D. Smith. An excellent introductory work on ciphers and their solution, the history of secret writing, and actual methods and problems in such techniques as transposition and substitution. Appendices describe the enciphering of Japanese, the Baconian biliteral cipher, and contain frequency tables and a bibliography for further study. Over 150 problems with solutions. 160pp. 5⅜ x 8. T247 Paperbound **$1.00**

PUZZLE QUIZ AND STUNT FUN, J. Meyer. The solution to party doldrums. 238 challenging puzzles, stunts and tricks. Mathematical puzzles like The Clever Carpenter, Atom Bomb; mysteries and deductions like The Bridge of Sighs, The Nine Pearls, Dog Logic; observation puzzles like Cigarette Smokers, Telephone Dial; over 200 others including magic squares, tongue twisters, puns, anagrams, and many others. All problems solved fully. 250pp. 5⅜ x 8.
T337 Paperbound **$1.00**

101 PUZZLES IN THOUGHT AND LOGIC, C. R. Wylie, Jr. Brand new problems you need no special knowledge to solve! Take the kinks out of your mental "muscles" and enjoy solving murder problems, the detection of lying fishermen, the logical identification of color by a blindman, and dozens more. Introduction with simplified explanation of general scientific method and puzzle solving. 128pp. 5⅜ x 8. T367 Paperbound **$1.00**

MY BEST PROBLEMS IN MATHEMATICS, Hubert Phillips ("Caliban"). Only elementary mathematics needed to solve these 100 witty, catchy problems by a master problem creator. Problems on the odds in cards and dice, problems in geometry, algebra, permutations, even problems that require no math at all—just a logical mind, clear thinking. Solutions completely worked out. If you enjoy mysteries, alerting your perceptive powers and exercising your detective's eye, you'll find these cryptic puzzles a challenging delight. Original 1961 publication. 100 puzzles, solutions. x + 107pp. 5⅝ x 8. T91 Paperbound **$1.00**

MY BEST PUZZLES IN LOGIC AND REASONING, Hubert Phillips ("Caliban"). A new collection of 100 inferential and logical puzzles chosen from the best that have appeared in England, available for first time in U.S. By the most endlessly resourceful puzzle creator now living. All data presented are both necessary and sufficient to allow a single unambiguous answer. No special knowledge is required for problems ranging from relatively simple to completely original one-of-a-kinds. Guaranteed to please beginners and experts of all ages. Original publication. 100 puzzles, full solutions. x + 107pp. 5⅜ x 8. T119 Paperbound **$1.00**

THE BOOK OF MODERN PUZZLES, G. L. Kaufman. A completely new series of puzzles as fascinating as crossword and deduction puzzles but based upon different principles and techniques. Simple 2-minute teasers, word labyrinths, design and pattern puzzles, logic and observation puzzles — over 150 braincrackers. Answers to all problems. 116 illustrations. 192pp. 5⅜ x 8.
.T143 Paperbound **$1.00**

NEW WORD PUZZLES, G. L. Kaufman. 100 ENTIRELY NEW puzzles based on words and their combinations that will delight crossword puzzle, Scrabble and Jotto fans. Chess words, based on the moves of the chess king; design-onyms, symmetrical designs made of synonyms; rhymed double-crostics; syllable sentences; addle letter anagrams; alphagrams; linkograms; and many others all brand new. Full solutions. Space to work problems. 196 figures. vi + 122pp. 5⅜ x 8.
T344 Paperbound **$1.00**

MAZES AND LABYRINTHS: A BOOK OF PUZZLES, W. Shepherd. Mazes, formerly associated with mystery and ritual, are still among the most intriguing of intellectual puzzles. This is a novel and different collection of 50 amusements that embody the principle of the maze: mazes in the classical tradition; 3-dimensional, ribbon, and Möbius-strip mazes; hidden messages; spatial arrangements; etc.—almost all built on amusing story situations. 84 illustrations. Essay on maze psychology. Solutions. xv + 122pp. 5⅜ x 8.
T731 Paperbound **$1.00**

MAGIC TRICKS & CARD TRICKS, W. Jonson. Two books bound as one. 52 tricks with cards, 37 tricks with coins, bills, eggs, smoke, ribbons, slates, etc. Details on presentation, misdirection, and routining will help you master such famous tricks as the Changing Card, Card in the Pocket, Four Aces, Coin Through the Hand, Bill in the Egg, Afghan Bands, and over 75 others. If you follow the lucid exposition and key diagrams carefully, you will finish these two books with an astonishing mastery of magic. 106 figures. 224pp. 5⅜ x 8. T909 Paperbound **$1.00**

PANORAMA OF MAGIC, Milbourne Christopher. A profusely illustrated history of stage magic, a unique selection of prints and engravings from the author's private collection of magic memorabilia, the largest of its kind. Apparatus, stage settings and costumes; ingenious ads distributed by the performers and satiric broadsides passed around in the streets ridiculing pompous showmen; programs; decorative souvenirs. The lively text, by one of America's foremost professional magicians, is full of anecdotes about almost legendary wizards: Dede, the Egyptian; Philadelphia, the wonder-worker; Robert-Houdin, "the father of modern magic;" Harry Houdini; scores more. Altogether a pleasure package for anyone interested in magic, stage setting and design, ethnology, psychology, or simply in unusual people. A Dover original. 295 illustrations; 8 in full color. Index. viii + 216pp. 8⅜ x 11¼.
T774 Paperbound **$2.25**

HOUDINI ON MAGIC, Harry Houdini. One of the greatest magicians of modern times explains his most prized secrets. How locks are picked, with illustrated picks and skeleton keys; how a girl is sawed into twins; how to walk through a brick wall — Houdini's explanations of 44 stage tricks with many diagrams. Also included is a fascinating discussion of great magicians of the past and the story of his fight against fraudulent mediums and spiritualists. Edited by W.B. Gibson and M.N. Young. Bibliography. 155 figures, photos. xv + 280pp. 5⅜ x 8.
T384 Paperbound **$1.35**

MATHEMATICS, MAGIC AND MYSTERY, Martin Gardner. Why do card tricks work? How do magicians perform astonishing mathematical feats? How is stage mind-reading possible? This is the first book length study explaining the application of probability, set theory, theory of numbers, topology, etc., to achieve many startling tricks. Non-technical, accurate, detailed! 115 sections discuss tricks with cards, dice, coins, knots, geometrical vanishing illusions, how a Curry square "demonstrates" that the sum of the parts may be greater than the whole, and dozens of others. No sleight of hand necessary! 135 illustrations. xii + 174pp. 5⅜ x 8.
T335 Paperbound **$1.00**

EASY-TO-DO ENTERTAINMENTS AND DIVERSIONS WITH COINS, CARDS, STRING, PAPER AND MATCHES, R. M. Abraham. Over 300 tricks, games and puzzles will provide young readers with absorbing fun. Sections on card games; paper-folding; tricks with coins, matches and pieces of string; games for the agile; toy-making from common household objects; mathematical recreations; and 50 miscellaneous pastimes. Anyone in charge of groups of youngsters, including hard-pressed parents, and in need of suggestions on how to keep children sensibly amused and quietly content will find this book indispensable. Clear, simple text, copious number of delightful line drawings and illustrative diagrams. Originally titled "Winter Nights Entertainments." Introduction by Lord Baden Powell. 329 illustrations. v + 186pp. 5⅜ x 8½.
T921 Paperbound **$1.00**

STRING FIGURES AND HOW TO MAKE THEM, Caroline Furness Jayne. 107 string figures plus variations selected from the best primitive and modern examples developed by Navajo, Apache, pygmies of Africa, Eskimo, in Europe, Australia, China, etc. The mostly readily understandable, easy-to-follow book in English on perennially popular recreation. Crystal-clear exposition; step-by-step diagrams. Everyone from kindergarten children to adults looking for unusual diversion will be endlessly amused. Index. Bibliography. Introduction by A. C. Haddon. 17 full-page plates. 960 illustrations. xxiii + 401pp. 5⅜ x 8½.
T152 Paperbound **$2.00**

Entertainments, Humor

ODDITIES AND CURIOSITIES OF WORDS AND LITERATURE, C. Bombaugh, edited by M. Gardner. The largest collection of idiosyncratic prose and poetry techniques in English, a legendary work in the curious and amusing bypaths of literary recreations and the play technique in literature—so important in modern works. Contains alphabetic poetry, acrostics, palindromes, scissors verse, centos, emblematic poetry, famous literary puns, hoaxes, notorious slips of the press, hilarious mistranslations, and much more. Revised and enlarged with modern material by Martin Gardner. 368pp. 5⅜ x 8. T759 Paperbound **$1.75**

A NONSENSE ANTHOLOGY, collected by Carolyn Wells. 245 of the best nonsense verses ever written, including nonsense puns, absurd arguments, mock epics and sagas, nonsense ballads, odes, "sick" verses, dog-Latin verses, French nonsense verses, songs. By Edward Lear, Lewis Carroll, Gelett Burgess, W. S. Gilbert, Hilaire Belloc, Peter Newell, Oliver Herford, etc., 83 writers in all plus over four score anonymous nonsense verses. A special section of limericks, plus famous nonsense such as Carroll's "Jabberwocky" and Lear's "The Jumblies" and much excellent verse virtually impossible to locate elsewhere. For 50 years considered the best anthology available. Index of first lines specially prepared for this edition. Introduction by Carolyn Wells. 3 indexes: Title, Author, First lines. xxxiii + 279pp. T499 Paperbound **$1.35**

THE BAD CHILD'S BOOK OF BEASTS, MORE BEASTS FOR WORSE CHILDREN, and A MORAL ALPHABET, H. Belloc. Hardly an anthology of humorous verse has appeared in the last 50 years without at least a couple of these famous nonsense verses. But one must see the entire volumes—with all the delightful original illustrations by Sir Basil Blackwood—to appreciate fully Belloc's charming and witty verses that play so subacidly on the platitudes of life and morals that beset his day—and ours. A great humor classic. Three books in one. Total of 157pp. 5⅜ x 8. T749 Paperbound **$1.00**

THE DEVIL'S DICTIONARY, Ambrose Bierce. Sardonic and irreverent barbs puncturing the pomposities and absurdities of American politics, business, religion, literature, and arts, by the country's greatest satirist in the classic tradition. Epigrammatic as Shaw, piercing as Swift, American as Mark Twain, Will Rogers, and Fred Allen, Bierce will always remain the favorite of a small coterie of enthusiasts, and of writers and speakers whom he supplies with "some of the most gorgeous witticisms of the English language" (H. L. Mencken). Over 1000 entries in alphabetical order. 144pp. 5⅜ x 8. T487 Paperbound **$1.00**

THE PURPLE COW AND OTHER NONSENSE, Gelett Burgess. The best of Burgess's early nonsense, selected from the first edition of the "Burgess Nonsense Book." Contains many of his most unusual and truly awe-inspiring pieces: 36 nonsense quatrains, the Poems of Patagonia, Alphabet of Famous Goops, and the other hilarious (and rare) adult nonsense that place him in the forefront of American humorists. All pieces are accompanied by the original Burgess illustrations. 123 illustrations. xiii + 113pp. 5⅜ x 8. T772 Paperbound **$1.00**

MY PIOUS FRIENDS AND DRUNKEN COMPANIONS and MORE PIOUS FRIENDS AND DRUNKEN COMPANIONS, Frank Shay. Folksingers, amateur and professional, and everyone who loves singing: here, available for the first time in 30 years, is this valued collection of 132 ballads, blues, vaudeville numbers, drinking songs, sea chanties, comedy songs. Songs of pre-Beatnik Bohemia; songs from all over America, England, France, Australia; the great songs of the Naughty Nineties and early twentieth-century America. Over a third with music. Woodcuts by John Held, Jr. convey perfectly the brash insouciance of an era of rollicking unabashed song. 12 illustrations by John Held, Jr. Two indexes (Titles and First lines and Choruses). Introductions by the author. Two volumes bound as one. Total of xvi + 235pp. 5⅜ x 8½. T946 Paperbound **$1.25**

HOW TO TELL THE BIRDS FROM THE FLOWERS, R. W. Wood. How not to confuse a carrot with a parrot, a grape with an ape, a puffin with nuffin. Delightful drawings, clever puns, absurd little poems point out far-fetched resemblances in nature. The author was a leading physicist. Introduction by Margaret Wood White. 106 illus. 60pp. 5⅜ x 8. T523 Paperbound **75¢**

PECK'S BAD BOY AND HIS PA, George W. Peck. The complete edition, containing both volumes, of one of the most widely read American humor books. The endless ingenious pranks played by bad boy "Hennery" on his pa and the grocery man, the outraged pomposity of Pa, the perpetual ridiculing of middle class institutions, are as entertaining today as they were in 1883. No pale sophistications or subtleties, but rather humor vigorous, raw, earthy, imaginative, and, as folk humor often is, sadistic. This peculiarly fascinating book is also valuable to historians and students of American culture as a portrait of an age. 100 original illustrations by True Williams. Introduction by E. F. Bleiler. 347pp. 5⅜ x 8. T497 Paperbound **$1.35**

THE HUMOROUS VERSE OF LEWIS CARROLL. Almost every poem Carroll ever wrote, the largest collection ever published, including much never published elsewhere: 150 parodies, burlesques, riddles, ballads, acrostics, etc., with 130 original illustrations by Tenniel, Carroll, and others. "Addicts will be grateful . . . there is nothing for the faithful to do but sit down and fall to the banquet," N. Y. Times. Index to first lines. xiv + 446pp. 5⅜ x 8.
T654 Paperbound **$2.00**

DIVERSIONS AND DIGRESSIONS OF LEWIS CARROLL. A major new treasure for Carroll fans! Rare privately published humor, fantasy, puzzles, and games by Carroll at his whimsical best, with a new vein of frank satire. Includes many new mathematical amusements and recreations, among them the fragmentary Part III of "Curiosa Mathematica." Contains "The Rectory Umbrella," "The New Belfry," "The Vision of the Three T's," and much more. New 32-page supplement of rare photographs taken by Carroll. x + 375pp. 5⅜ x 8.
T732 Paperbound **$1.65**

THE COMPLETE NONSENSE OF EDWARD LEAR. This is the only complete edition of this master of gentle madness available at a popular price. A BOOK OF NONSENSE, NONSENSE SONGS, MORE NONSENSE SONGS AND STORIES in their entirety with all the old favorites that have delighted children and adults for years. The Dong With A Luminous Nose, The Jumblies, The Owl and the Pussycat, and hundreds of other bits of wonderful nonsense. 214 limericks, 3 sets of Nonsense Botany, 5 Nonsense Alphabets, 546 drawings by Lear himself, and much more. 320pp. 5⅜ x 8.
T167 Paperbound **$1.00**

THE MELANCHOLY LUTE, The Humorous Verse of Franklin P. Adams ("FPA"). The author's own selection of light verse, drawn from thirty years of FPA's column, "The Conning Tower," syndicated all over the English-speaking world. Witty, perceptive, literate, these ninety-six poems range from parodies of other poets, Millay, Longfellow, Edgar Guest, Kipling, Masefield, etc., and free and hilarious translations of Horace and other Latin poets, to satiric comments on fabled American institutions—the New York Subways, preposterous ads, suburbanites, sensational journalism, etc. They reveal with vigor and clarity the humor, integrity and restraint of a wise and gentle American satirist. Introduction by Robert Hutchinson. vi + 122pp. 5⅜ x 8½.
T108 Paperbound **$1.00**

SINGULAR TRAVELS, CAMPAIGNS, AND ADVENTURES OF BARON MUNCHAUSEN, R. E. Raspe, with 90 illustrations by Gustave Doré. The first edition in over 150 years to reestablish the deeds of the Prince of Liars exactly as Raspe first recorded them in 1785—the genuine Baron Munchausen, one of the most popular personalities in English literature. Included also are the best of the many sequels, written by other hands. Introduction on Raspe by J. Carswell. Bibliography of early editions. xliv + 192pp. 5⅜ x 8.
T698 Paperbound **$1.00**

THE WIT AND HUMOR OF OSCAR WILDE, ed. by Alvin Redman. Wilde at his most brilliant, in 1000 epigrams exposing weaknesses and hypocrisies of "civilized" society. Divided into 49 categories—sin, wealth, women, America, etc.—to aid writers, speakers. Includes excerpts from his trials, books, plays, criticism. Formerly "The Epigrams of Oscar Wilde." Introduction by Vyvyan Holland, Wilde's only living son. Introductory essay by editor. 260pp. 5⅜ x 8.
T602 Paperbound **$1.00**

MAX AND MORITZ, Wilhelm Busch. Busch is one of the great humorists of all time, as well as the father of the modern comic strip. This volume, translated by H. A. Klein and other hands, contains the perennial favorite "Max and Moritz" (translated by C. T. Brooks), Plisch and Plum, Das Rabennest, Eispeter, and seven other whimsical, sardonic, jovial, diabolical cartoon and verse stories. Lively English translations parallel the original German. This work has delighted millions since it first appeared in the 19th century, and is guaranteed to please almost anyone. Edited by H. A. Klein, with an afterword. x + 205pp. 5⅝ x 8½.
T181 Paperbound **$1.15**

HYPOCRITICAL HELENA, Wilhelm Büsch. A companion volume to "Max and Moritz," with the title piece (Die Fromme Helena) and 10 other highly amusing cartoon and verse stories, all newly translated by H. A. Klein and M. C. Klein: Adventure on New Year's Eve (Abenteuer in der Neujahrsnacht), Hangover on the Morning after New Year's Eve (Der Katzenjammer am Neujahrsmorgen), etc. English and German in parallel columns. Hours of pleasure, also a fine language aid. x + 205pp. 5⅝ x 8½.
T184 Paperbound **$1.00**

THE BEAR THAT WASN'T, Frank Tashlin. What does it mean? Is it simply delightful wry humor, or a charming story of a bear who wakes up in the midst of a factory, or a satire on Big Business, or an existential cartoon-story of the human condition, or a symbolization of the struggle between conformity and the individual? New York Herald Tribune said of the first edition: ". . . a fable for grownups that will be fun for children. Sit down with the book and get your own bearings." Long an underground favorite with readers of all ages and opinions. v + 51pp. Illustrated. 5⅜ x 8½.
T939 Paperbound **75¢**

RUTHLESS RHYMES FOR HEARTLESS HOMES and MORE RUTHLESS RHYMES FOR HEARTLESS HOMES, Harry Graham ("Col. D. Streamer"). Two volumes of Little Willy and 48 other poetic disasters. A bright, new reprint of oft-quoted, never forgotten, devastating humor by a precursor of today's "sick" joke school. For connoisseurs of wicked, wacky humor and all who delight in the comedy of manners. Original drawings are a perfect complement. 61 illustrations. Index. vi + 69pp. Two vols. bound as one. 5⅜ x 8½.
T930 Paperbound **75¢**

Chess, Checkers, Games, Go

THE ADVENTURE OF CHESS, Edward Lasker. A lively history of chess, from its ancient beginnings in the Indian 4-handed game of Chaturanga, through to the great players of our day, as told by one of America's finest masters. He introduces such unusual sidelights and amusing oddities as Maelzel's chess-playing automaton that beat Napoleon 3 times. Major discussion of chess-playing machines and personal memories of Nimzovich, Capablanca, etc. 5-page chess primer. 11 illustrations, 53 diagrams. 296pp. 5⅜ x 8.   S510 Paperbound **$1.75**

A TREASURY OF CHESS LORE, edited by Fred Reinfeld. A delightful collection of anecdotes, short stories, aphorisms by and about the masters, poems, accounts of games and tournaments, photography. Hundreds of humorous, pithy, satirical, wise, and historical episodes, comments, and word portraits. A fascinating "must" for chess players; revealing and perhaps seductive to those who wonder what their friends see in the game. 48 photographs (14 full page plates) 12 diagrams. xi + 306pp. 5⅜ x 8.   T458 Paperbound **$1.75**

HOW DO YOU PLAY CHESS? by Fred Reinfeld. A prominent expert covers every basic rule of chess for the beginner in 86 questions and answers: moves, powers of pieces, rationale behind moves, how to play forcefully, history of chess, and much more. Bibliography of chess publications. 11 board diagrams. 48 pages.   **FREE**

THE PLEASURES OF CHESS, Assiac. Internationally known British writer, influential chess columnist, writes wittily about wide variety of chess subjects: Anderssen's "Immortal Game;" only game in which both opponents resigned at once; psychological tactics of Reshevsky, Lasker; varieties played by masters for relaxation, such as "losing chess;" sacrificial orgies; etc. These anecdotes, witty observations will give you fresh appreciation of game. 43 problems. 150 diagrams. 139pp. 5⅜ x 8.   T597 Paperbound **$1.25**

WIN AT CHESS, F. Reinfeld. 300 practical chess situations from actual tournament play to sharpen your chess eye and test your skill. Traps, sacrifices, mates, winning combinations, subtle exchanges, show you how to WIN AT CHESS. Short notes and tables of solutions and alternative moves help you evaluate your progress. Learn to think ahead playing the "crucial moments" of historic games. 300 diagrams. Notes and solutions. Formerly titled CHESS QUIZ. vi + 120pp. 5⅜ x 8.   T438 Paperbound **$1.00**

THE ART OF CHESS, James Mason. An unabridged reprinting of the latest revised edition of the most famous general study of chess ever written. Also included, a complete supplement by Fred Reinfeld, "How Do You Play Chess?", invaluable to beginners for its lively question and answer method. Mason, an early 20th century master, teaches the beginning and intermediate player more than 90 openings, middle game, end game, how to see more moves ahead, to plan purposefully, attack, sacrifice, defend, exchange, and govern general strategy. Supplement. 448 diagrams. 1947 Reinfeld-Bernstein text. Bibliography. xvi + 340pp. 5⅜ x 8.   T463 Paperbound **$2.00**

THE PRINCIPLES OF CHESS, James Mason. This "great chess classic" (N. Y. Times) is a general study covering all aspects of the game: basic forces, resistance, obstruction, opposition, relative values, mating, typical end game situations, combinations, much more. The last section discusses openings, with 50 games illustrating modern master play of Rubinstein, Spielmann, Lasker, Capablanca, etc., selected and annotated by Fred Reinfeld. Will improve the game of any intermediate-skilled player, but is so forceful and lucid that an absolute beginner might use it to become an accomplished player. 1946 Reinfeld edition. 166 diagrams. 378pp. 5⅜ x 8.   T646 Paperbound **$1.85**

LASKER'S MANUAL OF CHESS, Dr. Emanuel Lasker. Probably the greatest chess player of modern times, Dr. Emanuel Lasker held the world championship 28 years, independent of passing schools or fashions. This unmatched study of the game, chiefly for intermediate to skilled players, analyzes basic methods, combinations, position play, the aesthetics of chess, dozens of different openings, etc., with constant reference to great modern games. Contains a brilliant exposition of Steinitz's important theories. Introduction by Fred Reinfeld. Tables of Lasker's tournament record. 3 indices. 308 diagrams. 1 photograph. xxx + 349pp. 5⅜ x 8.   T640 Paperbound **$2.25**

THE ART OF CHESS COMBINATION, E. Znosko-Borovsky. Proves that combinations, perhaps the most aesthetically satisfying, successful technique in chess, can be an integral part of your game, instead of a haphazard occurrence. Games of Capablanca, Rubinstein, Nimzovich, Bird, etc. grouped according to common features, perceptively analyzed to show that every combination begins in certain simple ideas. Will help you to plan many moves ahead. Technical terms almost completely avoided. "In the teaching of chess he may claim to have no superior," P. W. Sergeant. Introduction. Exercises. Solutions. Index. 223pp. 5⅜ x 8.   T583 Paperbound **$1.60**

MODERN IDEAS IN CHESS, Richard Reti. An enduring classic, because of its unrivalled explanation of the way master chess had developed in the past hundred years. Reti, who was an outstanding theoretician and player, explains each advance in chess by concentrating on the games of the single master most closely associated with it: Morphy, Anderssen, Steinitz, Lasker, Alekhine, other world champions. Play the games in this volume, study Reti's perceptive observations, and have a living picture of the road chess has travelled. Introduction. 34 diagrams. 192pp. 5⅜ x 8.   T638 Paperbound **$1.25**

THE BOOK OF THE NEW YORK INTERNATIONAL CHESS TOURNAMENT, 1924, annotated by A. Alekhine and edited by H. Helms. Long a rare collector's item, this is the book of one of the most brilliant tournaments of all time, during which Capablanca, Lasker, Alekhine, Reti, and others immeasurably enriched chess theory in a thrilling contest. All 110 games played, with Alekhine's unusually penetrating notes. 15 photographs. xi + 271pp. 5⅜ x 8.
T752 Paperbound **$1.85**

KERES' BEST GAMES OF CHESS, selected, annotated by F. Reinfeld. 90 best games, 1931-1948, by one of boldest, most exciting players of modern chess. Games against Alekhine, Bogolyubov, Capablanca, Euwe, Fine, Reshevsky, other masters, show his treatments of openings such as Giuoco Piano, Alekhine Defense, Queen's Gambit Declined; attacks, sacrifices, alternative methods. Preface by Keres gives personal glimpses, evaluations of rivals. 110 diagrams. 272pp. 5⅜ x 8.   T593 Paperbound **$1.35**

HYPERMODERN CHESS as developed in the games of its greatest exponent, ARON NIMZOVICH, edited by Fred Reinfeld. An intensely original player and analyst, Nimzovich's extraordinary approaches startled and often angered the chess world. This volume, designed for the average player, shows in his victories over Alekhine, Lasker, Marshall, Rubinstein, Spielmann, and others, how his iconoclastic methods infused new life into the game. Use Nimzovich to invigorate your play and startle opponents. Introduction. Indices of players and openings. 180 diagrams. viii + 220pp. 5⅜ x 8.   T448 Paperbound **$1.50**

THE DEVELOPMENT OF A CHESS GENIUS: 100 INSTRUCTIVE GAMES OF ALEKHINE, F. Reinfeld. 100 games of the chess giant's formative years, 1905-1914, from age 13 to maturity, each annotated and commented upon by Fred Reinfeld. Included are matches against Bogolyubov, Capablanca, Tarrasch, and many others. You see the growth of an inexperienced genius into one of the greatest players of all time. Many of these games have never appeared before in book form. "One of America's most significant contributions to the chess world," Chess Life. New introduction. Index of players, openings. 204 illustrations. xv +227pp. 5¼ x 8.
T551 Paperbound **$1.35**

RESHEVSKY'S BEST GAMES OF CHESS, Samuel Reshevsky. One time 4-year-old chess genius, 5-time winner U. S. Chess Championship, selects, annotates 110 of his best games, illustrating theories, favorite methods of play against Capablanca, Alekhine, Bogolyubov, Kashdan, Vidmar, Botvinnik, others. Clear, non-technical style. Personal impressions of opponents, autobiographical material, tournament match record. Formerly "Reshevsky on Chess." 309 diagrams, 2 photos. 288pp. 5⅜ x 8.   T606 Paperbound **$1.25**

ONE HUNDRED SELECTED GAMES, Mikhail Botvinnik. Author's own choice of his best games before becoming World Champion in 1948, beginning with first big tournament, the USSR Championship, 1927. Shows his great power of analysis as he annotates these games, giving strategy, technique against Alekhine, Capablanca, Euwe, Keres, Reshevsky, Smyslov, Vidmar, many others. Discusses his career, methods of play, system of training. 6 studies of endgame positions. 221 diagrams. 272pp. 5⅜ x 8.   T620 Paperbound **$1.50**

RUBINSTEIN'S CHESS MASTERPIECES, selected, annotated by Hans Kmoch. Thoroughgoing mastery of opening, middle game; faultless technique in endgame, particularly rook and pawn endings; ability to switch from careful positional play to daring combinations; all distinguish the play of Rubinstein. 100 best games, against Janowski, Nimzowitch, Tarrasch, Vidmar, Capablanca, other greats, carefully annotated, will improve your game rapidly. Biographical introduction, B. F. Winkelman. 103 diagrams. 192pp. 5⅜ x 8.
T617 Paperbound **$1.25**

TARRASCH'S BEST GAMES OF CHESS, selected & annotated by Fred Reinfeld. First definitive collection of games by Siegbert Tarrasch, winner of 7 international tournaments, and the leading theorist of classical chess. 183 games cover fifty years of play against Mason, Mieses, Paulsen, Teichmann, Pillsbury, Janwoski, others. Reinfeld includes Tarrasch's own analyses of many of these games. A careful study and replaying of the games will give you a sound understanding of classical methods, and many hours of enjoyment. Introduction. Indexes. 183 diagrams. xxiv + 386pp. 5⅜ x 8.   T644 Paperbound **$2.00**

MARSHALL'S BEST GAMES OF CHESS, F. J. Marshall. Grandmaster, U. S. Champion for 27 years, tells story of career; presents magnificent collection of 140 of best games, annotated by himself. Games against Alekhine, Capablanca, Emanuel Lasker, Janowski, Rubinstein, Pillsbury, etc. Special section analyzes openings such as King's Gambit, Ruy Lopez, Alekhine's Defense, Giuoco Piano, others. A study of Marshall's brilliant offensives, slashing attacks, extraordinary sacrifices, will rapidly improve your game. Formerly "My Fifty Years of Chess." Introduction. 19 diagrams. 13 photos. 250pp. 5⅜ x 8.   T604 Paperbound **$1.45**

Fiction

FLATLAND, E. A. Abbott. A science-fiction classic of life in a 2-dimensional world that is also a first-rate introduction to such aspects of modern science as relativity and hyperspace. Political, moral, satirical, and humorous overtones have made FLATLAND fascinating reading for thousands. 7th edition. New introduction by Banesh Hoffmann. 16 illustrations. 128pp. 5⅜ x 8. **T1 Paperbound $1.00**

THE WONDERFUL WIZARD OF OZ, L. F. Baum. Only edition in print with all the original W. W. Denslow illustrations in full color—as much a part of "The Wizard" as Tenniel's drawings are of "Alice in Wonderland." "The Wizard" is still America's best-loved fairy tale, in which, as the author expresses it, "The wonderment and joy are retained and the heartaches and nightmares left out." Now today's young readers can enjoy every word and wonderful picture of the original book. New introduction by Martin Gardner. A Baum bibliography. 23 full-page color plates. viii + 268pp. 5⅜ x 8. **T691 Paperbound $1.50**

THE MARVELOUS LAND OF OZ, L. F. Baum. This is the equally enchanting sequel to the "Wizard," continuing the adventures of the Scarecrow and the Tin Woodman. The hero this time is a little boy named Tip, and all the delightful Oz magic is still present. This is the Oz book with the Animated Saw-Horse, the Woggle-Bug, and Jack Pumpkinhead. All the original John R. Neill illustrations, 10 in full color. 287 pp. 5⅜ x 8. **T692 Paperbound $1.50**

28 SCIENCE FICTION STORIES OF H. G. WELLS. Two full unabridged novels, MEN LIKE GODS and STAR BEGOTTEN, plus 26 short stories by the master science-fiction writer of all time! Stories of space, time, invention, exploration, future adventure—an indispensable part of the library of everyone interested in science and adventure. PARTIAL CONTENTS: Men Like Gods, The Country of the Blind, In the Abyss, The Crystal Egg, The Man Who Could Work Miracles, A Story of the Days to Come, The Valley of Spiders, and 21 more! 928pp. 5⅜ x 8. **T265 Clothbound $4.50**

THREE MARTIAN NOVELS, Edgar Rice Burroughs. Contains: Thuvia, Maid of Mars; The Chessmen of Mars; and The Master Mind of Mars. High adventure set in an imaginative and intricate conception of the Red Planet. Mars is peopled with an intelligent, heroic human race which lives in densely populated cities and with fierce barbarians who inhabit dead sea bottoms. Other exciting creatures abound amidst an inventive framework of Martian history and geography. Complete unabridged reprintings of the first edition. 16 illustrations by J. Allen St. John. vi + 499pp. 5⅜ x 8½. **T39 Paperbound $1.85**

SEVEN SCIENCE FICTION NOVELS, H. G. Wells. Full unabridged texts of 7 science-fiction novels of the master. Ranging from biology, physics, chemistry, astronomy to sociology and other studies, Mr. Wells extrapolates whole worlds of strange and intriguing character. "One will have to go far to match this for entertainment, excitement, and sheer pleasure . . . ," NEW YORK TIMES. Contents: The Time Machine, The Island of Dr. Moreau, First Men in the Moon, The Invisible Man, The War of the Worlds, The Food of the Gods, In the Days of the Comet. 1015pp. 5⅜ x 8. **T264 Clothbound $4.50**

THE LAND THAT TIME FORGOT and THE MOON MAID, Edgar Rice Burroughs. In the opinion of many, Burroughs' best work. The first concerns a strange island where evolution is individual rather than phylogenetic. Speechless anthropoids develop into intelligent human beings within a single generation. The second projects the reader far into the future and describes the first voyage to the Moon (in the year 2025), the conquest of the Earth by the Moon, and years of violence and adventure as the enslaved Earthmen try to regain possession of their planet. "An imaginative tour de force that keeps the reader keyed up and expectant," NEW YORK TIMES. Complete, unabridged text of the original two novels (three parts in each). 5 illustrations by J. Allen St. John. vi + 552pp. 5⅜ x 8½.
T1020 Clothbound $3.75
T358 Paperbound $2.00

3 ADVENTURE NOVELS by H. Rider Haggard. Complete texts of "She," "King Solomon's Mines," "Allan Quatermain." Qualities of discovery; desire for immortality; search for primitive, for what is unadorned by civilization, have kept these novels of African adventure exciting, alive to readers from R. L. Stevenson to George Orwell. 636pp. 5⅜ x 8.
T584 Paperbound $2.00

A PRINCESS OF MARS and A FIGHTING MAN OF MARS: TWO MARTIAN NOVELS BY EDGAR RICE BURROUGHS. "Princess of Mars" is the very first of the great Martian novels written by Burroughs, and it is probably the best of them all; it set the pattern for all of his later fantasy novels and contains a thrilling cast of strange peoples and creatures and the formula of Olympian heroism amidst ever-fluctuating fortunes which Burroughs carries off so successfully. "Fighting Man" returns to the same scenes and cities—many years later. A mad scientist, a degenerate dictator, and an indomitable defender of the right clash— with the fate of the Red Planet at stake! Complete, unabridged reprinting of original editions. Illustrations by F. E. Schoonover and Hugh Hutton. v + 356pp. 5⅜ x 8½.
T1140 Paperbound $1.75

THE PIRATES OF VENUS and LOST ON VENUS: TWO VENUS NOVELS BY EDGAR RICE BURROUGHS.
Two related novels, complete and unabridged. Exciting adventure on the planet Venus with
Earthman Carson Napier broken-field running through one dangerous episode after another.
All lovers of swashbuckling science fiction will enjoy these two stories set in a world of
fascinating societies, fierce beasts, 5000-ft. trees, lush vegetation, and wide seas. Illustra-
tions by Fortunino Matania. Total of vi + 340pp. 5⅜ x 8½.   T1053 Paperbound **$1.75**

RURITANIA COMPLETE: THE PRISONER OF ZENDA and RUPERT OF HENTZAU, Anthony Hope.
The first edition to include in one volume both the continually-popular "Prisoner of Zenda"
and its equally-absorbing sequel. Hope's mythical country of Ruritania has become a household word and the activities of its inhabitants almost a common heritage. Unabridged
reprinting. 14 illustrations by Charles Dana Gibson. vi + 414pp. 5⅜ x 8.
                                                                T69 Paperbound **$1.35**

GHOST AND HORROR STORIES OF AMBROSE BIERCE, Selected and introduced by E. F. Bleiler.
24 morbid, eerie tales—the cream of Bierce's fiction output. Contains such memorable
pieces as "The Moonlit Road," "The Damned Thing," "An Inhabitant of Carcosa," "The Eyes
of the Panther," "The Famous Gilson Bequest," "The Middle Toe of the Right Foot," and
other chilling stories, plus the essay, "Visions of the Night" in which Bierce gives us a
kind of rationale for his aesthetic of horror. New collection (1964). xxii + 199pp. 5⅜ x
8⅜.   T767 Paperbound **$1.00**

BEST GHOST STORIES OF J. S. LE FANU, Selected and introduced by E. F. Bleiler. LeFanu is
deemed the greatest name in Victorian supernatural fiction. Here are 16 of his best horror
stories, including 2 nouvelles: "Carmilla," a classic vampire tale couched in a perverse
eroticism, and "The Haunted Baronet." Also: "Sir Toby's Will," "Green Tea," "Schalken the
Painter," "Ultor de Lacy," "The Familiar," etc. The first American publication of about half
of this material: a long-overdue opportunity to get a choice sampling of LeFanu's work. New
selection (1964). 8 illustrations. 5⅜ x 8⅜.   T415 Paperbound **$1.85**

FIVE GREAT DOG NOVELS, edited by Blanche Cirker. The complete original texts of five classic
dog novels that have delighted and thrilled millions of children and adults throughout the
world with stories of loyalty, adventure, and courage. Full texts of Jack London's "The Call
of the Wild"; John Brown's "Rab and His Friends"; Alfred Ollivant's "Bob, Son of Battle";
Marshall Saunders' "Beautiful Joe"; and Ouida's "A Dog of Flanders." 21 illustrations from
the original editions. 495pp. 5⅜ x 8.   T777 Paperbound **$1.75**

THE CASTING AWAY OF MRS. LECKS AND MRS. ALESHINE, F. R. Stockton. A charming light
novel by Frank Stockton, one of America's finest humorists (and author of "The Lady, or the
Tiger?"). This book has made millions of Americans laugh at the reflection of themselves in
two middle-aged American women involved in some of the strangest adventures on record.
You will laugh, too, as they endure shipwreck, desert island, and blizzard with maddening
tranquility. Also contains complete text of "The Dusantes," sequel to "The Casting Away."
49 original illustrations by F. D. Steele. vii + 142pp. 5⅜ x 8. T743 Paperbound **$1.00**

**AT THE EARTH'S CORE, PELLUCIDAR, TANAR OF PELLUCIDAR: THREE SCIENCE FICTION NOVELS
BY EDGAR RICE BURROUGHS.** Complete, unabridged texts of the first three Pellucidar novels.
Tales of derring-do by the famous master of science fiction. The locale for these three
related stories is the inner surface of the hollow Earth where we discover the world of
Pellucidar, complete with all types of bizarre, menacing creatures, strange peoples, and
alluring maidens—guaranteed to delight all Burroughs fans and a wide circle of adventure
lovers. Illustrated by J. Allen St. John and P. F. Berdanier. vi + 433pp. 5⅜ x 8½.
                                                                T1051 Paperbound **$2.00**

**THE WAR IN THE AIR, IN THE DAYS OF THE COMET, THE FOOD OF THE GODS: THREE SCIENCE
FICTION NOVELS BY H. G. WELLS.** Three exciting Wells offerings bearing on vital social and
philosophical issues of his and our own day. Here are tales of air power, strategic bomb-
ing, East vs. West, the potential miracles of science, the potential disasters from outer
space, the relationship between scientific advancement and moral progress, etc. First
reprinting of "War in the Air" in almost 50 years. An excellent sampling of Wells at his
storytelling best. Complete, unabridged reprintings. 16 illustrations. 645pp. 5⅜ x 8½.
                                                                T1135 Paperbound **$2.00**

DAVID HARUM, E. N. Westcott. This novel of one of the most lovable, humorous characters
in American literature is a prime example of regional humor. It continues to delight people
who like their humor dry, their characters quaint, and their plots ingenuous. First book
edition to contain complete novel plus chapter found after author's death. Illustrations from
first illustrated edition. 192pp. 5⅜ x 8.   T580 Paperbound **$1.15**

TO THE SUN? and OFF ON A COMET!, Jules Verne. Complete texts of two of the most imaginative flights into fancy in world literature display the high adventure that have kept Verne's
novels read for nearly a century. Only unabridged edition of the best translation, by Edward
Roth. Large, easily readable type. 50 illustrations selected from first editions. 462pp.
5⅜ x 8.   T634 Paperbound **$1.75**

FROM THE EARTH TO THE MOON and ALL AROUND THE MOON, Jules Verne. Complete editions of two of Verne's most successful novels, in finest Edward Roth translations, now available after many years out of print. Verne's visions of submarines, airplanes, television, rockets, interplanetary travel; of scientific and not-so-scientific beliefs; of peculiarities of Americans; all delight and engross us today as much as when they first appeared. Large, easily readable type. 42 illus. from first French edition. 476pp. 5⅜ x 8.　　　　　T633 Paperbound **$1.75**

THREE PROPHETIC NOVELS BY H. G. WELLS, edited by E. F. Bleiler. Complete texts of "When the Sleeper Wakes" (1st book printing in 50 years), "A Story of the Days to Come," "The Time Machine" (1st complete printing in book form). Exciting adventures in the future are as enjoyable today as 50 years ago when first printed. Predict TV, movies, intercontinental airplanes, prefabricated houses, air-conditioned cities, etc. First important author to foresee problems of mind control, technological dictatorships. "Absolute best of imaginative fiction," N. Y. Times. Introduction. 335pp. 5⅜ x 8.　　　　　T605 Paperbound **$1.50**

GESTA ROMANORUM, trans. by Charles Swan, ed. by Wynnard Hooper. 181 tales of Greeks, Romans, Britons, Biblical characters, comprise one of greatest medieval story collections, source of plots for writers including Shakespeare, Chaucer, Gower, etc. Imaginative tales of wars, incest, thwarted love, magic, fantasy, allegory, humor, tell about kings, prostitutes, philosophers, fair damsels, knights, Noah, pirates, all walks, stations of life. Introduction. Notes. 500pp. 5⅜ x 8.　　　　　T535 Paperbound **$1.85**

Prices subject to change without notice.

Dover publishes books on art, music, philosophy, literature, languages, history, social sciences, psychology, handcrafts, orientalia, puzzles and entertainments, chess, pets and gardens, books explaining science, intermediate and higher mathematics, mathematical physics, engineering, biological sciences, earth sciences, classics of science, etc. Write to:

Dept. catrr.
Dover Publications, Inc.
180 Varick Street, N.Y. 14, N.Y.